Flying through Fire

And, as evening comes
And mists, like quiet ghosts, rise from the river bed
And climb the hill to wander through the cloisters,
We shall not forget them. Above the mist
We shall see the memorial still, and over it
The crown and single star. And we shall pray
As the mists rise up and the air grows dark
That we may wear
As brave a heart as they.

Paul Scott's words on the Runnymede Memorial Chapel Window

Flying through Fire

FIDO – the Fogbuster of World War Two

GEOFFREY WILLIAMS

Foreword by Marshal of the RAF Sir Michael Beetham
GCB CBE DFC AFC FRAeS

A SUTTON PUBLISHING BOOK

Published by Grange Books
An imprint of Grange Books Plc
The Grange
Grange Yard
London SE1 3AG

Copyright © Geoffrey Williams, 1995

Reprinted 1996

British Library Cataloguing-in-Publication Data

ISBN 1-85627-900-6

This books was designed and produced by
Sutton Publishing Limited
Phoenix Mill · Far Thrupp · Stroud · Gloucestershire

Typeset in 11/12 Times.
Typesetting and origination by
Sutton Publishing Limited.
Printed in Great Britain by
WBC, Bridgend, Mid Glam.

Contents

Acknowledgements

I am grateful to many people for their help in compiling this account of FIDO – a whole bookful in fact. The staff at Margate Public Library have obtained innumerable books for me from all parts of the UK. Archivists, curators, historians, keepers and assistants in every one of the institutions mentioned in the text and chapter notes have been most helpful; so have the editors of scores of newspapers, squadron association and aviation-related journals in Britain and overseas, who have allowed my requests for contacts to appear in their columns. In addition I have received valuable assistance from the United States Offices of History at Maxwell AFB, Alabama, and Elmendorf AFB, Alaska.

My particular thanks are due to hundreds of former airmen and civilians, some, alas, no longer with us, for sharing their remembrances. All of their contributions are appreciated; most are included.

I am grateful, also, to Marshal of the RAF Sir Michael Beetham for kindly agreeing to write a foreword. As a Lancaster pilot, Flt Lt Michael Beetham used FIDO at Fiskerton to make a safe landing in 1944.

I am indebted to the following publishers for permission to quote from books under their imprint: Square One Publications, *Chocks Away* by Robert E. Wannop; Ian Allan Ltd, *Lancaster at War 4* by Alex Thorne; Sidgwick & Jackson, *Glide Path* by Arthur C. Clarke; Department of Printing, School of Applied Design, Canberra, *To Fly Lancasters* by Clive Roantree.

To my wife, however, must go the biggest thank you, for coping with hundreds of pages of notes from a writer who has not yet entered the computer age. Sadly, Muriel died before my book was accepted for publication: I consider it a tribute to her for nearly fifty years of happy married life and for her enthusiasm and support for my project.

Foreword

MARSHAL OF THE ROYAL AIR FORCE SIR MICHAEL BEETHAM

GCB CBE DFC AFC FRAeS

Bomber Command, the main users of FIDO, normally returned from operations in the early hours of the morning, the worst possible time in winter for the formation of fog. One of the major worries of the crews was whether, after a long flight and having to cope with formidable German air defences, they would be able to to land safely at their home base. The blind landing aids of today were just not available. Many aircraft and crews were lost while trying to land in poor visibility, and many operations had to be cancelled because of the threat of widespread fog for return.

Unknown to most of the crews, work was going on behind the scenes to try and alleviate the problem. Some investigation had been done on fog dispersal before the war based on heating the atmosphere, but the large consumption of fuel involved prevented full-scale trials until the problem was recognized as acute in 1942. The impetus was then given to try and develop a workable system. That this was achieved in a remarkably short time is a tribute to the dedicated scientists and engineers who, with great skill and determination, overcame the many difficulties and frustrations to get an effective system into operational use.

Many are the crews, not just in Bomber Command, who have reason to be grateful to those 'backroom boys' for getting them down safely. Their experiences are recounted in the chapters which follow describing in meticulous detail the development, installation and operational use of FIDO on each of the airfields which was equipped. A broadly common thread for those using it for the first time was initial concern at seeing a red glow in the sky and wondering which city had been on the receiving end of a German raid, their relief at the realization that the glow was FIDO presenting them with the opportunity of a safe haven, followed by apprehension as they descended into the murk and lost sight of the glow; then relief again to break out into the clear with the flare path ahead, followed by further apprehension just after touchdown with roaring flames either side and then a final immense sense of relief to turn clear of the runway and realize that all was well for another night.

This is a fascinating story of British inventive genius. FIDO may have been a 'Heath Robinson' system but it worked and that, in war, was what really mattered. It is a story that needed to be told, it makes a most valuable contribution to our aviation history and I commend it to you.

Michael Beetham

Preface

The Second World War witnessed a spate of remarkable inventions and discoveries: from the horrific atom bomb to the humane penicillin; from the essentially practical radar-related devices to the exquisitely potty proposal to turn icebergs into aerodromes – or was it aircraft carriers?

Scarcely noticed, except to those who had occasion to use it, was the invention of the fog dispersal system, FIDO. Installed or planned at twenty airfields in Britain, on the continent and the far-away Aleutian Islands, FIDO enabled nearly 3,000 Allied aircraft and probably 15,000 aircrew to make safe landings when their own aerodromes were fogbound during the war. FIDO's welcoming glow was the salvation of many weary airmen at the end of a gruelling flight.

Research among official records has brought to light much hitherto unpublished material. Using this and the recollections of over 400 scientists, engineers, air and ground crew, by turns exciting, humorous and sad, the story of this life-saving invention is told. Illustrated with many plans and photographs, it makes a significant contribution to a little-known aspect of the Second World War.

Part One: A Deadly Hazard

ONE

Fighting the Enemy and the Weather

There is no need to fight the enemy and the weather at the same time!

Winston Churchill

The day war broke out, as the comedian Robb Wilton was wont to say, the writer was a pink, patriotic pupil at a North London technical college. There, we were well up on workshop practices and processes, but not too well informed on politics. Stanley Baldwin smoked a pipe, Neville Chamberlain carried an umbrella and Anthony Eden was good looking (or so our mothers said), and there our political enlightenment ended.

But we believed in the Empire – and to prove it we had recently beaten the Australians at cricket. The Royal Navy was without equal, as the Spithead Review or a visit to Chatham Dockyard on Navy Day would confirm. The Army ensured that large areas of the map of the world were coloured red. Most of all, however, we believed in the Royal Air Force. We held the altitude, the air-speed and the long-distance non-stop records; and if there were any records we didn't hold, it was because some foreigner had calculated in metric instead of imperial. Our homeland would be defended by Hurricane and Spitfire fighters, and if it came to taking the offensive, the Hendon Air Display showed with what accuracy flour bags could be dropped on a plywood enemy stronghold manned by erks dressed in old mattress covers.

We also believed, and completely misunderstood, Stanley Baldwin's phrase that the bomber would always get through. To us that meant British bombers, and we quite thought that the RAF had hundreds of these machines lined up and ready to pound Germany into submission ere the year was out. How wrong we were. Almost from the beginning our poorly armed, unescorted bombers fell prey to enemy fighters and anti-aircraft gunfire; over forty before the end of the year – but none inflicting serious damage on the enemy.

By night, leaflet raiders suffered less serious losses and gained valuable experience for many aircrew, but the loss of sixty-two aircraft and their crews during the so-called Phoney War, excluding crashes and non-operational casualties, was a rate which could not be supported without justifiable results.

The demands made on Bomber Command during the first years of the war were undoubtedly excessive, and we now know that few targets were located or attacked accurately, despite the courage and determination of aircrews.

The combination of operational losses due to enemy action, an alarming number of crashes on returning, and training casualties, meant that by the end of 1940 aircraft and their crews were being lost at a faster rate than they were being produced and trained; the losses to date far exceeded the total Bomber Command strength on the outbreak of war.

Despite their determination to pursue the bombing offensive against Germany to the utmost, neither Winston Churchill nor his War Cabinet was heedless of the toll being taken of Bomber Command by the enemy and the elements. They became especially aware of the drain due to crashes not caused by enemy action, and identified poor visibility, particularly fog, as a major contributory factor.

This phenomenon is probably more prevalent and less predictable over Britain than anywhere else in Europe, and where it descended on airfields being sought by tired, perhaps injured, crews in battle-damaged aircraft, probably short of fuel, its effects could be disastrous. In September 1940 there were twenty-one such crashes, in October thirty-two and in November thirty-four. In fact, during 1940 there were at least ten occasions when the number of aircraft crashing exceeded those brought down over enemy territory. At a time when a 100-plane raid was a major undertaking, such losses were grievous indeed. We cannot assume that all the crashes were caused by bad weather, but the fact that so many of them occurred during the autumn and winter months is significant.

The night of 16/17 October 1940 was particularly unfortunate. During raids by seventy-three bombers on various German targets, only three aircraft were shot down, but ten Hampdens and four Wellingtons crashed in England when attempting to land at their fog-covered bases on return. When this was brought to the attention of Winston Churchill, he immediately memoed his chief of air staff, who had only been in the job for two weeks: 'What arrangements have we got for blind landings for aircraft? How many aircraft are so fitted? It ought to be possible to guide them down quite safely as commercial craft were before the war in spite of fog. Let me have full particulars. The accidents last night are very serious.'

Three weeks later Sir Charles Portal received another prod, following raids on German cities during the night of 6/7 November:

Last night at least seven of our planes crashed on landing or were lost. The slow expansion of the bombing force is, as you know, a great anxiety to me. If bombing in this bad weather is imposing altogether undue risks on the pilots, the numbers might be slacked down in order to accumulate our strength while at the same time keeping various objectives alive . . . I see in the paper circulated, that the enemy last night used 210 bombers over Great Britain. Have they had losses similar to those we suffered? Or are our aerodromes far more weatherbound than theirs?

Before the chief of staff had much chance to formulate a reply, another missive was on his desk and that of the air minister, when eleven out of eighty-two bombers were lost from raids, mainly on Berlin, on 14/15 November:

I said the other day by minute that operations were not to be pressed unduly during these very adverse weather conditions. We cannot afford to have losses of this kind in view of your very slow replacements. If you go on like this you will break the bomber force down below a minimum of grave emergencies. No results have been achieved which would in any way justify or compensate for these losses. I consider the loss of eleven aircraft out of eighty-two, about 8 per cent, a very grievous disaster at this stage of our bomber development.

Even so, there is no record of any measures being taken to reduce the losses due to bad weather, which continued at a high level into 1941. 'Sometimes,' comments the author and historian Martin Middlebrook, 'risks were taken to keep the offensive going and the bombers suffered heavy casualties around their home airfields or in the more distant parts of the United Kingdom to which they were diverted.' By the autumn the casualty rate was mounting even higher.

At War Cabinet level, concern was again expressed after serious losses on the night of 28/29 September 1941, following raids on Frankfurt and Genoa. Of sixty-nine aircraft taking part, five failed to return and five more crashed on their return. 'The Chief of Air Staff undertook to look into the possibility of dispelling fog on aerodromes by heat or other means.' While he was doing this, Winston Churchill's scientific adviser, Lord Cherwell, began enquiries of his own, and reported to the prime minister:

> For some years, work was done in a leisurely fashion by the Air Ministry on the best way of clearing aerodromes of fog. Though the experiments were promising, they were discontinued. It may be that the expenditure is too great to justify the adoption of these methods in peace-time; but such arguments have no weight today. In view of the appalling losses we occasionally suffer from unexpected fogs . . . it seems urgent to take up this work again . . . If we have even two or three aerodromes fitted to disperse fog in case of need, the cost would be recovered in a very short time.

In the pre-war experiments referred to by Lord Cherwell, Professor David Brunt of Imperial College, London, had calculated that if the temperature of a given volume of fog could be raised by approximately 5° F, it would evaporate. Trials to this end were carried out between 1936 and 1939 by Dr J.D. Main-Smith, A.S. Hartshorn and their colleagues at Farnborough, Martlesham and Brough. Initially, 'trays containing various smokeless liquid fuels were arranged in lines and the effect of the heat evolved by the burning fuels on fog dispersal was observed'.

This system was not very satisfactory and was succeeded by a pipe laid on the ground, feeding a series of agricultural Four-oaks spray burners, on short standpipes, atomizing a mixture of 80 per cent alcohol and 20 per cent petrol. From this developed a layout consisting of two 600 ft pipelines at right angles to each other, with burners 10 ft apart. During 1938 and 1939 further experiments were carried out, doubling the lines and staggering the burners, so that they had the effect of being one every 5 ft (Plate 1). In these tests visibility was increased threefold for a fuel consumption of about 8 gallons per burner per hour. The heat generated was not considered sufficient to raise the temperature of a substantial volume of fog by the 5° F suggested by Professor Brunt, but its feasibility had been established. At that point the tests ceased.

Sir Charles Portal concurred with Lord Cherwell that tests should be resumed, but before any such resumption could take place, Bomber Command mounted what was to prove a

Plate 1 Two double rows of Four-oaks burners, set out at right angles, Martlesham, 1939 (RAE)

disastrous raid on Berlin on the night of 7/8 November 1941. Of the 392 aircraft, mainly Whitleys and Hampdens, thirty-seven failed to return or crashed in England. 'It is probable', recorded Martin Middlebrook and Chris Everitt in their *Bomber Command War Diaries*, 'that many of the casualties crashed in the North Sea, suffering from icing or fuel exhaustion in the bad weather conditions'. Such losses immediately called forth from the prime minister: 'I have several times in Cabinet deprecated forcing the night bombing of Germany without due regard to weather conditions. There is no need to fight the enemy and the weather at the same time!'

Max Hastings, in his book *Bomber Command*, summed up this and other late-1941 fiascos pointing out that

> It was unthinkable to continue operations at this rate of attrition when the Butt report made it clear that no significant results were being achieved. There was also a serious loss of confidence in Sir Richard Peirse's direction of Bomber Command. He seemed to have little grasp of operational realities and was a most convenient scapegoat. On 13 November the Air Ministry instructed him to curtail drastically the scale of sorties against Germany, especially in bad weather.

Despite this, there was considerable resistance to the Chief of Air Staff's request for further fog dispersal experiments to be carried out, and when Lord Cherwell reluctantly recommended postponement of any further experiments, Winston Churchill's interest in the subject seems to have dwindled, for on 29 November, accepting the proposal, he minuted Sir Charles Portal, '. . . Meanwhile, do what you think best.' This rather suggests that if anyone cared to take the matter further he would have no objection, but that fog dispersal was by no means his main war concern. Things were not going well in the Mediterranean, North Africa or the Atlantic, to which conflicts his energies were more urgently drawn.

So there the matter rested, for 1941 at any rate; a year in which on at least sixteen occasions more British aircraft crashed on their return from operations than fell prey to enemy flak or fighters; a year during which Chris Everitt's estimate of 966 bomber losses is supplemented by Max Hastings's that another 359 crashed on return. These estimates take no account of the drain due to training and non-operational casualties.

During the winter of 1941/2 the most significant of Bomber Command's operations were directed against the German battleships *Scharnhorst* and *Gneisenau*. They were not very effective and did not prevent the ships escaping through the English Channel, but the period saw a substantial fall in aircraft losses. Immediately following the escape of the German warships, Winston Churchill expressed himself 'in favour of the resumption of full bombing of Germany, subject always of course to our not incurring heavy losses due to bad weather and enemy resistance combined'.

Sir Arthur Harris succeeded Sir Richard Peirse as Commander-in-Chief (C-in-C) Bomber Command in March 1942 and inherited this policy, which he pursued unreservedly. But as the sorties rose so did the casualties. In the period February–May 1942 Bomber Command mounted attacks on sixty nights and thirty-seven days, with the recorded loss of 313 aircraft and their crews, and it is estimated that at least another eighty bombers crashed on return from operations.

Anxiety over the effects of fog on future bombing operations must have lurked in the minds of the War Cabinet and discussion took place, culminating in a memo from Sir Archibald to the prime minister on 23 April 1942, only part of which has survived: 'We under-rate neither the extreme value nor the extreme difficulty of the project, and although previous experiments have cast doubts upon its practicability, we should like the study of the problem and experiments to continue. I will inform the Ministry of Aircraft Production accordingly and at the same time ask them to send you a brief of previous investigations.'

Records show that following the 1,000-bomber raid on Cologne in May 1942, more than 10,000 sorties were flown during the next ten weeks, at a cost of over 500 bombers lost. In addition to these figures, over fifty machines are known to have crashed on their return, quite apart from non-operational losses.

During that time the total production of heavy bombers was less than 600. This was particularly galling to Churchill, for in a review of the war position compiled on 21 July he had urged that: 'renewed intense efforts should be made by the Allies to develop during the winter and onwards, ever growing, ever more accurate and ever more far-ranging bomber attacks upon Germany'. To compound the matter, the weather during the third and fourth quarters of 1942 mitigated against sustained operations.

With these factors in the background a proposal to construct emergency runways for the succour of aircraft returning with battle damage, crew injury, fuel shortage or just plain lost was considered. Three sites were earmarked: Woodbridge in Suffolk, Carnaby, near Bridlington, Yorkshire, and Manston in Kent (initially called the Canterbury site). Their benefits, however, were not to be experienced for many months.

Losses continued to mount, and reports of these caused urgent measures again to be considered by the prime minister's scientific advisers and his air minister, and at about this time (we can be no more specific than that), the Committee for the Co-ordination of the Bomber Offensive was asked to consider the problem and make recommendations. This they did, and on 2 September 1942:

> It was decided that the Air Minister for Supply and Organization (AMSO), in consultation with Lord Cherwell and Professor Dobson [an eminent meteorologist who was familiar with the earlier fog dispersal experiments] and the Petroleum Warfare Department (PWD), should undertake full scale trials in fog dispersal, making use of the research and design work carried out by the Air Ministry before the war.

Consultations went ahead and on 25 September Air Minister Archibald Sinclair added his support for the project in a letter to Winston Churchill:

> I am persuaded that the procedure which offers the best chance of rapid progress in fog clearance is to entrust the experimental work to the Petroleum Warfare Dept. Mr Geoffrey Lloyd, the Minister for Petroleum, is prepared to undertake it. The department has experience in dealing with analogous problems and they have a certain amount of plant and equipment which would enable them to get to work at once. Lord Cherwell agrees that this is the best line of action – indeed, the suggestion first came from him. It would help Mr Lloyd if you would send him a Minute authorizing him to proceed!

Within twenty-four hours a prime minister's personal minute was on Geoffrey Lloyd's desk: 'It is of great importance to find means to dissipate fog at aerodromes so that aircraft can land safely. Let full experiments to this end be put in hand by the Petroleum Warfare Department with all expedition. They should be given every support. W.S.C.'

FOG AND EARLY DISPERSAL EXPERIMENTS

Of the Petroleum Warfare Department, Major General Sir Donald Banks, its first and only director general, said:

> On 5 July 1940 I received a telephone summons from Sir Horace Wilson who wanted me to see Mr Geoffrey Lloyd, Secretary for Petroleum about an urgent and important job which he had in hand. Geoffrey Lloyd was of that rarer type of Minister who relishes novelties and cultivates enthusiasm. Most men in office have found that the long path of self-repression from the visionary ideals of the first election address to the ultimate opportunity to exercise power has transformed creative enthusiasm into more sedate qualities of reform. The number who, by the time they have reached ministerial rank, are still able to allow their enthusiasms rein are few and refreshing as springs of water in a dry land. Such Geoffrey Lloyd proved to be throughout our time together in PWD.
>
> On 9 July 1940 PWD was born. There was no specific authority for establishing a new department; indeed it had no documentary status at all beyond a Treasury letter creating me an

'Accounting Officer'. This latter step was all-important. It meant that subject to Treasury control and accountability we could spend such sums as we required, unfettered by recourse to other departments. How important it was, transpired only in the course of later developments, for our financial independence enabled us to go ahead with experiments and to pursue ideas with a flexibility which would have been difficult to obtain under the aegis of larger organizations.

Prior to this invitation, the department had already been involved in the construction of a south coast flame barrage as an anti-invasion precaution following Dunkirk, and flame thrower experiments, and some of its associated personnel had been developing the underwater petrol pipeline PLUTO ('Pipe Line Under The Ocean'). Pipes and pumps of one sort or another were its stock in trade.

Fog has been a hazard to travellers since men first ventured from their caves, causing mishaps ranging from mere delays to major disasters. The earth's atmosphere contains water vapour, which has been drawn up or evaporated from the seas, lakes and rivers which cover two-thirds of its surface. Once absorbed, the vapour, which is invisible, is distributed around the globe by its infinite variety of wind systems. The amount of vapour which can be borne in the atmosphere depends on the temperature and the air pressure in a given location.

On a British winter day, the air at, say, 40° F, is capable of carrying up to 6.8 g per cu. m of vapour. It is then said to be saturated, or at its dew-point. If the air temperature decreases or the barometric pressure falls to give equivalent effect, it becomes less and less able to hold that quantity. Its wetness, or humidity, is said to increase until moisture starts to coagulate into tiny drops, or condenses, and becomes visible.

As an example of this from the figures just used: if the air temperature should be reduced from 40° F to 38° F, only 6.2 of the 6.8 gms/cu. m of moisture can be borne and the remaining 0.6gms/cu. m forms into water droplets, which may impede visibility if the condensation takes place over a large enough area. When this phenomenon occurs above the earth's surface it is referred to as *cloud*, at ground or sea level it is termed *fog*. Conversely, of course, if the volume of fog at 38° F is heated, droplets evaporate until at 40° F they have all disappeared and the air is saturated with 6.8 g of water vapour per cu. m. If the air is heated further, it then becomes unsaturated again, i.e. capable of carrying even more moisture away.

On a clear, calm, autumn or winter night, the ground temperature falls considerably after sunset, chilling the air above it and reducing its capacity to retain its moisture. Its greatest effect is felt in the few hours before dawn. Because the heat has been lost due to radiation from the earth's surface, the fog which results when the air temperature falls below its dew-point is known as radiation fog and is the commonest on British airfields. Unfortunately the nights most favourable to the formation of radiation fog were the very times when Bomber Command was wont to be most active and the fog to have its most disruptive effect on its operation.

Sometimes fogs are caused when cool, moist, slow-moving winds, still above dew-point, are chilled as they creep over certain topographical features such as sodden fenland fields or sandy heathlands, which are poor retainers of heat, to the extent that their saturation point is reached and condensation takes place. The fogs so generated are referred to as advection fogs, and can occur at any time of year.

Poor visibility when approaching an airfield to land may be caused by, as one airman put it, 'fog which sits upon the ground or by cloud, which doesn't'. Stratus is the name given to the layered cloud with the lowest base of all. It seldom has a base above 1,500 ft and under some conditions is indistinguishable from fog. It is formed in the same way as advection fog, i.e. when moist air blows across a terrain whose temperature is below its dew-point, or where it is forced to rise to a height where the same thing happens. As the air moves along laden with its moisture suspended, it has the appearance of a layer of cloud, though if it encounters high ground en route, it will be observed as fog. As with advection fog, the south-west peninsula is a favourable region in Britain for stratus cloud, as the incoming air crosses a progressively cooler sea surface, followed by high cliffs.

The formation of fog over wartime Britain was often aggravated by pollution from millions of coal-fired factory and domestic chimneys. In these days it is perhaps difficult for many readers to picture the pea-soup fogs which accumulated before the Clean Air Act (1956). Road, rail and air traffic were frequently brought to a standstill for days on end, as was coastal and river-borne shipping. Even football matches were cancelled!

Emissions from chimneys consisted of millions of minute particles of soot which provided nuclei for condensation drops to form as they gradually drifted out to country areas where radiation fogs were forming and where airfields were situated. Oil-fired installations and waste fumes from chemical and metallurgical plant also contributed to the murk, for the minuscule microns of oiliness formed a film around each globule of moisture, making subsequent evaporation by natural or artificial means more difficult.

Following Mr Churchill's minute, things moved with commendable speed. Mr A.C. Hartley, chief engineer of the Anglo-Iranian Oil Co., who had played a leading part in the invention and development of the cross-Channel petrol pipe-line PLUTO, was appointed technical director of PWD on 30 September, and shortly afterwards Mr E.G. Walker, civil and aeronautical engineer, became chief engineer (Plate 2). Mr Walker's Christian names were Edward George, but he was invariably known as E.G. His daughter, Mrs Darnborough, said of him: 'Our family were often puzzled when on foggy nights he used to disappear into the wilds of Kent in a government issue donkey jacket with torch and boots instead of his usual city suit. It was not until after the war that we understood the reason for this strange behaviour, though we realized that he was on highly secret work.'

Plate 2 FIDO Chief Engineer E.G. Walker (standing, with trilby) examining a postwar FIDO project (Mrs M. Darnborough)

Discussions between Geoffrey Lloyd, Sir Donald Banks, Messrs Hartley, Walker and others, took place. Mr Lloyd then set off to consult fruit farmers in Kent on how they combatted frost and fog in their orchards. He was quite pleased with his outing:

> We duly arrived at Canterbury and saw Mr E.J. Mount, one of four men of this name who are among the most substantial fruit farmers in the country . . . he proved exactly the type of man with whom I wished to talk, and had on view one of his orchard heaters. . . . Mr Mount quickly warmed to the idea of the experiments I proposed and spontaneously suggested that he should carry out tests himself with his own heaters . . . and is putting in hand the collection of some two hundred in a field particularly susceptible to fog.

Meanwhile Mr Hartley and the director general consulted with officials of the Gas, Light & Coke Co. and the Metropolitan Water Board, and together with Mr Walker surveyed the then incomplete No. 2 reservoir at Staines (now the King George VI reservoir) with a view to taking it over for fog dispersal experiments. It was an ideal site and was immediately placed at the Department's disposal by the Water Board (Plate 3).

On 8 October 1942 the PWD's liaison officer Wing Commander (Wg Cdr) Wooldridge, contacted Air Marshal (later Marshal of the Royal Air Force) Sir Arthur Harris, First World War confrere of Mr Hartley, to establish what were his requirements. He considered that a landing area 1,000 yd long and 100 yd wide would need to be cleared to a height of 100 ft, and suggested that he saw Gp Capt (later Air Vice-Marshal) Basil Embry, Commander of the Wittering Sector of 12 Group Fighter Command, which covered the approaches to the Midlands through the area of the Wash. Accordingly, Mr Hartley visited Wittering with Gp Capt Embry and Wg Cdr John Wooldridge. The latter had already carried out nearly 100 operations over Germany and by way of a rest had been seconded to act as a liaison officer between Bomber Command and the Petroleum Warfare Department. It was then that Major R.H. Mayo, another First World War colleague of Mr Hartley, suggested that Gp Capt (later

Plate 3 Incomplete Staines reservoir, placed at disposal of Petroleum Warfare Department by Metropolitan Water Board. See Fig. 1 (PWD)

Air Vice-Marshal) D.C.T. Bennett, whose Pathfinder Force (PFF) had recently been established, might have some useful suggestions to make. Until then it was decided to proceed with 'preliminary arrangements in connection with research on the dispersing of fog' at the Staines reservoir, based on the pre-war experiments at Farnborough and Martlesham, and to erect similar burners at Moody's Down farm in Hampshire. Coke-burning was also considered, and to this end the Gas, Light & Coke Co. agreed to construct a series of coke-burning braziers at Staines.

Up to this time the fog dispersal project had no convenient name. A meeting at the Petroleum Warfare Department on 5 October 1942 was to 'consider the preliminary arrangements in connection with research on the dispersal of fog'. Referred to as 'a fog dispersal provisional investigation plan' on 8 October, this did not trip lightly off the tongue, and 'a fog dispersal investigation operation' used on a document of the following day was not much better. But then Lyn Urwick, a major on Sir Donald's staff, noticed that if the positions of the two middle words in this phrase were reversed the meaning would not be seriously altered and the initial letters FIDO would make a useful companion for PLUTO which already existed. At some time in 1945, Sir Donald says, it was 'readjusted in RAF jargon to "Fog, Intensive Dispersal Of".' Winston Churchill's minute, that 'means to dissipate fog' be pursued, was dated 26 September 1942. Documents referring to FIDO without any full stops between the letters exist from 9 October. A.C. Hartley uses it thus for the first time on 22 October 1942.

After a flying visit to Moody's Down and lunch at the oil company's experimental station at Kempshott on the 10th, Mr Hartley picked up Geoffrey Lloyd and Wg Cdr Wooldridge and headed for Gp Capt Bennett's Pathfinder headquarters at Wyton in Cambridgeshire. Gp Capt Bennett recalled:

> A moustached wing commander called Wooldridge knocked on the front door of my quarters and asked to see me. It was just about dinner-time, so I invited him in. He came diffidently inside the door and said that he had some friends outside. Before inviting them in, however, he waved a letter in my face and asked me to read it. I glanced at it and saw that the signature was that of Winston Churchill. Briefly it said that the scientists had promised that fog could be cleared and that he wished all concerned to grant the best cooperation in bringing this about.

Gp Capt Bennett more than welcomed Wg Cdr Wooldridge and his companions and was delighted at such a prospect:

> The four visitors looked at each and almost burst with laughter. The contrast of finding someone who was keen to have fog cleared, compared to the discouragement which had faced them in the northern groups was almost too much for them. The C-in-C Bomber Command, who was enthusiastic about the idea, had sent them to the main force groups first as he did not want me to be diverted by a development not peculiar to our needs.

Mrs Bennett, who entertained them, recalled that the minister was 'a very excitable man who kept walking up and down puffing his pipe'. Airfield plans and photographs of Wyton were made available to the party on their return to London the next day. Initially it was intended to install two rows of Four-oaks burners (see Plate 1) on each side of the runway, 50 yd back from its edge. While the planning was going on, the reservoir at Staines was 'commissioned' as Station I. Denys Fox, an Anglo-Iranian Oil Co. (AIOC) production and maintenance engineer, was appointed research engineer and later research and experimental engineer (Plate 5). Under his direction a series of pipelines up to 650 yd long was laid on the bed of the reservoir, with standpipes every two feet for the burners, and work was begun on a line of braziers for the coke-burning experiments.

On 16 October, however, there was a hitch. In conference with representatives of civil engineers William Press, Wyton was considered to be unsuitable for the installation of the

Plate 4 Geoffrey Lloyd, Minister for Petroleum, and AVM Donald Bennett with Pathfinder aircrew, late 1943 (IWM)

system. So Mr Hartley and his advisers examined Wyton's satellite airfield at Graveley, the home of 35 (PFF) Squadron, and found it admirable for their purpose. The very next day William Press's engineers began surveying the site. Graveley was designated Station II, and all full-scale operational trials of FIDO were subsequently conducted there. A few days later Frank Gill, another physicist with the AIOC, who had been working with the PWD for some time, joined the staff at Staines as technical officer with particular responsibility for the design of burners.

It was quickly realized that the PWD brought a wide degree of expertise to the problem, but that the large-scale assemblies of piping and pumping equipment were not very flexible of variation. It was decided therefore to carry out calculations on model installations, scaled down so that only small quantities of fuel would be required and desired conditions of air movement could be imposed at will. Data could be assembled from which it would be possible to predict the behaviour of the installations at Staines and airfields chosen for full-scale trials.

Accordingly, the director general and Dr Oliver Rankine, Anglo-Iranian's senior physicist, visited a number of potential venues for such a project, and by 22 October the Empress Hall, Earls Court, was decided on. On the concrete floor of the ice rink a wind tunnel 163 ft long, 30 ft wide and 12 ft high was constructed. A large fan at one end, suitably geared down, provided the means of inducing artificial winds of from 1 to 5 ft per second in the tunnel (Plate 6). Alongside the wind tunnel was built a smaller wind channel, with no roof, in which calm air conditions of minimal wind speed could be reproduced. Under the direction of Dr Rankine (Plate 7) assisted by Mr L.F.G. Simmons, thousands of readings were taken in the two installations over a period of many months. This information was passed on to the

*Plate 5 Research and Experimental
Engineer Denys Fox at Staines (Denys Fox)*

engineers at Staines, enabling them to pursue their experiments regardless of weather conditions.

Meteorologist Fred Gee and others had a great affection for the dedicated doctor, who was completely immersed in his work:

> One of my lasting memories is of sitting on the floor of the now demolished Empress Hall, over what had been an ice rink and on which had been constructed a large wind tunnel for the simulation of fog. Next to me on a low stool sat Oliver Rankine, Professor of Physics at Imperial College, who was in charge of scaled-down experiments aimed at calculating the amount and distribution of heat needed to disperse fog once it had been formed. In my hands was a potentiometer on which I took readings from sets of thermo-couples spread around the tunnel. In the Professor's hand was a cigarette which he had just taken from a packet of Wills' Goldflake; behind his ear was a pencil. A thought crossed his mind and he stared at the instruments. Then, quite slowly, he put the cigarette behind his other ear, placed the pencil in his mouth, and tried to light the end of it with a match.

Stanley Crawford also recalled: 'I'm sure too that all members of the Met. unit working closely with Professor Rankine greatly appreciated his help, his kindness and constant good humour. The only day of the week when he insisted on getting back home in good time was on Thursdays to catch the Tommy Handley programme, ITMA.' Professor Peter Broadhurst, a twenty-year-old meteorological assistant at the time, also spoke well of Dr Rankine: 'He took a kindly interest in "us lads" and taught us many lessons of ingenuity and precision which we carried with us into our subsequent careers.'

While Dr Rankine was setting up his wind tunnel, much activity was taking place elsewhere. Not only was Graveley earmarked for full-scale trials, but the emergency airfield under construction at Woodbridge was considered as well. There a 4,000 yd long runway with 3 miles of open country beyond was in mind. A coke-burning installation was erected by the Gas, Light & Coke Co. at Staines, consisting of a series of rectangular braziers in line, and there and at Moody's Down farm in Hampshire parallel lines of Four-oaks burners were also set up. Fortunately, the burners used in the pre-war experiments had been put in storage and were rapidly made available (Plates 8 and 9). The system was tested in shallow fog on the night of 28/29 October 1942 (only a month after FIDO's inception). Two parallel lines of

Plate 6 The wind tunnel at Earls Court Ice Rink, powered by a London Underground ventilation fan (PWD)

Plate 7 Professor Oliver Rankine conducting air speed experiments in the Earls Court wind tunnel (IWM)

Plate 8 Moody's Down in its heyday. Burner lines operating left and right. Remains of burns centre. Concrete pipes related to induction type burner not proceeded with (IWM)

Plate 9 Moody's Down in 1992. Waving corn stands where once FIDO burners flamed (Alex Wright)

burners 90 yd long and 8 ft apart were laid out and an 85 ft high turntable ladder was raised halfway along. As reference points four hurricane lamps were fixed to the ladder at intervals and observations taken at distances up to 250 yd away. When the burners were lit, sufficient clearance was obtained to encourage further experimentation.

With the Four-oaks type of burner it had been found impossible to obtain a smokeless burn using petrol alone as a fuel, and a mixture of 80 per cent alcohol to 20 per cent petrol was used. Edward Ryder drove a tanker to Liverpool for supplies of commercial alcohol for the purpose:

> On our first trip we found that going up steep hills the alcohol came pouring out of the rear filler cap breather on top of the tank, and going downhill it poured out of the front cap and all over the driver's cab. As you can imagine, we dreaded the thought of anyone throwing away a lighted match or cigarette end in our path, and we crawled back to Moody's Down. When we off-loaded the lorry we examined the inside of the tank, to find that there were plenty of struts in position, but no baffle plates had been fitted!

Flame-throwers mounted on Bren-gun carriers were also under test at that time and a flame-thrower had in fact been used for fog dispersal itself, in an experiment at the AIOC's proving station at Kempshott on 28 October. A Cockatrice had been brought out in thick fog with a visibility of only 80 yd. Six 1½-second bursts had been fired and the fog in the immediate vicinity of the flame-thrower cleared immediately, passing down wind. Two Cockatrices were then stationed facing each other some yards apart and fired, but the results are not recorded. Edward Ryder recalls that on one occasion the machines gave several hefty squirts in a strong wind, drenching everyone within range; but fortunately the fuel did not ignite. It meant, however, that nobody dared smoke for a week!

Meanwhile construction of similar Four-oaks burner lines and coke-filled braziers had been going ahead at Staines. A number of young meteorologists under Principal Meteorologist Harry Edge and meteorological officers Leslie MacPherson and Charles (needless to say, Dickie) Bird took up residence. Several of them had pleasant recollections of the place and the work they did there. Said Fred Gee:

> Many of our experiments were full scale in the bottom of a dried up reservoir at Staines. Here the Ministry of Works had built a hut in which Leslie MacPherson, Peter Broadhurst and I housed our instruments, cooked scrambled eggs (from imported dried egg and powdered milk) and snatched some sleep while waiting for fogs to form. When conditions were right I would be strapped to the ladder of a London Fire Brigade appliance and shot to the dizzy heights of 60 . . . 80 . . . maybe 100 ft to measure the air temperatures before and after the burner lines on either side of me were lit. I cannot pretend that I was ever scorched, nor was I ever scared, but I was sometimes hard pressed to read the instrument scale in the initial gloom and subsequent glare.

Fred recalls that the road into the reservoir from the street (see Fig. 1) was designated 'private', although 'primitive' would have been a more apt description:

> It stretched over several contours for more than a mile, and to save time, if not trouble, we acquired transport in the form of a clapped-out Morris saloon. On that vehicle I first learned to drive. Not having to take it on the public highway, there was no need for a licence, but I ought to have been insured! Lurching up a narrow ramp and down the side of a steep slope into the bottom of a fog-filled reservoir on a cold night, with frosted windscreen, was a hazard for an accomplished driver; for a novice it was a nightmare! Compensation for such a risk was the sense of importance in being entrusted with the burning of thousands of gallons of petrol at a time – more in an hour than many of us have consumed in the lifetime since.

Peter Broadhurst, too, regarded the experience as exciting. The terrain inside the unfinished reservoir was like a beach. Off-duty they could sunbathe by quarry-like pools. He first learned to drive there too, driving the battered old car used for transportation to and from the

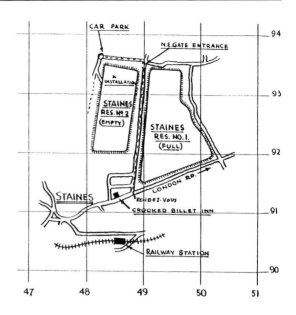

Fig. 1 Section of Ordnance Survey Map 114 – Windsor, showing site of PWD Station I, Staines. See Plate 3

gate, up and down the embankments to the huts in the middle where the staff slept when fog, and therefore a burn, was expected: 'At Staines I first encountered the concept of control measurement of air temperature before and after a burn, and my first taste of responsibility in being the senior person (at 20!) on the spot when a fog descended and required the order to burn some ten thousand gallons of petrol.' He also recalled being spoken to by the minister of petroleum himself, no less; but as he only wanted to know why the fire engine bell was ringing, not much of a conversation developed.

Dickie Bird observed, during wind tunnel tests at Earls Court, that when a 'runway' was completely enclosed by burners the efficiency of the installation was less than might have been expected. (Perhaps because of controlled as opposed to haphazard supply of air to the burners, it was advantageous actually to leave a gap between the cross-burner at the beginning of a runway and the side burners. The space could be as much as 80 yd and permitted a much more even level of flame. The gap became known as the Bird gap – with a capital B for obvious reasons.)

Engine fitter Ron Dill spent some time at Staines. In his recollections, the first and most important building he noticed was the cookhouse at the south end of the reservoir, and what there was of FIDO to the north:

> The small office was manned twenty-four hours a day and to here came messages when the boffins wanted to come down to experiment. There was a standing order on the wall instructing whoever was on duty that 'When you cannot see the parapet for fog, ring Whitehall'. We would then go into our routine – first ring the NFS for fire crew; second ring living quarters for service staff; third ring duty cook. These instructions were usually at some unearthly hour of the night, often in thick fog.
>
> The NFS crews manned the escapes with two men to each tender, one with a stop-watch and the other hanging on to the bell-rope. The Whitehall folk would decide on a height for the ladder, which was raised by set distances at set intervals. At each interval, indicated by a bell, the duty meteorologist would note the barometric pressure, temperature, height, etc., while he clung to the top of the ladder. Of course not all burns were carried out at night or in fog. Sometimes they were carried out in daylight or when some modification had been carried out or if variations of pump pressures were required.

Parallel experiments with Four-oaks burners had been carried out at both Moody's Down and Staines, and on 4 November 1942 came an unusual opportunity to see both systems at work at the same time, and the coke-burning braziers at Staines too. Fog had been predicted and the director general with Geoffrey Lloyd and others made their way to Moody's Down in the middle of the night. Sir Donald recalled:

> The stage was set when we arrived, and the burners 200 yd in length and 100 yd apart were being lit. In the centre was an 80 ft fire escape borrowed from the Southampton Fire Brigade, and up it climbed a local fireman, to disappear after a few rungs into the empyrean, like the boy in the Indian rope trick. As the burners got going, however, he came into view at the top of the ladder. Incredulous, we had the burners turned down and the fog closed round and blotted him out. Then they were turned up again and he reappeared.

The test was repeated at dawn to the great satisfaction of all present. During the same foggy night a petrol and a coke-burning demonstration had been arranged by Denys Fox and his colleagues at Staines, while the director general was en route from Moody's Down. Unfortunately the Four-oaks burners did not perform very well and the system created more smoke and fog than it cleared. It was Fred Gee's turn to perform the Indian rope trick that night:

> . . . when a party of 'top brass' arrived at about four in the morning to witness the way in which fog could be dispersed by a FIDO installation. From the top of my fire escape I watched the burners light up, and cheered as the visibility rose from a few feet to several hundred yards. Then, as I noted down the increase in temperature, I looked down to discover that the fog had suddenly returned. I could hear excited chatter from the audience below, expressing no doubt their displeasure at being robbed of sleep as much as at the spectacle they had witnessed. It was decided afterwards that the water droplets in the fog that night were larger than usual and that when the surrounding air rushed in to replace the hot air above the burners, FIDO was producing insufficient heat to maintain the evaporating.

The coke burners behaved much better and cleared the air in their immediate vicinity remarkably quickly (Plate 10). As a result of this early success the Air Ministry agreed to an experimental coke-burning installation at the Bomber Command airfield at Lakenheath.

Plate 10 Coke braziers – a trial burn at Staines. A lorry-load for recharging, right centre (PWD)

Although some fog clearance had been achieved, it was thought that the Four-oaks petrol-burning system did not have very great potential; the throughput of fuel was low and the double row of standpipes on each side of a runway would pose a serious obstacle to any aircraft which might swerve and collide with them.

FIRST SUCCESSFUL BURNERS

Such difficulties were not permitted to hold up developments for long. During the trials held on 4 November it had been noticed that some of the heaters burned clearer than others, and the conclusion was reached that heat from the flames had warmed the standpipes beneath them so that the petrol mixture was vaporizing as it entered the burners, much as it does in a painter's blowlamp. Mr Hartley wondered if a plain drilled pipe lying on the surface would function just as well. With characteristic verve he asked Frank Gill to tackle the problem, produce a design and have it ready 'by next Thursday'.

Frank was equal to the task and carried out some preliminary experiments at the oil company's research station at nearby Sunbury on Thames. Transferred to Staines, the unit was further developed under the supervision of Chief Engineer E.G. Walker and Resident Engineer Denys Fox, until the burner depicted in Plate 11 was produced. The corrugated iron sheets were intended to maintain an even burn in cross-winds and the piping was staggered, an old AIOC pipeline trick to permit expansion without distortion. As it was Mr *H*artley's idea, using *Anglo-I*ranian expertise, and as the petrol was being burned in the form of a *gas*, the system was christened Haigas, later to be known as the Mk 1 burner.

The theoretical work for much of the Staines project had been carried out at Earls Court by Dr Oliver Rankine and his assistant Mr Simmonds and the good doctor jumped at the

Plate 11 Haigas, or Mk I burner. Petrol enters the system via pipe 1, zigzags 50 yd along pipe 2, returns via pipe 3, travels another 50 yd along pipe 4 and comes back along pipe 5, the burner pipe, which is pierced every 6 in along its top surface (PWD)

chance to observe a fog-bound trial at Staines on 10 January 1943. The director, Lord Suirdale, came with him and observed the proceedings from the banks of the reservoir. This was not good enough for Dr Rankine, and he had himself hoisted 100 ft up on the fire escape ladder to make his own temperature and humidity recordings from there. He was able to report that: '. . . with a cross-wind at ground level of approximately 7 mph, heat evolution at the rate of 20 therms per yd per hour sufficed to clear the fog to a height of at least a hundred feet. This is compatible with theoretical expectations,' justifying many of those long hours of painstaking observation in the chilly ice rink tunnel. Following the success of this experiment, the Air Ministry proposed setting up a second airfield to be so equipped. Work at Graveley was already under way and Lakenheath (Station III) being earmarked for coke-burning experiments, the next aerodrome to have petrol-fired equipment was the Pathfinder station at Downham Market in Norfolk, designated Station IV.

Even before Dr Rankine saw the consummation of his work, the potential of the Haigas system was becoming obvious, and orders were given for all work using Four-oaks burners to be stopped. As it had been planned for installation at Graveley and, provisionally, at Woodbridge too, not everyone was pleased. Wg Cdr Wooldridge told Gp Capt Bennett that at the current rate it would be six months before the changeover at Graveley could be effected, and that the engineers at Woodbridge were feeling 'very Bolshie' about the scheme being changed again. On 19 November 1942 Gp Capt Bennett wrote to him: 'I have just heard from the Station Commander what an awful mess has been made out at Graveley – if it is wrong it will all have to come out again. In any case it is taking six times as long as was anticipated. Please excuse such a bad-tempered letter, but my excuse is that I appreciate only success.' Nevertheless, progress was gradually made over succeeding weeks and order proceeded out of chaos, though as a safeguard it was decided to carry on with the coke-burning experiments.

Burning coke as a means of dispersing fog was of interest not only to the RAF and the PWD, and we might take space here to follow its brief career as an alternative to petrol. It became known that the London Midland and Scottish Railway Co. was also concerned with fog as a hindrance to freight and passenger services alike. The willing cooperation of their Derby works was obtained and a site chosen near the company's power station between the river and the canal, where fog conditions were likely to be bad.

Lewis Patrick was a fitter at the carriage and wagon works, and recalls being directed to a variety of odd jobs:

> One of our tasks was to carry out an experiment on FIDO (though the word was not used) which was something completely new to us; and we struggled without drawings and specifications as time was of paramount importance. As steel was being put to other uses, wherever possible we had to improvise. However, we improved with experience and the War Office sent us all the materials we needed.

Eventually 340 braziers, each 9 ft 6 in long and 3 ft 9 in wide were built, which enclosed an area 425 yd long and 150 yd wide, about the equivalent of a third of an airfield runway. The braziers were charged with 70 tons of wood shavings, 90 tons of firewood and 200 tons of coke. A tower was erected at the centre to enable observations to be made up to 100 ft above ground level. It was equipped with a bosun's chair which could be laboriously winched to the top. To speed up combustion, it was considered advisable to spray the shavings with paraffin beforehand. Needless to say, foggy days were immediately in short supply, and it was not until 20 February 1943 that the first trial took place. 'When the day arrived [continued Lewis Patrick], the boffins were there in full force, but were not very impressed, for the fire itself created more black smoke than the fog and due to the intense heat most of the wire mesh and some of the angle-iron supports became distorted and were of no further use.'

Plate 12 Static coke braziers and trolleys for intersecting runways at Lakenheath, 1943 (PWD)

On this day fog began to form at about 7 o'clock but light-up was delayed in case the fog dispersed naturally. The braziers had, however, been sprayed with paraffin, and the coke was well alight within an hour. The improvement in visibility inside the rectangle was striking. The great heat created, however, caused a marked change in local weather conditions, noted by Lewis when a second trial was held on 15 March 1943. He recalled that shortly after light-up the heat created a breeze of its own, 'which dispersed the fog but blew burning debris on to a local farmer's barn and haystacks and on to our own wooden stores shed, destroying the lot'.

A complete installation was laid down at Lakenheath, including braziers on rails to cover intersecting runways (Plate 12). No operational use of this installation was ever made, and on 5 June 1943 orders were given for FIDO to be dismantled as 'it constitutes a serious obstruction to any aircraft which might swing from the runway'. Though never used in earnest, the vast quantities of coke acquired for FIDO did not go amiss, and it is said that the Nissen huts at Lakenheath were the best heated in East Anglia!

FIRST SUCCESSFUL LANDINGS

. . . I had vague thoughts of seeing lions jumping through a hoop of flames at the circus
AVM Donald Bennett

The Haigas installation at Graveley (Fig. 2) was completed at the end of January 1943, and in early February Mr Hartley sought an opportunity to view it in operation from the air. Flying Control Officer Henry Hemming organized a light-up for him around midday on 5 February, and the now Air Commodore (Air Cdre) Bennett flew over the burners in a Gypsy Major. He landed to pick up Mr Hartley and they 'flew low over the burners without any

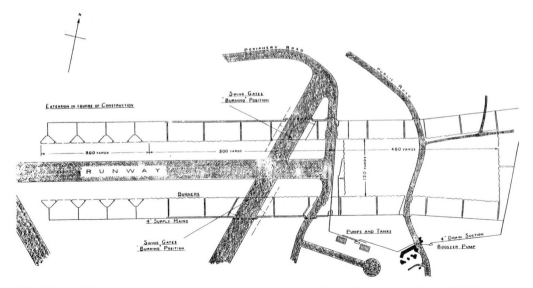

Fig. 2 Initial FIDO installation at Graveley. Approach box and first 500 yd were Mk I and Mk II burners. See Fig. 17 and Plates 11 and 15

bumps'. Their only misgiving was that by night or in fog, the long approach box might mislead pilots into landing too soon, depositing them into an orchard which lay before the airfield perimeter.

No doubt urged on by Mr Hartley, the system was tuned up and on 18 February Air Cdre Bennett put FIDO to the test for the first time by night. At 10.15 p.m. in poor, though not foggy, visibility he flew over from Oakington in a Lancaster of 156 Squadron. As he put it: 'I had vague thoughts of seeing lions jumping through a hoop of flames at the circus. The glare was certainly considerable and there was some turbulence, but it was nothing to worry about.'

After flying over the runway at 30–40 ft he came round again and made a successful landing and take-off. Air Cdre Bennett said that he could see the runway from a distance of 60 miles, whereas searchlights were only visible from 5 to 10 miles. He immediately wanted the system at Graveley to be extended and work to be expedited at Downham Market, so that the Pathfinders would always have an alternative aerodrome to use in foggy weather.

On 23 February Mr Hartley went to see the Bennetts and then on to Graveley. Aircraft were returning from a raid on Cologne when he arrived, and when the crews were de-briefed and bedded down, a demonstration of FIDO was organized. Flt Sgt Jordan i/c erks, only had six or seven men available to rush up and down the lines, which caused some delay in obtaining a full burn. What they lacked in speed they more than made up for in enthusiasm, however, for, according to Mr Hartley's diary, grass, hedges, trees and telegraph poles all went up in flames at the approach end of the system which, rather unwisely, passed through an orchard and across a country lane en route.

MORE AIRFIELDS ARE EQUIPPED

... consult the Chief Bomber and let me know what he thinks

Winston Churchill

Shortly after Graveley was earmarked as the first operational airfield to be equipped with FIDO, a number of proposals were considered concerning future work. Photographs of a successful fog clearance at Graveley early in April 1943 had been shown to the prime minister, who expressed a desire to have the scheme expanded: 'I should have thought it would be well to have half a dozen installations at different parts of the country so as to avoid a disaster if a sudden fog comes down upon our returning bombers. Also, this will give us greater freedom to act on doubtful nights. Will you consult the Chief Bomber and let me know what he thinks.'

Evidently the 'Chief Bomber', Sir Arthur Harris no less, was in favour and a provisional list of sites was drawn up. In addition to the experimental station at Staines (I), Graveley (II), Lakenheath (III) and Downham Market (IV), the following airfields were allocated station numbers: Lindholme (V), Blyton (VI), Melbourne (VII), Kirmington (VIII), Marston Moor (IX), Woodbridge (X), Carnaby (XI), Manston (XII), Fiskerton (XIII), Bradwell Bay (XIV), Hartfordbridge (XV), and St Eval (XVI). Coastal Command had asked that the Northern Ireland base of Ballykelly should be included, but settled for St Eval.

By July 1943, priority had been given to Melbourne, Fiskerton, Bradwell Bay, Hartfordbridge and St Eval, and when it was decided that the Airborne Cigar (ABC) Lancasters (see page 123) of 101 Squadron should accompany all bombing raids when the squadron took up station at Ludford Magna, that airfield was included as Station XVII.

On 4 December 1943, by which time construction at all the English airfields was under way, Bomber Command requested an increase to twelve in the number of airfields to be

Fig. 3 Distribution of FIDO-equipped airfields in England (R Met Soc)

installed with fog-dispersing equipment. The PWD did better than that. As well as proceeding with Woodbridge, where work had been carried out only tentatively because of the problems anticipated with its vast 250 yd wide runway, they also activated plans to construct FIDO at, in order of priority, Tuddenham (XIX), Metheringham (XX), the other two emergency airfields at Carnaby and Manston, Sturgate (XXI) and Foulsham (XXII); a total of fifteen in a great boomerang shape from Yorkshire to Kent to Cornwall (Fig. 3). Finally, in early 1945, the 2nd Tactical Air Force base at Epinoy near Cambrai was equipped with a portable FIDO system – as befits an air force on the move – and designated Station XXV.

As can be seen from Fig. 2, the early installation at Graveley did not cover the whole length of the runway. There was reluctance at this stage to put a line of burners across the far end of the runway to seal it off, as much for the morale of aircrew as anything. Investigations were carried out with heat blowers to see if they might act to seal off the upwind end of the airstrip, or even, if sufficient heat could be generated, to clear fog from the runway itself.

Plates 13 and 14 show that the blower consisted of an aeroplane engine with its propeller fitted back to front and mounted on a wheeled chassis, with a petrol burner like a flaming blowlamp. Bill Moore recalls being withdrawn from a project with ICI:

> . . . to supervise the testing of a heat blower unit for fog dispersal which had been made by ICI at Billingham and delivered to Staines. I was given an assistant to operate the blower, and my job was to obtain parts for same and have manufactured in the London area five more. The blowers used Merlin engines and 30 ft trailers together with operating controls, petrol vaporisers and burners and about thirty parts to connect the engine to the trailer. It proved no easy task to prise these parts out of various departments during wartime. All telephone lists had been withdrawn, and when I found the right person they would never answer direct, but would ring back to ensure authenticity.
>
> The blowers were a fearsome sight and the public must have wondered when seeing them transported to their various sites from Dagenham, where they were made by W.J. Reynolds Motors. The operation could be frightening and hazardous too, and my assistant had to be sent home after losing his nerve following a fire which burnt a tyre off the trailer. The temperature had to be judged high enough before the large petrol valve was quickly opened. The roar of the engine and of the burner made operating very uncomfortable. However, one got used to sensing when the vaporiser was hot enough.

Leslie MacPherson was a senior meteorologist with the PWD. On heat blowers he recalled:

> Analysis of the observations made at Staines clearly indicated the inadequacy of the unit. Despite this, the powers that be decided that it should be demonstrated on an airfield before an invited audience. The unit was trundled up to Graveley to await the right conditions. When these duly arrived, the audience was assembled and the demonstration took place late one night. I had never seen the unit working at night and I must confess it looked a fearsome sight. I could well understand the reluctance of members of the audience to get too near to it.
>
> Mr Lloyd was the most venturesome. I suppose that as the minister responsible for FIDO he thought that he should show an example. I kept an eye on him. He was moving about in line with the unit, holding up his hand to detect any heat moving past him. He started about 60 yd from it and gradually moved nearer to it. When he was about 30 yd away, a change in wind direction blew the hot air jet straight at him. He beat a hasty retreat, but his bowler hat blew from his head and sped on before him and was not recovered until the following morning, way across the airfield.

In practice, it was found that if the side-burners were extended upwind, any fog which did penetrate the open end would be 'burnt off' before entering far enough to constitute a hazard to taxiing aircraft. Experiments with an upwind cross-burner line, rapidly extinguishable and sunk into the runway so as to provide no obstructions, were pursued and are referred to later on.

Plate 13 Heat blowers made by W.J. Reynolds of Dagenham. A Merlin aero engine drove a pusher propeller (PWD)

Plate 14 Close-up of vaporizer coils and burners

THE HAIGILL SYSTEM

> . . . Demonstration very successful and christened HAIGILL
>
> *A.C. Hartley's diary*

Although the Haigas burners, later referred to as Mk 1s, were reckoned to be capable of raising the air temperature by the approximately 5° F necessary to disperse the fog which might descend upon them, they were not thought by any means to be the final design. They had yet to be subjected to rigorous operational conditions and were not the easiest of systems to construct in any quantity. Simpler design and improved performance were sought. One step to this end was to reduce the number of lengths of piping accompanying the burner pipe from three to two (Plates 15 and 16). This was designated the Mk II.

Within a short time Frank Gill devised a simple but most effective variation on the Mk II burner. He proposed that, instead of having a burner pipe in the middle with a vaporizer on each side, their roles should be reversed. The centre pipe was raised above the level of the outside burner pipes (so that the end view of the burner was of an equilateral triangle) and became the vaporizer, feeding the other two. The overall length of the burner was reduced from 50 to 20 yd, and was no longer required to be staggered.

Step by step over a period of months the design was improved until the design in Fig. 4 was produced. Initially the new burner was in the form of a 12-in equilateral triangle, but trials eventually determined that the best results were obtained with a triangle of only 7-in sides, which also reduced the obstruction factor. RAF ground crews later expressed their approval as this height was more convenient when propping up their camp bicycles! Eventually a heat output of over 50 therms per yd per hour was achieved, well in excess of the nominal 30 therms required to disperse fog.

Referring to burners as generating so many therms per yd per hour was a convenient measure of their heat output; the exact amount which evaporated the fog and the quantity which went to waste or warmed frozen operators is impossible to calculate. Thirty therms per yd per hour could be achieved by the consumption of 21.4 gallons of petrol per yd per hour; 40, 50 and 80 therms/yd/hour were obtained by burning 23.6, 35.8 and 57.3 gallons/yd/hour respectively. The therm values were much easier to remember.

The performance of the new type of burner was such an improvement on its predecessors that it was promptly named Haigill in honour of Frank and also referred to as the Mk III burner. As Mr Hartley's diary records it: 'Sunday 14 March – To Staines. Met Mr Lloyd, Rankine and Gill. Demonstrated original Graveley burner [Mk I], Graveley modified 12 in 3-pipe, and 7 in 3-pipe. Demonstration was very successful and christened the 3-pipe burner HAIGILL.' The only snag at this stage was that in May 1943 all petrol was treated with tetraethyl lead, which caused a hard deposit to accumulate in the jets at high temperatures and could cause output to decrease by as much as 10 per cent after a two-hour burn. Since unleaded petrol was unobtainable for the rest of the war, there was nothing for it but for someone to get down on his hands and knees and poke the holes clear every so often – or 'every too often,' as one victim said.

All of this necessarily took time, and it was October 1943 before the materials necessary for installing Mk III burners at Graveley were assembled. They were used to extend the original Graveley system by another 300 yd in the first instance and then gradually to replace all the Mk I and Mk II burners. As the guinea-pig, Graveley had to bear the upheaval of the progressive replacements, and later stations were spared the disorder involved. The next airfield to be equipped with FIDO, Downham Market, began with Mk IIIs and all subsequent aerodromes began with the next progression from that.

The first operational landings with FIDO took place at Graveley on 19/20 November 1943, followed before the end of the year by others at Downham Market, Fiskerton and Bradwell Bay; landmarks which are dealt with in their appropriate chapters in Part 2.

Plate 15 A Mk II burner converted from a Mk I. Length still 50 yd. Petrol enters far end of pipe 1, travels to loop in foreground, returns via pipe 2 and comes back along raised burner pipe 3 which is pierced along its top surface (PWD)

Plate 16 Mk II burner alight at night. Flames are coming from raised centre pipe. Corrugated iron windshield beyond (PWD)

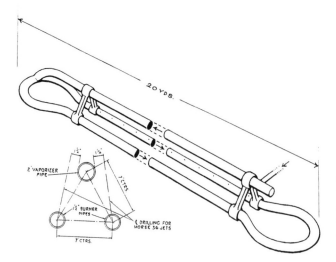

Fig. 4 Haigill or Mk III burner.
Workshop made, only 20 yd long.
Petrol flow as per arrows. Top pipe
is now the vaporizer and bottom
two are burners, whose jets
impinge their flames upon it

Figures: Jack Peppiatt

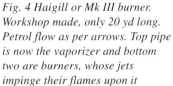

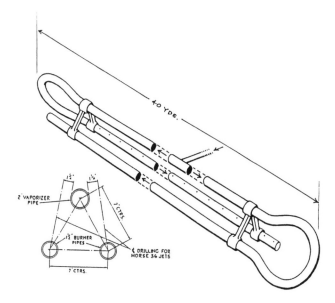

Fig. 5 Mk IV burner. Installed at
all British FIDO airfields. 40 yd
long. Petrol flow as per arrows.
Simplified for on-site airfield
construction

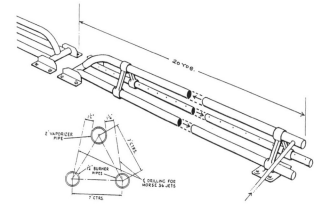

Fig. 6 Mk V burner. Progressively
replaced Mk IVs. Workshop
produced. Only 20 yd long. Petrol
flow as per arrows

Plate 17 Trial burn with Mk IV burners at Staines, 07.30, 20 May 1944. Ten minutes before light-up (PWD)

Plate 18 Ten minutes after light-up completed. The embankment is 700 yd from the camera (PWD)

Plate 19 Mk IV burner, detail showing somewhat crude airfield construction of end loop (IWM)

Pressure of time did not allow all the inherent faults in the system to be identified before they were subjected to the rigours of operational use. Manufacturing and technical difficulties and the proposed rapid expansion of FIDO-equipped airfields required simplification of the Mk III burners for quantity production, preferably on the airfields themselves. The design adopted before the end of 1943 was the Mk IV burner. The principle remained the same, as did the triangular form, but to reduce on-site welding the burner was doubled in length to 40 yd and the loop at each end was simplified (Fig. 5). The end-product was easier to construct, but operational experience revealed that the greater length was accompanied by a bigger distortion factor, as some of the plates show, due to the inadequate supply of spreaders and anchorage points; so much so that within six months, serious rethinking of the problem had to take place.

Therefore, after as much experimentation as time would allow, the Mk IV was replaced by the Mk V (Fig. 6), when the availability of labour and materials permitted a gradual overhaul of installations. The main differences were that the length of the Mk V burner was reduced to 20 yd again and the reverse-flow bend occurred at one end only. This section was made up in contractors' workshops, but the remainder could if necessary be welded on airfield sites. More and improved spreaders and anchorages were fitted and the nose or non-feed end was simplified.

TWO

Variations on a Theme

HAIRPIN BURNERS

Most experimental work at Staines and Moody's Down had involved surface burners of the Haigas and Haigill types, but consideration had also been given to setting burners in slots alongside the runway. Experiments at Staines were involved in the possibility of building a hairpin, two-pipe burner. Drs P.O. Rosin, H.R. Fehling and C.H. Lander of Imperial College were asked to investigate. Three days later they came back with a proposal to stand the hairpin on its edge with one leg of the pipe above the other, the lower pipe pierced to impinge its flames on the upper one, vaporizing the petrol passing through it (Fig. 7).

Experiments were carried out at the PWD station at Langhurst in Sussex and on a larger scale at Moody's Down. The decision was taken to opt for a hairpin burner in a much shallower trench. This meant that the flames would project above the covering grating, but ensure better air circulation within the slot. Eventually an optimum length of 10 ft 6 in for

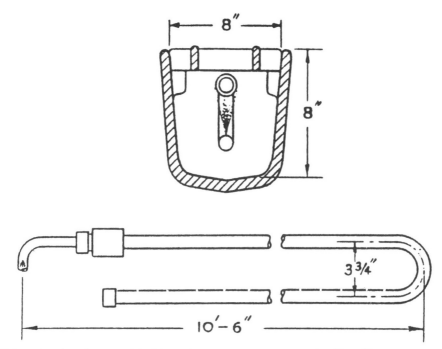

Fig. 7 Hairpin, alias slot, alias Blackbushe type burner, basic layout. See Plate 20

Plate 20 Hairpin burner in slot. Flames from jets in lower pipe impinge upon top, vaporizer pipe 3 in above it. Made in units 10 ft 6 in long. See Fig. 7 (PWD)

each burner was decided on. The hairpin pipe, ¾ in bore diameter, was set in a specially shaped cast-iron trough 8 in wide and 8 in deep (Plate 20), and the trough was fitted into a heat-resisting concrete trench. Half-inch steel bars formed a grid over the burners, somewhat thicker where the burners crossed intersecting runways. Ten double burners of seven yd each formed a section, each initially under the control of an operator, but subsequently under remote control for both fuel supply and ignition.

For major repairs or replacement it was a comparatively simple matter to disconnect and remove a 10 ft 6 in burner; but for the despised task of reaming or pricking out the jets when they became fouled by leaded petrol, the poor operator had to get down on hands and knees. As the upper pipes were only a few inches above the burners, and both were below ground level, aching backs and barked knuckles were frequent complaints.

Slot burners, also known as Blackbushe burners, were installed at that airfield from the middle of 1944. They were not noticeably more powerful in thermal output than the Haigill burners which they first complemented and then replaced there, but they were less intrusive and less subject to distortion. All cases of thick fog at Blackbushe were dealt with by the slot burners and Bill Beaumont, who was flight sergeant in charge of the system commended it as: ' . . . being much more efficient; one reason being that lighting was carried out simultaneously by electric igniters, whereas the old type had to be lit by hand with perhaps only a dozen men available to cover the whole length of burners'.

It was intended that the Blackbushe type of slot burners should equip the fog dispersal system at Heathrow Airport, but postwar economic conditions and the eventual introduction of superior landing equipment ruled out this proposal after the construction of a number of experimental burners had been completed.

HADES

By April 1943 the general principles of a FIDO installation had been established, but attention was focused on a problem still outstanding. The system could deal with the majority of fogs, but sometimes with a flat calm or a wind blowing 'up' the runway, intrusion could occur at the open end. As has already been noted, heat blowers had not overcome this difficulty. At this time experimental work at ICI suggested a possible solution by providing a rapidly extinguishable burner, flush with the surface across the end of the runway. W.T. (Bill) Moore (Plate 21), who had been brought down from ICI to work on heat blowers, became very much the developer of what transpired.

The project was discussed with A.C. Hartley on 19 April 1943. The system (Fig. 8) was to consist of four main elements: a vaporizer (1) alongside the runway in which the petrol would be converted into vapour before entering the burner line (2) crossing the runway. A bypass burner line (3) was fitted, into which the vapour output could be diverted when it was desired to extinguish the cross-line burner, and a blowdown line (4) which would have the effect of sucking back any vapour in the cross-line and speeding up extinction.

As developed, the vaporizer was a 75 ft long hairpin burner laid alongside the runway at its upwind end. Leading from it across the runway was the rapidly extinguishable (Rapex) burner, 150 yd long. By 25 July the cross-line burner was ready and Mr Hartley recorded in his diary: 'Saw ICI cross-burner for first time successfully. Walked across 20 seconds after turn-off.' Modified and improved, Rapex was satisfactorily demonstrated on 17 November 1943.

Almost immediately it was realized that for use on the much wider emergency runways (250 yd wide as against 50 yd), a more powerful burner with vaporizer and cross-line below

Plate 21 W.T. (Bill) Moore, designer of the Hades and Rapex burners at Staines (W.T. Moore)

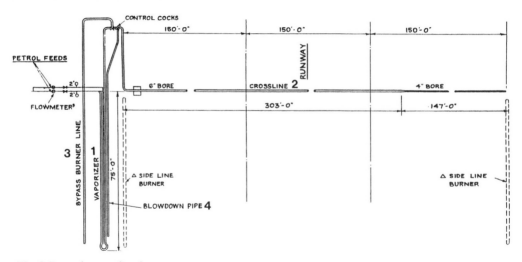

Fig. 8 Rapex burner, first layout

ground was required. By 21 February 1944 Moore's technicians had a new installation ready for test.

The new 130 ft long vaporizer now consisted of a bank of sixteen pipes in four rows of four, sunk into a trench 3 ft wide and 3 ft deep. Fig. 9 indicates its size and complexity. Being parallel to the runway the vaporizer contributed to the line-side dispersal of fog and was also powerful enough to supply a cross-line burner no less than 270 yd long. Its output, at 80 therms per yd per hour was twice that of any previous burner. Little maintenance was required and the Rapex experimental burner 'was eventually burned for a total of 150 hours, and at the end of this period no accumulation of carbon could be found in any part of the burner'.

At a later date Rapex cross-line burners were installed at Carnaby and Woodbridge but, as Bill Moore records:

> It was found that RAF flying personnel did not like the idea of landing with a line of flames across their path and a pilot on one occasion refused to land. In spite of the assurance and demonstration that the flame can be extinguished, opposition to the cross-line remained. There were a number of installation faults at Woodbridge . . . these difficulties could have been overcome, but Messrs Shell had to remove their labour before testing and the burners stood incomplete for several months. On 13 March 1945 it was decided that owing to the reluctance of the station authorities to use the Rapex burner, labour could not be diverted to complete the burners at the time.

To retrace our steps awhile: late in 1943, when the Rapex burners were still being perfected, another application of the principle was sought. With FIDO now operational or under construction at a total of eight airfields, the existing Mk IV Haigill burners (Fig. 5) ran into snags where runways intersected. Aircraft were either prevented from using the other runways because FIDO ran across them, or else FIDO had to be mounted on a cumbersome angle iron gate. Two remedies were adopted. The first was to build a triangular burner more powerful than the Mk IV and install it next to the intersecting runway. In addition to providing its own evaporational heat it would supply vaporized fuel through a pipeline laid in a channel trenched across the intersecting runway (Plate 22). This system worked quite well and was installed at most of the standard FIDO aerodromes; the burners were named intersecting runway burners, or IRBs.

The second project was to manufacture smaller versions of the Rapex burners and position them in the same way as the surface IRBs. In the event, the sub-surface IRB was only

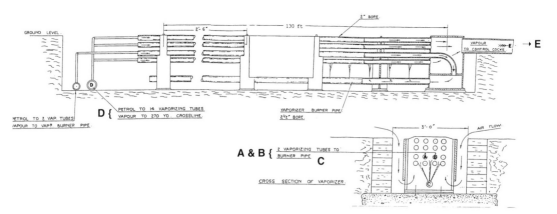

Fig. 9 Rapex/Hades vaporizer detail. On light-up, vaporizer tubes A and B feed burner pipe C in closed circuit. This heats the other 14 tubes. At approx 250°C valve D is opened, passing petrol along tubes as per arrows, vaporizing en route to runway burner line control cocks E

Plate 22 Vaporizer of intersecting runway burner (IRB) on test. When burning cleanly, the vaporized petrol would be taken along the burner line in a trench. The runway which the burner line crosses is just visible on the left (IWM)

installed at RAF Tuddenham. Its development had, however, held up progress which Bill Moore had planned for the Rapex burner.

He envisaged a like apparatus, used in series along the sides of an emergency runway. Similar in construction to the Rapex, but omitting the rapid extinguishing elements 3 and 4 in Fig. 8, the flames from Bill's pride and joy when well stoked up caused the burner to be named Hades 'because of the resemblance of the vaporizer flames to the classical pictures of that region'. Fig. 9 and Plates 23, 24, 25 show some details of Hades, and Plates 53, 54 and 55 show it in operation. Calling on the experience gained with the Rapex burner and later incorporating remote control ignition, it became possible for a burner to attain a full burn of 200 gallons per minute in 12 minutes. On one occasion the Hades burner was: ' . . . started up with a layer of snow 1½–2 in thick covering all parts. No difficulty was experienced during starting up and burning, the flames lighting through the snow before this melted'.

Manston was the only airfield to be equipped with Hades. Alongside 6,000 ft of its giant runway were entrenched seventeen 80-therm and two 40-therm burners as illustrated. The designed lengths of burners were varied to suit the position of crash bays which they could cross without impeding the egress of wrecked machines. They ranged from 425 to 1,024 ft. Individual burners were tested as they were installed over a period of many months and a full-scale test was carried out on 3 May 1945, and with only minor faults the installation proved to be fully operational (see Chapter Twelve, pp. 135–52).

W.T. Moore's enthusiasm for the development of the heat blowers, the Rapex and the Hades burners, caused the director general, Sir Donald Banks, to dub the inventor 'the indefatigable Mr Moore'.

Plate 23 Hades vaporizer and burner line under construction (PWD)

Plate 24 Experimental Hades/Rapex vaporizer and burner (PWD)

Plate 25 'Header', where vaporized petrol was collected and fed into the burner pipe, bottom left (PWD)

. . . A TRANSPORTABLE FOG-CLEARING APPARATUS

During preparations for the invasion of Europe in June 1944, thought was given to the fact that with the advance of the front line, support to the troops would need to be given by aircraft operating from captured airfields not up to Bomber Command standards, and that temporary airfields might have to be used. The approach of winter fogs would hamper operations if no fog dispersal system was available.

Sir Basil Embry, Air Officer Commanding of 2 Group within the 2nd Tactical Air Force and, it will be recalled, one of Mr Hartley's first supporters, asked him to devise 'a transportable fog-clearing apparatus'. At Staines this project became the responsibility of Denys Fox. Such an installation would need to be easily transported and suitable for erection by military labour, with the minimum of welding and concrete. It was anticipated that storage tanks, pumps and pumping engines would be readily available.

Initially, modification and adaptation of existing types of burner was considered, but experiments led to the conclusion that it was not possible to scale down the size of the units without loss of output and efficiency. Drawing on his considerable expertise, by the end of August 1944 Denys had devised a burner in which the straight length of vaporizing pipe (the top pipe on a triangular Haigill burner) was replaced by a coil or coils before leading on to the burner pipe (Fig. 10 and Plate 26). Over a period of time it was found possible for the system to generate the 30 therms per yd per hour required to evaporate fog, but at only half the weight of a comparable length of Haigill burner; the portable installation was named the Haifox.

Each coiled burner unit was 7 ft 6 in long, with 76 ft of burner line. Four such units were controlled from a single valve, giving 120 yd per assembly. The installation was designed to give 1,200 yd of continuous burners for operational airstrips. A system was installed on the airfield at Epinoy in January 1945 and brought into use for the Mosquitos of 138 Wing which operated from there during the spring of 1945. Sir Basil Embry paid tribute to the system: 'Our bases were all fogbound throughout this period and we were only able to operate at night because we had a transportable fog-clearing apparatus known as FIDO installation at Epinoy, where 138 Wing was based. I had asked for this apparatus to be

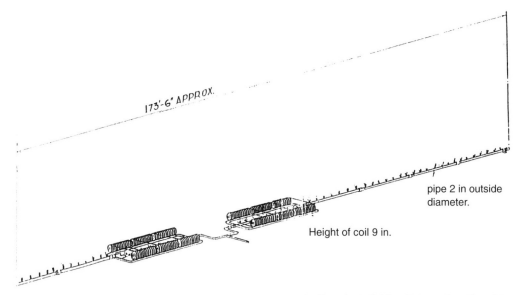

173'-6" APPROX.

pipe 2 in outside diameter.

Height of coil 9 in.

Fig. 10 Layout of a portable, Haifox burner unit as used on the French airfield at Epinoy. See Plate 26

Plate 26 A single vaporizer unit for a Haifox portable fog dispersal installation. See Fig. 10 (PWD)

specially made before D-Day and thanks to the good offices of my friend Clifford Hartley, who was the inventor of FIDO, it had been possible to provide it.'

Frank Tolliday was an apprentice with Essex tubemakers Brown and Tawse at that time, and had the job of manufacturing coils for the Haifox burners. The coils were much tighter than those usually made by the company and Frank had to make a jig around which the tubing could be bent. With a bore diameter of 1 in and a coil diameter of 5½ in he found that the steel behaved like coiled springs. To prevent kinking during the bending, the tubing was filled with sand and had to be plugged at the ends. He often found that if the coils did not spring off the spigot they spat hot sand at him instead.

THREE

FIDO's Record

SUPPLY AND STORAGE

Storage tanks, sufficient in capacity to permit six hours continuous burning at the maximum rated output, had to be installed at each FIDO-equipped airfield. At the early installations of Graveley and Downham Market the only available storage was the standard Air Ministry horizontal welded cylindrical steel tank, 30 ft long, 9 ft in diameter and holding about 12,000 gallons. These were replenished by convoys of road tankers. From the time of the expansion of the FIDO system in late 1943 they, and all subsequent airfields, were equipped with several vertical steel storage tanks, with capacities ranging from 80,000 to a quarter of a million gallons each. These were erected above ground level, encased in brickwork, with earth blast walls for protection (Plate 57).

Initially the tanks were supplied by road tanker, each carrying about 3,000 gallons, a system which in some cases continued throughout the war. When the later FIDO airfields were commissioned, delivery was by underground pipeline from a railway siding at the nearest convenient spot, not necessarily in a station yard. The line-side system consisted of a 6 in main running parallel to the siding for about 150 yd. At tanker-length intervals were welded twenty or so 2½ in standpipes fitted with control valves, to which flexible hoses were connected, making union with the 10-ton, say 3,000-gallon, wagons. On demand, the pumping engines on the airfield site would suck away thirstily, disgorging their contents into the storage tanks nearby. The distances involved varied a great deal. At Carnaby the siding was only a field away, whereas at Woodbridge it was over four miles from the siding at Melton and the pipeline had to be carried under the River Deben en route. At Manston the petrol was pumped for a mile and a half from a siding near Minster and ascended about 150 ft in the process. In this case an additional pump and engine were installed at the siding to help it on its way. How common this was we do not know (see Plates 49–51).

The FIDO installations were originally equipped with pumps driven by Coventry Climax engines, which were used on NFS trailers during the war. Later airfields were equipped with Sulzer Mk V pumps driven by Ford V-8 engines, each of which could deliver up to 700 gallons per minute, and so could empty a tanker in less than five minutes. The standard FIDO airfield pumphouse contained five Sulzer pumps, three of which were normally in use at any time to deliver up to 1,500 gallons per minute to the burners, i.e. up to 90,000 gallons per hour. The emergency aerodromes at Carnaby, Manston and Woodbridge had two pumphouses each, with six Sulzers apiece (Plate 27). Eight were usually required to provide about 500 gallons/min each at a pressure of 90–100 lb/sq. in. If required a total of 240,000 gallons per hour could have been pumped through the burners, although nothing like that amount was ever demanded. To a civilian populace nearly four years into the war and accustomed to many shortages and privations, the quantity of petrol used by FIDO would have seemed prodigious. In comparison with a heavy raid on Germany, of which many were

Plate 27 Bank of six Ford V8 engines driving Sulzer Mk V pumps, Manston (PWD)

mounted at approaching two million gallons a time, it was not so bad as it seemed. The supply position was considerably improved as the loss rate of shipping in the Atlantic dropped dramatically towards the end of 1943. An Air Ministry memo of 3 December noted that 'for the purposes of fog dispersal it may be said that there is no shortage of petrol, but that the limitation is one of delivery'! Fortunately, the Ministry of Petroleum had organized a network of pipelines and tanker trains from ports such as Bristol, Liverpool and Southampton early in the war so that supplies were never critically short.

FIDO'S ACHIEVEMENT

This revolutionary change in the air war was made possible by FIDO
Bomber Command appreciation

From the time of the first operational use of FIDO at Graveley on 19/20 November 1943 until the end of the year, thirty-nine successful landings were made. By the spring of 1944, eight Fido-equipped airfields were in operation, and seven more, including the emergency aerodromes at Woodbridge, Carnaby and Manston, were under construction. By the end of April 1944 the total of landings had reached 231, with 93 in that month alone. An expected reduction in Fido's use during May and June was followed by an increase in the third quarter of 1944, so that by the end of September 500 landings had been made and nearly fifty take-offs achieved in safety. The total continued to rise, 407 machines landing with the aid of FIDO in November alone, the total of 1,000 safe landings being passed in early December. At this time Sir Arthur Harris expressed his appreciation of its/his assistance in a letter to Geoffrey Lloyd:

Now that FIDO installations are operational, I must write and thank you personally, in particular, for the enthusiasm and efficiency with which all concerned have tackled this problem, which many thought might be impossible of solution. We are already getting to the stage where FIDO is taken as a matter of course.

The numbers so far landed this Autumn with the aid of FIDO are, September 43, October 33, November 261 [in fact they were considerably higher]. Sixty-one of these were Americans accommodated at Woodbridge. Without exception their crews expressed the greatest astonishment and enthusiasm over the working of the system.

At Ludford Magna on 20 September, fourteen heavy bombers were landed safely by pilots who had no previous experience of FIDO. On 22 September at Woodbridge, a Stirling with its windows and ailerons iced up was de-iced by flying for five minutes over the installation before landing. We are also increasingly using FIDO for taking off under bad conditions for operations and I think that this has very great possibilities.

We are all very grateful, and in particular I realize that if it had not been for your personal enthusiasm and push we should never have got anywhere with this essential, and now highly efficient safeguard.

FIDO rendered its most signal service during the period of the Ardennes offensive. From over 400 landings in November the total increased to 704 in December, plus 107 take-offs, bringing the total of operational movements by the end of the year to over 1,800. Giving credit where it was due, Bomber Command recorded its appreciation of the part played by FIDO during this critical period covering Christmas and the New Year: 'Over a thousand aircraft landed with the aid of FIDO. Of these about 300 were American. Also, nearly 150 British bombers took off in fog from runways cleared by FIDO.' The statement continues:

This revolutionary change in the air war was made possible by FIDO. During the Christmas week of von Runstedt's offensive, Pathfinders were able to take off and return from operations involving the marking of seven marshalling yards, two airfields in the Ruhr and the all-important direct army support attack against St Vith in the Ardennes bulge. The attack on St Vith took place on one of the worst days in the week. Thanks to FIDO the operation was possible, the attack was a great success and did everything the army wanted it to. Despite the fog the crews were able to do their job thoroughly, knowing that when they returned the weather would not stop them from landing.

Such commendations and statistics, however, should not distract from the fact that during December over 120 British and at least as many American aircraft were lost due to enemy action, with an unknown additional number of crashes. Although percentage losses may have been acceptable to statisticians, it is nevertheless the case that upwards of 2,000 Allied airmen lost their lives in that month. In January, only ten nights were fit for heavy bomber operations. A grand total of 11,000 sorties were flown and 443 aircraft landed safely with the aid of FIDO; but over 130 failed to return, even to FIDO's welcoming glow.

Operations were fewer in February and March 1945 with 233 and 54 FIDO landings respectively, at which point PWD records cease, with the total at 2,541. Landings continued, however, albeit on a decreasing scale and we can quote a survey carried out for PWD by Sqn Ldr W.F. Reid, formerly flying control officer at Fiskerton, as shown in Table I (to 31 May 1945):

FIDO General Survey
Section 8 (a): The role played by FIDO in operations.

Number of landings in fog and conditions of low visibility when the whole or a major part of the installation was used.	1,068
Number of landings in poor visibility when a few burners were used as markers.	1,456
Number of take-offs	182
Total	2,706

To his survey Sqn Ldr Reid adds the comment: 'In a great many cases records are incomplete, many landings being made without official return thereon, especially when only a limited number of burners were used.'

In their report upon *The Meteorological Aspects of Fog Dispersal*, Sqn Ldr Harry Edge and Leslie MacPherson analysed the performance of FIDO during the worst of the weather. When FIDO was equal to the task and records have survived, the landings shown in Table II are recorded.

Visibility	Occasions when fog lifted	Landings
0–55 yd	14	28
55–110	29	51
110–220	28	57
220–550	46	170
550–1100	44	416
Total 161		722

From November 1943 until the end of the Second World War it is estimated that about 2,700 Allied aircraft took off or landed with the aid of FIDO. Since not all occasions were recorded, or records have not survived, the figure may well have been higher, perhaps by as many as 100. The value of such service cannot be calculated. Approximately 700 aircraft landed with FIDO under conditions of fog and probably three times as many when the system enabled the runway to be identified rather than clearing the fog from it. If we take the former group alone, something in excess of 3,500 aircrew can be said to owe their lives to FIDO. Of 10,000 others, many would aver that, at the very least, a dangerous situation was made easier.

However, admiration which we may have for the achievements of FIDO has to be tempered by the overall picture. As Max Hastings, never averse to ruffling a few feathers, put it:

> The weather remained as central an element in the bomber offensive in April 1945 as it had been in September 1939. Despite the FIDO burners that were established at key airfields to keep runways clear of fog, crashes on take-off and landing remained a major cause of lost aircraft. With the approach of winter [1944–5] the sortie rate declined severely even in the last year of the war.

Aircrew also had misgivings, as witness *Tail-end Charlie*, alias John Wainwright:

> To get back to base and find the place fogbound isn't comforting. FIDO was, to say the least, Heath Robinson-ish. Run pipes along both sides of the landing strip, with holes drilled along the top. Come the fog, and the return of the wandering boys, all you have to do is to belt fuel into the pipes until the juice squirts out of the holes; then, in effect, drop a match. The fog goes like magic. But it's a little like landing into the mouth of hell, and you'd better not fishtail off that runway. I, for one, never fell in love with FIDO.

There is undoubtedly truth in these dampeners. It is the case, however, that, but for the availability of FIDO, the number of sorties flown would have been fewer and the casualties suffered far higher.

Part Two: The Hazard Overcome – FIDO in Operational Use

FOUR

Hartfordbridge/Blackbushe

. . . we saw the reddish glow

Adam Szajdzicki, navigator

To summarize Trevor Harvey's *A History of Blackbushe*, during 1941 plans were drawn up for an airfield to be built at Hartfordbridge, an area on the borders of north-east Hampshire and Surrey, near the village of Yateley. At the beginning of 1942 work started on clearing the huge area of trees and brush to facilitate the task of building a major airfield with three all-weather runways. Flying began long before buildings were completed, and initially there was no electric light. All meals had to be finished by 17.30 hours. The station's operations record book opened on 7 November 1942, with the airfield described as a satellite of RAF Odiham.

In June 1943 Hartfordbridge was earmarked as a diversion field for Bomber Command. When in July 1943 a list of additional aerodromes (additional that is to Graveley and Downham Market) to be equipped with FIDO was drawn up, Hartfordbridge was one of them, designated Station XV. Geoffrey Adams, who was already at work as a surveyor on the PLUTO project for construction engineers J.L. Eve & Co., recalled being withdrawn from that task in August 1943. He was sent on a brief introductory course to Staines and then to Hartfordbridge to survey the locations for petrol tanks, pumphouses, etc.

> Arriving, I was horrified to see the whole area covered with RAF motor transport. Enquiry from a senior NCO brought out the alarming news that it had been chosen for the permanent station M/T park. On telling the MT officer that I was afraid he would have to move (without daring to mention FIDO), he obviously thought that I was mad and drove me off to the station HQ with the intention of having me shot. He did not take me in to see the Commanding Officer; but after five minutes returned and in a very different manner asked me if it would be okay if he cleared the site by midday; with which arrangement I was happy to agree. I then got on with the survey . . .
>
> Apart from the novelty, the job was not particularly interesting, for the burners were pretty elementary and posed no difficulties in setting out; after all an airfield is a fairly level and uncomplicated area on which to work.

While Geoffrey Adams was at work, 2 Group had been formed and squadrons of Venturas and Bostons took up residence at Hartfordbridge.

A FIDO progress report of 20 September 1943 records 'slight delay, owing to continuous operational flying during the day. Difficulties have been eliminated by close co-operation with Station Commander. Should be operational on schedule' [20 November]. Geoffrey was very much aware of these 'difficulties':

> The station was of course operational as a medium bomber unit, flying mainly Lockheed Venturas and Douglas Bostons. This made life somewhat complicated, as we always had to be ready to move off in the event of an emergency. After all, we were operating well within the prohibited areas of

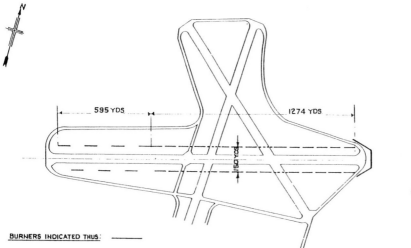

595 YDS   1274 YDS

1150 YDS

PUMP HOUSE AND
STORAGE TANKS

BURNERS INDICATED THUS:

Fig. 11 Hartfordbridge/Blackbushe, original FIDO layout. See Plate 28

runway safety where in normal circumstances nobody and nothing would be permitted, let alone such objects as mechanical diggers, trenchers and welding machines.

The job proceeded relatively smoothly and I can recall only two alarming incidents. In the first, Nobby Clarke, with the Cleveland trencher, dug up the airfield ring main of umpteen thousand volts, fortunately without injury to himself or the machine.

In the second, I was crossing one of the subsidiary runways which was out of action as we had trenched across it, when I heard a great roar and saw a Ventura which had landed on it coming straight at me. I broke into a gallop, but the more I ran the nearer he came. Flying control put up a barrage of reds and fortunately the pilot realized that he should not have been there and took off again. I threw myself flat and he cleared me with about 15 ft to spare. I was even less amused when I tore along to complain to Control, to find them laughing their heads off with the excuse, 'he doesn't belong to us'.

By October we had a number of burners in action, and on 11 November, with all setting out complete and the work in its final stages I was suddenly transferred to an assignment in Essex.

The east-west runway at Hartfordbridge was lined with a series of Haigill Mk IV burners (Fig. 11), set 50 yd back from the edge, which at full burn could consume as much as 90,000 gallons of petrol per hour. Trials of Hartfordbridge's installation took place on 19 and 20 November 1943. During the first of these, fog 300–500 ft thick was lifted in forty-five minutes, but a number of joints failed due to faulty welding. The burn was generally satisfactory though a 10 mph cross-wind blew the clearance well to the leeward of the runway.

Before making use of FIDO as a pilot with 342 (Free French) Squadron, François Rozoy found it very useful in another way: 'October and November 1943 were dull days with poor weather. We were in the crews' Nissen hut when somebody told us of the things going on. From the pipes on each side of the main runway fuel was burning. We enjoyed it because it was a cold day and a cheap way of keeping warm.' François also commented on the efficiency of FIDO:

As far as the aim of FIDO, it was deceiving; mixture too rich and it gave black smoke and visibility poor. Later on another test was done, probably after changing mixture on a foggy day. This time the effect of warmth was good and from time to time we could see a patch of blue sky above the runway but, bad luck, there was a slight side wind and it was not perfect. Consumption was said to be very great.

Plate 28 Blackbushe aerial, runway 26. FIDO burners most obvious at runway intersections, FIDO tanks almost off photograph to east of approach box. See Fig. 11 (Crown)

Plate 29 Mk IV burners on test at Blackbushe, probably eastern end by touchdown (Nat Met Lib)

One of the great complaints for operators of the burners was that with the introduction of leaded petrol in 1943 a hard deposit formed around the jet holes, which required constant reaming out. James Allan recalls:

> When I think back to my days there, I remember first the back-breaking work that was necessary to keep the unit ready for an emergency. You may wonder what was so back-breaking about it, but if you realize that every few inches along the burner pipes, which were laid directly on the ground, was a small jet hole which had to be kept carbon free, you will understand what I mean. The unit burned about 60,000 gallons of fuel per hour and the holes soon began to decrease in size with a rock-hard deposit from the fuel.

Malcolm Lucas recalled that lighting the burners was much more exciting: 'The method of ignition was to open the inlet valve to each section, wait until the cool petrol spurted out of the burner holes and then throw a match at it. The first time I did it I lost my eyelashes, which were the envy of many a woman; never to regain their former glory. The only maintenance as I recall was to ream out the holes in the burner lines.' He also had the job of seeing that sufficient petrol was on order to keep the tanks topped up: 'Each morning I had to ring PWD in London, giving the ullages. I recall one day saying that we were down *to* 50,000 gallons, instead of *by* 50,000. Ten minutes later PWD rang back to say that we would receive a tanker every fifteen minutes until we were full again. As the tanks at Hartfordbridge held over half a million gallons I then had to point out my error in phraseology, and sanity was eventually restored.'

Although FIDO had been tested as early as November 1943 and frequently in the following weeks, it was not until February 1944 that operational landings first took place. One such day was 24 February 1944, when twelve Bostons of 88 Squadron and six of 342 Squadron based at Harfordbridge raided V1 sites at Bois de la Justice, while six home-based Mitchells of 226 Squadron and twelve of 320 (Dutch) Squadron from nearby Dunsfold attacked Le Groseiller, escorted by a substantial force of Spitfires. Numerous Mosquitos were also aloft. On a hazy day it was difficult for many pilots to pick out the runway as they made shallow approach runs on their return, and the approach box and the first few burners on each side of the runway were lit at 11.20 a.m. Over the next five hours the Hartfordbridge aircraft all put down safely, together with quite an armada of other machines to whom the airfield was a more attractive proposition than their own mist-shrouded aerodromes. Altogether twenty Bostons, twelve Mosquitos, eight Mitchells and twenty-two Spitfires landed, together with seventeen other aircraft who came in such a welter that they were all lumped together as 'unidentified' – seventy-nine in all!

Gerald Baker of 107 (Boston) Squadron brought to mind the feelings of aircrew on such occasions early in 1944:

> . . . when we came back from a raid – in daylight as I was on Bostons – it was quite a relief to see the FIDO glow down through the gloom. So far as I can remember we could see it from about 2,000 ft. We had to come much lower and managed to keep it in sight during the circuit as my pilot judged his approach. I don't think that I need to tell you that it was a very frightening experience landing between the two lines of flames. The really worrying part was the uneasiness that there had been some damage to the aircraft which might make it swerve off the straight and narrow. Understandably, there were a few problems with it in the early stages and I seem to remember one time when it would not light and the officer in charge had to run down and throw lighted matches in order to get it going.

Early in March 1944 Trevor Harvey reports that an airfield construction flight moved on to the airfield to begin installing a new system of burners. The Haigill Mk IVs were comparatively easy to build on site but they did not stand up very well to prolonged operational use. On most aerodromes they were replaced by Mk V surface burners as materials and labour became available, but at Hartfordbridge a different system was tried. This, sometimes referred to as a slot, trenched or, later, a Blackbushe burner, is described and depicted on pp. 29–30 and in Fig. 7 and Plate 20. The new system was built alongside the existing Haigill burners and covered 1,815 yd of the runway. It took several months for the job to be finished, during which time the Mk IVs continued to operate as best they could.

On 18 April 1944 the whole of Hartfordbridge was in uproar as word got around that General Eisenhower would be making a visit [recalled Trevor Harvey]. Boots were given a special shine and uniforms an extra press. Towards 10 o'clock sergeants were sent to assemble all personnel inside the largest hangar on the airfield . . . The morning was extremely foggy and when the hangar doors were opened, the thick pea-souper started its damp surge inside. At just after 11 o'clock two yellow headlights appeared through the gloom and a car drew up and out stepped Ike. Following the formal salutes he shocked everyone with an informal greeting of 'Hello boys!' and asked them to gather round him. He then proceeded to thank the squadron for the hard work they had already carried out and went on to tell them something of the plans for them in the build-up for the invasion. He then saw a demonstration of FIDO, appropriate on this cold foggy morning, and left, very impressed.

Bill Beaumont, flight sergeant in charge of FIDO, to whom I am indebted for copies of his fog dispersal reports, remembered General Eisenhower's visit: 'While in flying control he was asked if he would like to see FIDO in operation. We were on standby at the time and ordered to "light up". Before we were completely alight, somebody mentioned that the consumption of fuel was something in the region of 80,000 gallons per hour. Ike promptly said "Shut it down quick. I have to bring that stuff to England!"'

FIDO was not required on D-Day itself. Curiously enough Hartfordbridge's own Bostons were actually engaged in making smoke rather than clearing it during the prelude to the invasion, screening the first wave of assault craft from the eyes of German gunners as they made their hazardous approach to the beaches. Perhaps it was just as well that visibility over England was good at that time, for the FIDO contractor's agent, Mr Russell, reported on that day that the high winds which had delayed the landings in Normandy had also worked some mischief at Hartfordbridge. Sand and loose, heat-crumbled earth had blown over everything, choking burner jets and filling up the operating pits. Nevertheless, during three months operations some 164 aircraft had landed with FIDO's aid; more than at any other station.

In the early morning of 9 June, six Hartfordbridge Mosquitos of 264 Squadron struck at targets behind the beachhead in very poor weather conditions. Nearly 2 in of rain had fallen and as they returned it was still pouring, with the cloud base down to 200 ft. As they crossed the English coast, two burners at the head of the runway were lit to establish its line and location and all six Mosquitos put down safely. 'The pilots were most appreciative of the guide the burners had given them', although only one considered himself to have been 'saved' by it. In markedly similar conditions a single Mosquito landed early in the morning of 16 June, the half-hour burn necessary to ensure its safe arrival costing the taxpayer 1,500 gallons of petrol; a small price to pay for the survival of a Mosquito and its crew.

Installation of the more efficient slot system (referred to on p. 30) began in the spring of 1944 and by mid-July was well under way and reckoned to be ten days ahead of schedule – the impending visit of the King and Queen may have had something to do with this. Throughout August and September the work progressed, but despite satisfaction with the trial burns, it was not until December 1944 that the burners were put to the test, operationally, in fog. Malcolm Lucas remembered both systems in use:

Every time fog was forecast, PWD personnel would appear in numbers, but it was many months before we actually had a fog in which to test-burn. I'll never forget it. Perhaps five to ten yards visibility outside the burner lines and as clear as can be inside, seeing the whole length of the runway. Until well after D-Day the whole system was never burnt in anger, although we regularly used the first 180 yards or so on each side when a squadron was returning in poor weather. Apparently it could be seen from the south coast.

The slot system was much tidier and all underground. It was in pre-cast concrete sections with iron grids over. Perhaps one of the best sights was the cross-runway burners. They were similar to the Hades burners (pp. 31–4) with a large pre-heater which gradually vaporized the fuel until it extended across the fifty yard gap.

During July raids continued to be made both by day and night on enemy troop and armour concentrations, bridges, marshalling yards, V1 sites and communication centres. For example, on 25 July nine Mitchells of 226, fifteen Bostons of 88 and fifteen more from 342 Squadrons were detailed to attack the Bourgebus troop concentrations again, the attack timed to take place within the space of only two minutes: 07.17–19. To ensure the most compact take-off it was decided to light the whole of the burners on the southern side of the runway, which was also the windward side. All thirty-nine machines took to the air in swift succession just after 06.00. This was the first recorded occasion on which FIDO was used for an operational take-off at Hartfordbridge. By the time of their return the sun had burnt off the mist and normal landings were made. When Petroleum Minister Geoffrey Lloyd heard of the occasion, he asked for confirmation to be sent direct to the prime minister.

There are no reports that FIDO was used during the month of August 1944. This was the period when the changeover from the old Haigill to the new slot burners was at its height. As the new system was progressively installed it was tested section by section with good results, although on one occasion the heat-proof concrete failed because a sizeable piece of damp wood had been buried with it. The resulting explosion had everyone diving for cover.

The late summer months saw the Allies advancing across France from the Normandy bridgehead. Keeping pace with the battle line, 83 and 84 Group's fighters crossed to operate from French airfields during July, with 2nd TAF HQ going over on 9 August. Although the fighters were away, the medium-range bombers still operated from Hartfordbridge, Lasham,

Plate 30 Mk V burners alight alongside slot burner at Blackbushe (Nat Met Lib)

Dunsfold and Hunsdon. Entering September, the old Haigill system at Hartfordbridge was examined and declared to be in very poor shape. A full-scale burn was planned, after which it was proposed to give it a complete overhaul. Sufficient of the slot burners were now in place to operate a complete burn if necessary; a trial of the remote control lighting system was planned for 25 September.

During this period 2nd TAF was heavily engaged in Operation 'Market Garden', the large-scale series of airborne landings designed to capture key bridges in Holland. On 21 September seventeen Mitchells and seventeen Bostons of 137 Wing were detailed to attack German forces moving against the British 2nd Army's corridor reaching to Nijmegen. The ever-common thick haze hung over Hartfordbridge at the time of take-off and it was decided to give the old Mk IV system a chance to go out in a blaze of glory. It did its best, coughing and spluttering, as did many of the ground crew, for three welded joints failed, spewing out smoke instead of clean flames. Nevertheless it was possible for all thirty-four machines to take off in safety and accomplish a three-and-a-half-hour mission without loss and to land with FIDO re-lit for the occasion. The station ops record book gives the Mk IV's last report as, 'Conditions were such that the operation was only possible through the use of this installation.'

On 29 October visibility was poor all day with advection fog reducing horizontal vision to under 1,000 yd, but angular sighting nearly impossible. For pilots seeking haven, instruments may have said that England lay not far below, but there was no confirmation of this from the Mk I eyeball, and in response to numerous requests FIDO was lit at about 14.30. Between 14.50 and 17.00 hours a variety of aircraft made safe landings, namely an Anson, two Bostons, a Dakota, a Fairchild and a Mosquito. The Mosquito, P-Peter of 305 (Polish) fighter-bomber squadron was probably the first to descend at about 15.00. Its navigator, Adam Szajdzicki, recalled:

I have brought the aircraft with the help of the GEE on the beginning of the runway at 1,500 feet. Then the pilot made the instrument circle and we came into funnel. Flying over the runway we saw the reddish glow. When we have turned in the final and started approaching the threshold, we saw the red ring with the black tunnel in the ring of light with the red line above disappearing in the milky fog with the reddish line above it. Above the threshold we felt bump and we have heard terrific row. After touch-down I have realized that the noise was coming from the flames. We were very glad when we have reached the end of the runway and turned into taxiing way.

On the following day Hartfordbridge was re-named Blackbushe, apparently to avoid confusion with a namesake in Norfolk. On 25 November the system was lit in low cloud to assist a Fortress far from home and lost. Its pilot said that FIDO was a great help as a beacon. By the end of the month it is estimated that 333 operational landings and take-offs had been made with FIDO.

The first occasion when the new FIDO system at Blackbushe was operated under conditions of thick fog was 13 December 1944. A test-burn took place at noon with visibility only 50 yd in fog 50 ft thick. Within the space of ten minutes the fog had been completely evaporated over the runway to show blue sky overhead. As if awaiting the opportunity of making an entrance, an Anson, homeward bound from Brussels with R/T unserviceable, hove into view and, making a long careful approach, landed safely on the last 800 yd of clearway. After an hour the burners were extinguished, whereupon visibility again reduced to 50 yd.

At 15.00 on the same afternoon, by which time there had been no improvement in the weather conditions, a number of aircraft were heard circling the base above the fog. After several of them had made unsuccessful attempts to land, it was decided to light FIDO and put them out of their misery. Unfortunately, the burners did not perform as well as they might have done, and although the fog was cleared, considerable smoke was caused by numerous time-expired units. Nevertheless, the station commander's comments were: 'Burn successful, semi-operational. Fog was cleared very satisfactorily, but large number of defective burners produced extensive smoke, mostly due to old burners. It is evident, however, that when fully installed and with increased experience of PWD personnel, the new installation will be very successful.' In the seventy-five minutes during which FIDO was alight, two Dakotas, a Mosquito and a Wellington landed without difficulty. Air-gunner aboard the Wellington NC537 was Gerard Timney, homeward bound from Melsbroeke:

> Crossing the line of the runway before the approach was extremely bumpy and I recall a wait on the circuit until the system was in full operation and the height of the flames reduced. Then a first sight of the runway through the banks of fog and the approach when the twin lines of flames were diminished.
>
>   Two features stand out in my mind: firstly the thickness of the fog viewed from above, with nothing but a church steeple or an occasional tall tree showing; and then the short interval which elapsed before the fog closed in again once FIDO had been turned off.

In fact, within ten minutes of extinguishing the burners, it was impossible to see more than 30 yd on the airfield. The burn had consumed a total of 38,000 gallons of petrol.

Only one more aircraft used FIDO before the end of the war – a Christmas present, one might say. On the evening of 25 December 1944, Fortress RX-K from 305th Bomb Group at Chelveston was short of fuel and requested assistance in landing somewhere – in fact, anywhere! Rain and low cloud at 600 ft made approach to any airfield difficult over strange terrain, so FIDO was lit at 17.25 hours. It did not affect the cloud base, but the pilot was able to home in on the glow and eased himself in below the stratus to make a safe landing. He expressed great approval of FIDO as a beacon – with justification, for two of his engines petered out as he touched down!

For the rest of the war FIDO at Blackbushe was not further recorded in action. Our best estimate is that 266 aircraft landed and 73 took off using FIDO, but additional, unrecorded landings may well have increased the 339 to a total in excess of 350. FIDO continued in use during the postwar years. We have record of a further twenty-eight FIDO landings before the RAF departed in 1946. Following this a series of civilian charter companies operated from the now Blackbushe Airport, reopened in 1947.

The installation was again overhauled during 1952 'and put on standby for the Manston unit', but not used. FIDO was finally dispensed with in May 1958 and dismantled in 1960. Blackbushe is currently a busy private airfield. Runway 26 has lost the eastern half of its length, but traces of the FIDO trenches can still be seen at the head of the present airstrip, running on eastwards into the scrub beyond.

FIVE

Bradwell Bay

. . . like a sponge cake with a slice cut clean through the middle

Stuart Davis, pilot, 122 Squadron

The airfield at Bradwell Bay was just over a mile north of Bradwell-on-Sea, alias Bradwell-Juxta-Mare, in pre-war days a large village and parish on a promontory to the south of the Blackwater estuary in Essex. The airfield site was formally requisitioned in 1940 and in February 1941 work began on the three runways, the main one of which was about 1,600 yd long on a NE–SW line. This was extended by some 200 yd to the north-east during the summer. Because it was so close to the coast, Bradwell Bay frequently became a haven of refuge for bombers suffering battle damage and for escorts running short of fuel. This was no doubt taken into account when potential sites for the installation of FIDO were under review.

Bradwell Bay was first considered as a FIDO airfield in addition to Graveley and Downham Market in a list drawn up on 26 July 1943, and designated Station XIV. It was noted that Bradwell was subject to sea fogs, ' . . . but owing to its advantageous geographical position and the fact that it was also subject to much radiation fog, every endeavour should be made to install the apparatus'. Construction of FIDO began in August 1943. William Press were the contractors and progress reports indicate that they found it a very inaccessible site for heavy road transport and earth-moving equipment.

Despite setbacks construction went ahead with early November set for the system to become fully operational. The main runway alongside which FIDO was laid was on a compass bearing 240°–060° (approximately NE–SW). Coming in from the North Sea aircraft would make their approach over water and saltings, but, curiously enough, when using FIDO an approach was made from the south-west (Plates 31 and 32).

As can be seen from Fig. 12, Bradwell Bay had an approach box of 280 yd terminating at a perimeter track which acted as a Bird gap (see p. 15). Then followed 1,195 yd of Haigill Mk IV burners (see Fig. 5), which crossed runways 17 and 12 by means of sunken intersecting runway burners (see Plate 22). The last 510 yd were covered by burners placed on alternate sides as shown in the diagram. A total of nearly eighty burners lined the runway, requiring over 15,000 yd of various diameter piping to supply them. The FIDO storage tanks in the south-west corner of the airfield contained over half a million gallons of petrol, and had to be kept full by convoys of road tankers negotiating tortuous country lanes from a depot at Maldon.

Even before the system was completed Gp Capt Roland Beamont had occasion to make use of FIDO's services in Typhoon G-George of 609 Squadron when 'on the way back from an intruder patrol over north-west France'. His log-book entry reads 'Intruder. Weather u/s Cap Griz Nez. Directed to Bradwell Bay (fog Manston). 55 mins (night). FIDO very good.' Enlarging, Gp Capt Beamont recalled:

I found Manston, 609's base, fogged in, and a kindly controller suggested I might go to Bradwell Bay which was also in fog, 'but they should be able to help'. Duly arriving there after about fifteen minutes flying over the flat, moonlit sheet of fog in the Bradwell area, I was impressed to see a

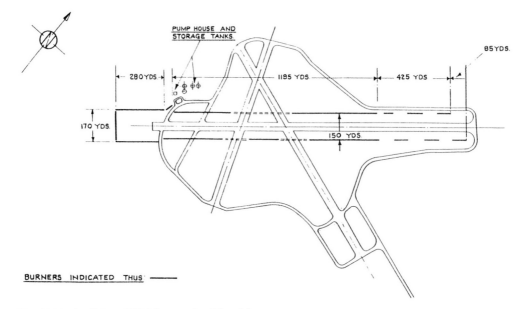

PUMP HOUSE AND
STORAGE TANKS.

85 YDS.

280 YDS.

1195 YDS.

425 YDS.

170 YDS.

150 YDS.

BURNERS INDICATED THUS: ———

Fig. 12 Bradwell Bay, FIDO layout. See Plate 31

bright orange glow ahead. Bradwell set me a nice GCA, which became a little disorienting as I passed five hundred feet with the voice saying, 'You are on the centre line of the glide path', with grey fog all around except ahead where the fog seemed to be on fire.

Then, miraculously, at 150 feet, two big fiery bars appeared, slightly left and ahead. A quick sidestep brought the Typhoon safely into the centre and firmly on to the runway. It then seemed very desirable to keep straight and not veer off into the lines of leaping flames on each side. It was very impressive, descending into the glaring 'tunnel' in the fog which, at fifty ft or less, gave about 1500 yd of clearish, if smoky, visibility in what was otherwise a solid 'clamp-in' of fog all around.

Air Vice-Marshal Roderick Hill, Deputy C-in-C Fighter Command, and his entourage, visited the station on 6 November 1943 to witness a full burn of the apparatus. Although not officially handed over, FIDO at Bradwell Bay was ready for operational use.

Just before dusk on 29 December, Sqn Ldr Bunting of 488 Squadron took off in his Mosquito to intercept a reported enemy aircraft. While he was aloft a thick haze descended over the whole of the Blackwater estuary. Sqn Ldr Bunting saw nothing of the enemy machine and as he approached Bradwell Bay he could see nothing of the airfield either. Instructions were given for FIDO to be lit. The fog dispersal report describes the atmosphere as partly advection fog but mainly smoke, probably from the London area, 200–300 ft deep. Apparently, most of the aircrew on the station turned out to watch, but inexperienced ground crews and an incomplete Tannoy system hampered a good quick clean burn. Nevertheless, Sqn Ldr Bunting made a safe landing and the observers 'were favourably impressed'.

It was another three months before the next recorded use of FIDO occurred. Ronnie Sherward brought to mind:

I was a flight commander in 137 Squadron and we were flying rocket-firing Typhoons out of Lympne. On 13 March 1944 I did a night-flying test and then led five aircraft to Bradwell Bay. We did many landings and take-offs in moonlight and dark periods, and after the initial landing and getting used to all the fire down each side of the runway we found it a 'piece of cake', and a real life-saver in duff weather. Our idea was to give Typhoon pilots some experience of FIDO in case of bad weather during the Normandy landings, as 2nd TAF was to operate in poor weather as well as in good.

Plate 31 Bradwell Bay aerial. Runway 06. FIDO burners most obvious at runway intersections. Storage tanks north of touchdown. See Fig. 12 (RAF Museum)

Plate 32 Oblique of FIDO alight at Bradwell Bay. Pewet Island to left, River Blackwater beyond (IWM)

Four nights later FIDO was in use again and curiously enough Sqn Ldr Bunting was involved once more. A thick haze lay over the aerodrome as he and Flying Officer (Flg Off) Bergmann (NZ) were returning from the attempted interception of enemy aircraft over London just before 10 p.m. on 17 March 1944. The burners did not ignite cleanly and the Tannoy system was still not complete; the flying control officer said that FIDO should not have been used at all. Both pilots took a dim view of the occasion: Sqn Ldr Bunting complained that he 'had to orbit for nearly half an hour before the fog dispersal was ready for use and even then there was some smoke'; and Flg Off Bergmann found that the flarepath, funnel lights and glide path indicator were all lost to view in FIDO's glare. As his windscreen was completely iced over, his touchdown was a bit like landing on an aircraft carrier, peering through the side window and trying to keep straight. However, they both landed safely, the system having consumed 56,000 gallons of petrol in the process.

J.F. Maughan was on detachment from Lympne at the time this event took place and commented on it from an erk's eye view: 'One afternoon the airfield was hit by a very thick fog and our CO rang through to say that we could have the evening off. Two of us decided to have a drink at the local which was just outside the camp boundary, and cut across the runway having to step over some pipes which had been installed along both sides by some workmen. We couldn't imagine what they were for.' They had a pleasant couple of hours in the pub and left at about 10 o'clock to return to their hut. As they stepped outside they could see a bright light from the direction of the airfield, and thought it must be some of the buildings on fire:

> However, as we reached the perimeter fence we saw flames rising in jets from those pipes several feet in height. Although the fog around the airfield was as thick as ever, where the flames where it had lifted and we could see the concrete runway between the two lines of flames. As we were standing there, we heard the noise of aircraft engines and a Mosquito landed on the runway, seeming to run through a tunnel of fire, followed quickly by another Mosquito. As soon as they had landed, the jets were turned off and the night seemed blacker than ever.
>
> We heard the next day that the controller who authorized the use of the equipment was given a 'rocket' by the Air Ministry for using it for only two Mosquitos. He was told that he should have told the pilots to bale out and let the aircraft fly out to sea and crash!

G.H. Porter, who was an Air Ministry civil engineer during the war, spent some time at Bradwell Bay. At about the time of the Arnhem operation he brought to mind:

> . . . it was used as a beacon for returning aircraft if there was a certain amount of fog about. The overall effect was quite something to remember. My wife and I walked up to the airfield to see the main runway lined with light, accompanied by the roar of many burners. Everything appeared to be in glorious technicolour. Our cottage was about seven minutes walk from the airfield, but we could easily have read a newspaper in the garden.

This could well have been on the evening of 21 September 1944. A number of Dakotas had been diverted to Bradwell during the day with fading visibility over East Anglia, and as evening drew on, mist from the marshland and north of the airfield spread over all. Seven Dakotas from 310 and 62 Squadrons requested permission to land. FIDO was lit for them, but it was not a good burn from a technical viewpoint, a smoke pall adding to the fog. Despite the adjustment of burner pressures the problem was not completely solved, but all seven aircraft made safe landings, which, the fog dispersal report says, 'was of great operational value as they had no alternative base'.

Sometimes FIDO was put to a use which its designers had not originally intended. Ron Hills recalls:

> I was in the National Fire Service, and we had the enormous job of keeping the station water tanks filled, 'just in case'. I remember FIDO being tested on one occasion and some smart guy decided to

fry some sausages. He took up position, squatting on his haunches, pan in hand, by the nearest burner pipes, but to his horror pan and sausages flew sky-high when the burners were ignited by a lad pedalling hell for leather on his bicycle!

September was a quiet month for FIDO at Bradwell, and October was even quieter. The weather was seldom good during November but it deteriorated further during the second half of the month. As has been noted already 16 November 1944 was a particularly hectic day for the Allied air forces, bombers and fighters alike. Nearly 3,000 sorties were flown in ever-dwindling visibility and many aircraft had to be diverted on their return to England. There were poor conditions everywhere when Wg Cdr (later AVM) Harold Bird-Wilson (Birdy) led the Bradwell wing as escort to a force of 418 Lancasters on a raid to Aachen. The attack was completed with few losses but a 'moderate' fog hanging over most of East Anglia gave anxiety to pilots as they sought safe landings. This was particularly the case for single-engined machines, with or without long-range fuel tanks. Although no fog dispersal report survives covering Bradwell Bay's use of FIDO on that day, 'Birdy' recalled such an occasion:

> After an escort sortie over Germany, the wing leader knows that the return to base is going to be a problem with the 36 Spitfires when there is an appalling weather forecast including fog. Nevertheless, as each squadron descended into the fog on a given order, it was the greatest relief to gradually see a reflection from FIDO which truly penetrated the sky over the aerodrome. The next relief was when all the Spitfires had landed.
>
> The flying skill of all the squadron pilots from the most experienced to the youngest member was magnificent. I do not recall a single accident when operating FIDO. It certainly gave the pilot the maximum confidence in their role to 'press on regardless'.

Czechoslovakian pilot Miroslav Liskutin, who flew with 312 Squadron from North Weald and Bradwell Bay, paid tribute to Birdy and to FIDO in his book *Stormy Skies*:

> I remember him with great admiration. He was the sort of man who inspired confidence at all times and particularly when we were operating in awful weather conditions. One could not help admiring the wing leader's accurate navigation when the usual departures were made in poor visibility and cloud base below 500 ft and frequently returning into thick fog. Our accurate rendezvous with bombers above cloud over Germany looked most impressive. The accurate arrival back to base, or to a diversion airfield, in extremely limited visibility, seemed almost unbelievable. The landings between the flaming jets of the fog dispersing system FIDO after descending in a tight formation through the dark clouds down to ground level . . . this was a fearfully dramatic experience. Some of these returns home were bordering on the miraculous.
>
> The FIDO system was frequently our only salvation, because the weather seemed to be so unpredictable, so vile, so bad. These unfavourable meteorological conditions remained without much change for many weeks, but operations had to continue just the same. Although it is true to say that FIDO gobbled up thousands of tons of fuel, it also saved hundreds of aircraft and crews. Of course, there were cases when aircraft, after landing, swung off the runway and into the flames. For such eventuality we had a man on duty with his hand on the fuel valve, who was able to shut down the system and prevent the destruction of aircraft, As far as I know only one aircraft was lost at Bradwell Bay in this kind of accident.

On 27 November, nine Mosquitos of 29 Squadron based at Hunsdon were diverted to Bradwell Bay following intruder operations which had been hampered by bad weather. FIDO was lit at 22.00 and according to the fog dispersal report, six of 29 Squadron's Mosquitos and another of 654 Squadron's landed safely. The crews reported that the burners had provided 'considerable visual help, enabling the aerodrome and appropriate runway to be discerned'. On the 29th Wg Cdr Bird-Wilson led 126 and 312 Spitfire Squadrons as escorts to the vanguard of 270 Lancasters on their withdrawal from targets at Dortmund. The weather conditions are described as 'deteriorating during the morning to poor'. FIDO was used to light the Bradwell Bay aircraft home. If the squadrons were at full strength, about twenty-four Spitfires would have been involved.

The same machines were off again next day acting as an escort to the rear of sixty Lancasters targeted to Osterfeld. Anti-aircraft gunfire was intense and the weather conditions, which were described as mainly cloudy with slight rain, remained poor all day due to smoke haze. FIDO was used to assist Wg Cdr Bird-Wilson and some two dozen aircraft to put down safely. Shortly afterwards two Mosquitos from 29 Squadron at Hunsdon were diverted after patrols over the continent had been aborted owing to 10/10 cloud.

December 1944 was the month when the greatest demands were made on FIDO, at Bradwell Bay and countrywide. 'Diver' anti-V1 patrols were still the order of the day (or night) for 501 Squadron's Tempests as they had been since June, and the Spitfires of 64, 126 and 312 Squadrons were constantly on escort duty. Despite weather reports of 'severe icing', 'visibility poor', 'weather very bad', 'cloudy, rain', 'fog', 'thick fog', 'visibility reduced by London fog', day after day operations still proceeded, and it is no small wonder that 140 landings or take-offs with FIDO are credited to Bradwell Bay during the month. Bradwell's own Spitfires and Tempests were only some of the aircraft which sought sanctuary as the days shortened.

The first of such visitors arrived at 11.30 on 3 December: twenty-five Mustangs from Andrewsfield near Braintree, which had been unable to return to their own base after escort duty. A few burners on each side of the runway were lit at the western end, enabling the pilots to distinguish the line of approach without difficulty. The poor conditions were caused by a pall of London smoke which had drifted eastwards.

During 11 December, there was a major daylight raid on Osterfeld, in which 150 Lancasters of 3 Group took part. More fighters than ever before were put up for escort duty on a day which saw 468 Bomber Command sorties. Bradwell's three squadrons were engaged, as well as those from 150 Wing at Andrewsfield and the Czech Wing at North Weald. The raid was carried out successfully, but for the eighth day in succession a swathe of pollution from London's chimneys hindered the vision of low-flying pilots on their return. The majority groped their way down unaided, but a posse of Andrewsfield's Mustangs opted to divert when they saw FIDO alight for the tail-end of Bradwell's own Spitfires. Just on noon, seven home-based aircraft landed, followed by thirteen from 19 and 65 Squadrons. The fog did not lift as the afternoon wore on and a couple of hours later FIDO had to be lit again to bring five Bradwell Tempests safely down, with a 278 Squadron Air Sea Rescue Warwick bringing up the rear.

On 16 December 1944 the Germans launched their Ardennes offensive against American ground troops, under conditions which made it almost impossible for the Allied air forces to intervene. British airfields in eastern England were fogbound, ground traffic was disorganized and sea and riverborne shipping paralysed. Not until 22 December were some squadrons able to strike at German troop concentrations and route centres. From poor, the weather deteriorated to worse and as the aircraft groped their way home through ever-lowering skies towards 7 o'clock, FIDO was successively lit at seven airfields, concluding an hour later with Bradwell Bay. James Riach, flight engineer on a 626 Squadron Lancaster from Wickenby making its way back from Koblenz, remembered it well:

On our return eighteen of us were diverted to Bradwell Bay because of fog. Upon arrival we were stacked up at 500 ft intervals, which meant that the top aircraft was around 10–11,000 ft. I recall that our aircraft was at about 4,000 ft and that we could see the glow of FIDO on occasions as we circled above the airfield. We circled for the best part of an hour, with the ground controller requesting us to stay at our nominated height. However, as time went by there was considerable complaining by pilots over the R/T on the amount of time spent awaiting instructions to land.

Eventually the pilot of the top (11,000 ft) aircraft stated that he was running out of fuel and was coming in to land . . . and the air was 'blue' with his comments about hanging around up there.

We were all gradually lowered, and when eventually came our turn to circuit, we could see on the downwind run, the flames of the system quite clearly on each side of the runway. However, as we turned in for our line-up to the runway (probably about three miles out), we ran into dense, thick, black, oily smoke. This permeated the whole aircraft and we all suffered streaming eyes.

Suddenly we burst out of this, and there was the runway just ahead with the flames on either side. As we touched down and ran along, I slid the window beside me to let in some fresh air and I was surprised to feel the heat of the flames. I remember remarking to Jim Fisk, my pilot, to keep it straight, otherwise we'd catch fire . . . I believe that this was the first time they'd had Lancasters landing at night, which was the reason for the controller stacking us so high.

Eventually we were de-briefed and went to the mess, where £100 was voted out of the funds so that we could have a Christmas party before our return to Wickenby.

Bradwell's aircraft, together with 133 Wing machines, acted as top cover for 200 Halifaxes to Mulheim and 100 Halifaxes and 60 Lancasters to Dusseldorf on 24 December. Also escorting the force were 19, 65 and 122 Squadrons of 150 Wing from Andrewsfield. The Andrewsfield Wings were unable to return there as the weather had closed in and nearly 100 aircraft returned to Bradwell Bay. Stuart 'Snow' Davis of 150 Wing recalled that the air was clear for their landing. The pilots left their Mustangs at Bradwell overnight and were taken back to Andrewsfield by bus:

The following morning we were taken back to Bradwell Bay in the dark and pea-soup fog, and briefed for a sortie which my logbook describes as a fighter sweep over the Frankfurt-Koblenz area. Because of the fog we were confident that the sortie would be abandoned and that we could return to base for our planned Christmas party. To our amazement we were soon briefed to scramble and when we queried the possibility of being able to take off we were told that the 'drome was equipped with FIDO.

However, as the CO of 122 Squadron's aircraft would not start I had the dubious honour of leading the squadron that day. It was a harrowing experience which I can vividly recall; and while the take-off was uneventful it was more than a little nerve-wracking to see the fog close back in after they turned FIDO off. By the time the Wing was formed up there was just solid fog below us and as far as the eye could see.

Bradwell's ops record book notes that twenty-five Mustangs of 133 Wing were aloft at the same time as the thirty-two of 150 Wing. It records that mist hampered operations and that both Wings returned to Bradwell together with an ASR Warwick and an American PRU machine. 'Snow' Davis continued his recollections:

Perhaps the thing most fixed in my mind is the size of the airfield on our return 3 hours 20 minutes later when 122 Squadron was first back. I called the Control Tower and told them I thought we were in the vicinity. They replied that we were overhead – what a coincidence! – and that they would turn FIDO on. The fog was just solid white, but was soon penetrated by billowing black smoke; enough to make me lead the squadron some distance away. The smoke and fog quickly disappeared and there, looking like a sponge cake with a slice cut clean through the middle was the runway. When we were cleared to land, I recall my apprehension at the possibility of an undercarriage or tyre failure, but fortunately all three squadrons landed safely.

January's weather was no better than December's; only ten days in the month were suitable for Bomber Command operations and fewer daytime sorties were flown than during the previous six months. At Bradwell Bay this was reflected in the fact that operations were prevented on eighteen days. Considerable reconnaissance was carried out on 2 January by the USAF 7th Photographic Group based at Mount Farm near Oxford. A PRU Spitfire and six PRU Lightnings escorted by a total of thirty Mustangs carried out observations over western Germany in two separate sorties. We do not know how their plates came out for the time spent over the continent, but the weather was so poor that on return some of them had to be diverted. At 11.30 the Spitfire and an escort of eight Mustangs, which had operated from Downingford, requested guidance and FIDO was lit to bring them safely down; and at 17.30 two of the Spitfires from Bradwell's 312 Squadron, which may have been despatched as shepherds, brought three of the Lightnings back with them to a FIDO-lit return. Following this the only newsworthy event occurred on the 30th, when a V2 rocket landed on one of the runways to relieve the monotony, leaving a crater 25 yd wide for the janker wallahs to fill in.

On 7 February the Spitfires of 310, 312 and 313 Squadrons led by Wg Cdr Hlado escorted outward-bound bombers targeted on Western Germany and landed on one of the captured continental airfields to refuel. They returned the following day, having first escorted a force of 617 Squadron Lancasters to the E-boat pens at Ijmuiden. The weather was 'cloudy with rain and drizzle', and visibility was greatly reduced by the presence of London fog. FIDO was lit, just two burners on each side, to establish the approach heading, and the whole Bradwell Wing touched down safely, thirty-five home in fewer minutes. The wing commander 'expressed his appreciation and considered the burn very helpful'. Three Spitfires from Biggin Hill also landed after escorting a VIP to Brussels, seven more Spitfires and a Mustang, and finally four PRU Mosquitos from Benson.

Nearly 900 B–17s and B–24s of 1, 2 and 3 Air Divisions of the US 8th Air Force, escorted by 183 P–51s set out to raid synthetic oil plants on 17 February. Deteriorating weather forced the recall of the whole of the 1st and 2nd Air Divisions before reaching enemy airspace. The conditions were so bad that some aircraft controls froze and several had to jettison their bombs. Of the armada, nine Liberators were diverted to Bradwell Bay just after 10 a.m. Visibility at ground level was 3,000 yd, but the cloud base was down to 300 ft. It was only necessary to light a few burners at the head of the runway as 'line-up' and the B–24s landed without difficulty. The FIDO runway at Bradwell is roughly SW–NE, heading out to the North Sea. Legend has it that as the Liberators passed along the River Blackwater on the downwind leg they jettisoned their bombs, which exploded to the consternation of all within earshot.

On 22 February Allied air forces began Operation Clarion, a major assault on German rail and road communication centres.

The operation continued next day, with almost 3,000 USAF bombers and fighters aloft and Bomber Command mounting raids on Gelsenkirchen, Essen and Oberhausen. Three hundred of 3 Group's Lancasters had been on a daylight raid to Essen, escorted by Mustangs from Bentwaters. FIDO was lit at 15.52 with poor visibility and a cloud base below 500 ft and, spread over a period of just over two hours, forty-one Bentwaters Mustangs of 64, 118, 129 and 165 Squadrons, two Fortresses from Podington in Bedfordshire and a Liberator from Saltby, short of fuel, made safe landings. They were joined by a further three USAF P–51s and all stayed overnight.

This brought the number of confirmed landings by FIDO during February to 109, nearly half of all recorded occasions for the month. Only one more instance occurred before the end of hostilities; on 15 March when two Mosquitos returning from night-flying training exercises had difficulty in picking out the runway. The ubiquitous London haze had spread eastwards and the afternoon sun was reflected from its upper surface, dazzling the pilots. FIDO was lit at 14.15, but according to the fog dispersal report it was 15.45 before the system was extinguished.

We know of approximately 300 landings and take-offs with the use of FIDO at Bradwell Bay during the war. There may have been more, for many fog dispersal reports are niggardly in the information they give and some incidents may well not have been recorded at all.

Finally, not long before the last personnel left the station, FIDO and its crew earned their highest commendation. On 21 November 1945 a C–47 piloted by Major Wood with VIP General John Lee, General Eisenhower's deputy, aboard made a forced landing: 'All other airfields within 150 miles radius were clamped.' On 26 November came a congratulatory message from General Lee, 'particularly singling out Flg Off F.M. Mowatt, the flying control officer, and paying warm tribute to the crews of FIDO and flying control for their efficiency.' On 30 November 1945 Bradwell's last bods departed, unrewarded but not disregarded.

SIX

Carnaby

... this igloo-shaped hole into which we were about to fly

Bill Tiltman, flight engineer, 1658 HCU

The idea of emergency aerodromes, capable of accepting aircraft in distress regardless of weather conditions, emanated from a Flt Lt Broadhead of 5 Group Bomber Command in October 1941. Subsequently three sites, at Woodbridge, Manston and Carnaby were earmarked for such a project. Construction at Carnaby began early in 1943. As a site for an emergency airfield Carnaby was a sound choice. The land is reasonably flat, although it rises somewhat to the north towards the East Yorkshire Wolds. The aerodrome is not much more than a mile from the sea, ensuring uninterrupted approach from the east. Although considered to be on the Yorkshire Moors, it is only about 30 ft above sea level, a great relief for pilots nursing engines on their last legs. Bridlington lies about two and a half miles north-east and the airfield was alongside the railway line to Hull, close to Carnaby station. It was therefore comparatively easy to transport building materials and equipment to be unloaded at specially built sidings there.

In December 1943 Woodbridge, Carnaby and Manston appeared in a list of seven airfields to be equipped with FIDO under an expansion scheme approved in that month. Carnaby was designated Station XI. Messrs A. Monk were the contractors and set about their task of building the largest runway in the north. A 3,000 yd runway, 250 yd wide (five times the normal width) was laid down on an approach of 259° (approximately WSW) which lined up almost directly with Flamborough Head. In addition, 500 yd undershoots and overshoots were cleared. The runway surface was made from a special easily repaired sea-sand mix covered with bitumen, and at the south-west end was added an enormous loop 300 yd in diameter, around which aircraft could be dispersed after landing. Two were originally planned, but only one was completed. The runway was divided into three lanes. That on the left or south side was the emergency lane, marked by white-painted lines and green lights at night. Aircraft in distress could land at will here, without the necessity for contacting flying control. The centre lane was illuminated by white and the northern line by yellow lights at night, and on these lanes standard landing procedure was followed.

As planned, the runway at Carnaby was to be flanked by a double row of Haigill Mk IV burners (see Fig. 5) on each side, set back 20 and 40 ft respectively from its edge. On the north side the series of burners would be uninterrupted for a distance of 2,000 yd. On the south side a perimeter track ran parallel to the runway about 75 yd back. Connecting the runway with the perimeter road was a series of exit points at intervals of about 200 yd, so that any damaged aircraft which did not make it safely to the far end of the runway could be quickly towed or bulldozed clear. A double row of burners was laid across the runway at the touch-down point, and a rapidly extinguishing burner (Rapex; see Fig. 8) laid in a trench approximately a mile down the runway. When eventually completed, over 180 Mk IV burners in double rows lined the runway, requiring over 30,000 ft of various diameter piping to supply a potential 120,000 gallons of petrol per hour.

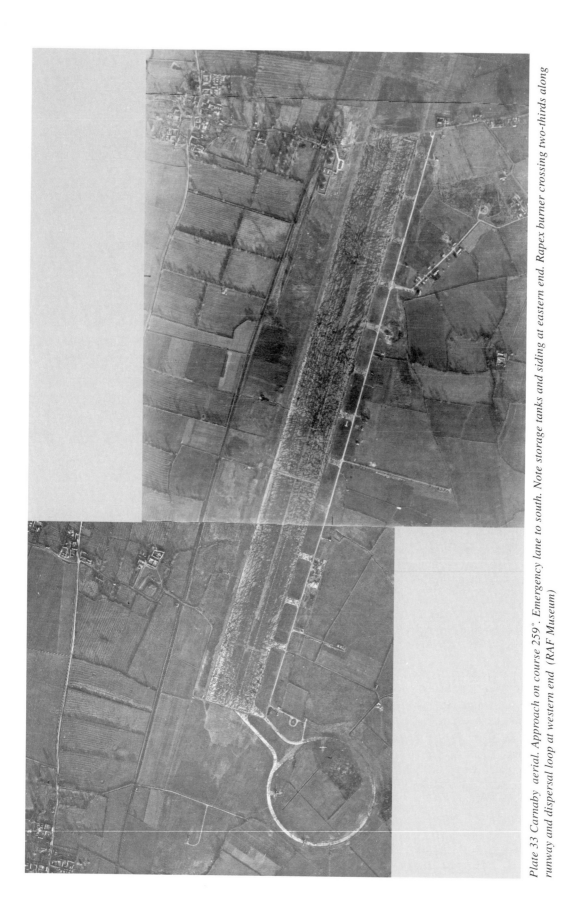

Plate 33 Carnaby aerial. Approach on course 259°. Emergency lane to south. Note storage tanks and siding at eastern end. Rapex burner crossing two-thirds along runway and dispersal loop at western end (RAF Museum)

A special siding was built adjacent to Carnaby railway station, only a field away. The layout of the siding and its equipment would have approximated to that in Fig. 19 and Plates 49–52, although the pumphouse might not have been needed. The burners themselves were served by two pumphouses, each containing six Sulzer pumps driven by Ford V8 engines.

Work on the installation of FIDO was very much dependent upon progress of the runway generally, and as it covered about 280 acres of Yorkshire there was a considerable amount of earth moving and grading to be done. Nevertheless, Carnaby was officially opened for business on 20 April. The following day the site engineer grumbled:

> We are held up on this aerodrome while grading of the sides of the runway is being completed, but it is anticipated that work on the burners will be able to proceed on the north side very shortly. All burners have been installed on the south side, including the IRB dispersal track crossings, but the laying of the 1½ in feed-lines has been delayed due to grading. Work on the touch-down end is still held up due to lack of grading.
>
> Owing to objections being put forward by the railway company to shunting on the main line, the location of the rail off-loading siding had to be altered to one of the existing Air Ministry sidings. We have shown a revised operational date of 10 June, but this is entirely dependent upon the progress of airfield construction.

With much work still to be done and vast quantities of petrol to be delivered to the storage tanks it is perhaps not surprising that it was not until 19 July 1944 that Sqn Ld Harry Edge, the senior PWD meteorologist, was able to observe the system's first practice burn. A postwar feature in the *Bridlington Free Press* recalls the trial:

> Bridlington people saw a great glow in the sky. It was accompanied by dense volumes of thick, black, oily smoke. Then the smoke disappeared and the fog was tinted red. It grew brighter until people in Bridlington could have read newspapers by the light. 'What a fire!' they said. Fire brigades fifty miles away said the same thing and stood by for a call which never came. One or two fire brigades actually clanged their way towards Bridlington without waiting for the call. Their dash was in vain, for there was no fire. What Bridlington was seeing for the first time was that faithful watchdog of distressed aircraft, the Carnaby FIDO!

When primed prior to burning the enormous system frequently overflowed into local dykes and streams. Tom Walker remembered that leakages were a boon to the locals.

> Drips of petrol at one point of the installation totalled five gallons a day and were of course collected, petrol being rationed. One can of five gallons was given to a farmer, with strict instructions not to pour the last half gallon or so into his motor because of the sediment. Unfortunately, he took no notice, being of a greedy disposition and subscribing to the idea that it couldn't happen to him, used the whole contents of the can – and ruined his engine. I should think that was the most expensive petrol he ever used!

The first record of an operational burn of FIDO occurred on 1 August 1944 when 777 aircraft were detailed to attack flying bomb sites in the Pas de Calais. Visibility remained poor throughout and Bomber Command records show that only seventy-nine aircraft were able to bomb their targets. A force of sixty-five Halifaxes from 4 Group set out for Chapelle Notre Dame. Cloud base at take-off was 1,000 ft with 10/10 cloud all the way to the target, and nothing better was expected on the return flight. In fact, as midnight approached, the stratus was down to 250 ft over the Yorkshire coast and diversion orders were issued. Many of the aircraft still had bombs on board as the raid had been abandoned just before H-hour.

Instructions were given to light FIDO at Carnaby at 23.30. The distances involved caused some delay in getting the operating crews to their stations quickly, but the approach burners were well alight within ten minutes and shortly afterwards the whole of the outside lines were blazing away. The effect was to raise the cloud base to 500 ft, where it seemed to stick. What followed, told by three different people, would have qualified as a 'spiffing yarn'.

The first Halifax landed safely just before midnight, followed by five others. Dorien Freeman was watching from a position near the control tower when the next group approached. One of them, Q-Queenie, was known to be short of fuel:

> The Halifax approached the runway from the west (normally all landings took place east–west) and asked permission to land. The pilot was given a course to clear the runway and join the other aircraft already in the circuit. He, however, ignored the instructions and carried on his approach with wheels and flaps down, heading straight for an aircraft making an emergency landing. A crash seemed inevitable, when the pilot of the aircraft approaching from the west opened his throttles and literally bounced over the other aircraft.

The circumstances were not quite as terrifying as they might have seemed to an observer, though hairy enough. Fred Papple had been pilot of W-Willie diverted from Leconfield, one of the earlier Halifaxes to land:

> Being an abandoned mission we were always told to bring our bombs back, only dropping enough to correct our landing weight. We dropped two 500 lb bombs on the way back. We had taken off at 20.08 and were over Carnaby at 23.54. FIDO was working, lifting the cloud base to 500 ft, a lovely sight to see.
>
> We landed without difficulty, parked our aircraft and made our way over to the control tower. There were many aircraft coming in, and while we were watching we suddenly saw two coming in to land at the same time. This was okay, but they were coming from opposite ends of the runway, and from where we were standing they looked to be on a collision course. Knowing that they had bombs on board, we began to move backwards very smartly; and then we remembered that Carnaby had three runways side by side, and to our relief watched them touch down and pass on different tracks.

The machine which Q-Queenie, flown by Flt Sgt Billy Bishop, had threatened to decapitate was in fact O-Orange, diverted from Lissett a few miles away. Piloted by Flg Off Leonard on the last trip of his tour, O-Orange had suffered battle damage and Gp Capt Tom Sawyer, station commander at Lissett, thought it was wise to send him to Carnaby:

> . . . who were only too pleased to oblige and lit up the fog dispersal flare path to help him. We saw his navigation lights circling at Carnaby and then he went straight in to land, although approaching very low in the final moments. In the light of the fires there we could see an engine suddenly burst into flames just before he sank out of sight on to the runway, and waited anxiously for a telephone call from Carnaby.
>
> It came soon to reassure us that the pilot had landed safely and the crew were all right, but that they had been so low in the approach funnel that the aircraft had struck the chimney of a disused farmhouse during the final approach, an airscrew had been knocked off and the engine had caught fire. They had just scraped in over the boundary.

All in all, this was a spectacular beginning to FIDO's service at Carnaby.

As autumn advanced, airfield conditions deteriorated. Wg Cdr Fowle had to report: 'Some civilian aircraft maintenance employees refused to work under the terrible conditions, but service maintenance parties carried on and overcame the same conditions; but not without considerable hardship.' There were no permanent accommodation or repair facilities at Carnaby and relations must have been very strained at times. 'It is appalling,' grumbled Wg Cdr Fowle, 'that after a long operational sortie, aircrew cannot be received in a suitably warm building and be interrogated in conditions which even allow them to sit down, particularly as the establishment of only one coach for the dispersal of the crews necessitates the lapse of two, three and even four hours before they can be transferred to Lissett for feeding and sleeping.'

As an example of this on the night of 15/16 November, among other operations a number of RCM missions were flown over Western Germany, one of them including Fortress A-Apple of 215 Squadron. Jimmy Southgate was rear-gunner:

On our homeward leg the fog got worse and eventually we were diverted to RAF Carnaby. I was sitting in the rear turret, thinking that this was the worst fog we had ever seen, when up came the navigator on the intercom with the startling remark 'ETA two minutes'. I must admit that I was very concerned for I knew that there was no way in which we would be clear of fog in that time.

After what seemed an age there came a yellow glow in the sky and then we came over a runway with fires on each side. I did not know that we were going to a FIDO 'drome, although I had heard of them. My skipper did a couple of circuits and we landed at 05.55 on 16 November. It is certainly a memory which will always stay with me – and it was a very long two minutes. I was convinced that we would have to bale out. I don't know if it was the only 'drome open, but there was every type of plane you could think of. They were all over the place, from Lysanders to four-engined bombers and crews of every nationality.

There was nowhere to sleep as the place was so crowded. Our bomb aimer went to the mess to play cards and managed to win a few pounds, which enabled us to scrounge a lift into Bridlington and sleep in a bed-and-breakfast place.

Altogether during the month of November, Carnaby received 221 Allied machines – seven damaged by enemy action, ninety with technical troubles, twenty-two short of fuel and 102 diverted because of bad weather at their own aerodromes. The station commander's monthly summary concluded: 'Appalling weather conditions have not only increased the fifth element, MUD, against which the station is fighting, but has increased the difficulties and troubles of the maintenance and servicing sections.'

Conditions in December 1944 were, if anything, worse than in November. The first recorded FIDO landing of the month took place on 13 December just before 5 p.m., a calm evening with 300 yd visibility and radiation fog just deep enough to mask any final approach. Although no operational aircraft were aloft, a number of machines en route, exercising or on test flights, were caught out over various Yorkshire bases and were diverted to Carnaby. As they reached Carnaby's orbit and their altitudes decreased, so did visibility. The whole length of the inner line of burners was lit at 16.53 and over a period an unidentified Halifax, two more, L and Z of 426 Squadron and, oddly enough, a 5 Group Spitfire K9871 made safe landings. J.R. Smith, pilot of Z-Zebra, voted 'FIDO a decided advantage, in fact really wizard!'

The first Halifax to land may have been unidentified in PWD records, but it was well known to Bill Tiltman, its flight engineer. Halifax LW193 from 1658 HCU at Riccal had been engaged in bombing and air to sea firing exercises when the weather closed in and she was recalled: 'I remember seeing this igloo-shaped hole into which we were about to fly, plus of course the roaring, red, short wall of fire at the base of each side. There was plenty of smoke with the fog really rising up.' The length of the burn is not recorded, but 124,000 gallons of petrol were consumed. One pre-heater burst during the operation.

Later that evening FIDO had to be lit again. By this time visibility was down to 100 yd with the fog deepening to 200 ft. At about 9 o'clock Lancaster R2 of 166 Squadron landed, its pilot experiencing 'no difficulty, only in estimating distance from runway on approach'. The CO was not satisfied, however, and complained that nothing had been done about the access road he had requested to be built parallel to the north side of the runway. Once FIDO had been extinguished visibility remained good enough for a while after the burn so that the FIDO crews could return safely to their quarters – the problem had been in getting them to their operating pits in the first place.

On 16 December 1944 the great German offensive in the Ardennes began, with the object of capturing Brussels and the port of Antwerp, and splitting the Allied armies into two parts. The attack was launched under conditions of poor weather with low cloud and mist, and it was several days before Allied air forces could intervene in the battle.

As the Christmas period approached, however, the number of sorties flown against the German forces increased, though there was no let-up in the weather. Raids on Trier, Politz, Cologne, Koblenz, St Vith, Rheydt, Bonn and other communication centres and airfields took place in an almost round-the-clock series of attacks. FIDO was in frequent use throughout, and the installation at Carnaby took quite a hammering.

Early on 22 December conditions were very bad for aircraft returning from the continent; 542 bombers had been engaged on targets such as Bonn and Cologne and the synthetic-oil refinery at Politz near Stettin on the Baltic. Three Lancasters were lost on the Politz raid and five more crashed in England. But for FIDO the figure would have been much higher. It was raining heavily in the north by 01.30 and there was radiation fog 40 ft deep at Carnaby where to cap it, literally, 10/10 cloud was down to 400 ft. It took some twenty minutes from light-up to clear horizontal visibility to 1,500 yd throughout a three-hour burn. Seven 5 Group Lancasters made safe landings in the middle of that period – T, A, S and G of 463 Squadron, R and Q of 619 Squadron and X-X-ray of 630 Squadron. Flg Off J.B. Grant of R-Robert enthused: FIDO was wizard, could not have landed without it. Just like coming in to daylight; while E.T. Foster (S-Sugar) reported, 'Bang on! No trouble from glare.'

Although no USAF bombing missions were recorded on the 22nd plenty of their aircraft were aloft, and at 11.35 FIDO had to be lit again for thirteen Fortresses which were lost. Communication difficulties often arose with American aircraft, but it was only found necessary to light the burners at the eastern end for them to find their way down. 'All crews agreed that had FIDO not been lit, they would not have been able to locate the airfield.' The burn was spread over almost three hours, by the end of which time the FIDO tanks were running dry and it was necessary to couple up the pumps direct to the railway tankers and feed the lines from the sidings.

When FIDO was turned off at 14.40, the crews worked furiously to top up the storage tanks. They were well backed up by the LNER which kept trainloads of wagons on their way for several days on end. Dorien Freeman recalled the state of the burners after many hours of continuous use without repair or maintenance. 'When we eventually turned FIDO off, the pipes alongside the runway were so distorted by the heat that whole lengths looked like pieces of spaghetti and had to be replaced.'

The urgency of the situation was such, however, that there could be no question of closing the system down for wholesale reconstruction. On 26 December 1944 Bomber Command was able to mount a concentrated attack on German forces near St Vith. Nearly 300 aircraft took part, but the improvement in the weather was only temporary and by lunchtime it was necessary to light FIDO against the return of the 4 Group Halifaxes. Markers only were lit initially, as visibility was half a mile, though radiation fog 70 ft deep made a final approach hazardous. Using the markers, one Halifax landed safely, but the fog gradually thickened to allow only 80 yd visibility. The whole of the inner lines of burners was alight by 16.10, which cleared the runway to 1,500 yd. Nineteen more Halifaxes landed without difficulty over a two-and-a-half-hour period, although each machine was able to put down in an average time of less than three minutes from Flying Control taking over. A number of the Halifaxes were on only three engines and all pilots expressed the opinion that a landing would have been impossible without FIDO.

Alan Arthurson was navigator aboard L-Love of 102 Squadron which touched down at 16.45 that day:

> On arrival back over England we were diverted to Carnaby. It was a hair-raising experience, as we were unable to see other planes while we were stacked waiting to come in. We finally got into the thinner fog and could see the FIDO flames. As we were coming in to land – there were six of us coming in at the same time, some landing short, some on grass and some half-way down the runway – a French pilot flew down just in front of us. How the skipper missed him I do not know. Taxiing off the runway was a nightmare, but flying control did a wonderful job.

One of those trying to unscramble the chaos was Hugh Tyson of 102 Squadron whose aircraft:

. . . had been out on a 'gardening' trip, returning in the early hours of Christmas Day, to be diverted to Carnaby because of fog. I was a member of a ground party sent to Carnaby to sort out various engine snags which had developed on some of our Halifaxes. The weather was grim (freezing fog) and we finally arrived at our destination to find the FIDO installation there going at full bore. To add to the awe, a Halifax actually came in to land in the middle of this conflagration.

We were unable to reach our aircraft that night and the next morning we went down to the loop at the southern end of the strip. This loop was used to park visiting machines nose to tail as they arrived, and the sight which met our eyes was staggering. The loop was packed full of Halifaxes, Lancasters and Stirlings; there must have been fully 100, parked with the utmost precision, the nose of each machine being well over the tail of the one in front. It was the next day, Boxing Day plus one, before we were able to get our own kites out and away to Pocklington.

On 29 December there was a major daylight raid on Koblenz, a main centre serving the Ardennes battle front. Nearly 200 of the participating aircraft were from 4 Group. As they headed for home in the early afternoon, fog consisting mainly of smoke haze 100 ft deep brought visibility down to only 600 yd. Flying Control recorded that none of the aircraft in 4 Group was equipped with SBA instrumentation and the FIDO markers at the entry to the system were lit to guide pilots to the airfield. Halifaxes O and A of 76 Squadron, and I and R of 78 Squadron were able to land with this aid, but by 4 o'clock the fog had thickened and a full burn was ordered. Unfortunately, the whole of the inner line of burners was clapped out by this time and the outer line had to be burned at maximum pressure to maintain clearance. Another six Halifaxes and a Lancaster were able to set down safely on a runway cleared to 1,600 yd visibility within the burners. They were O and W of 78 Squadron, T and X of 10 Squadron, L-Love of 150 and B-Baker of 158 Squadron from nearby Lissett. Temperatures were down to 20° below zero at the time, and the expansion and contraction of the FIDO pipes caused numerous breakages; and although emergency welding took place, in most cases complete replacement was the only real solution. During the course of the burn which lasted from 12.45 to 18.33, 264,764 gallons of petrol were burned.

The station ops record for the month reports:

Sixty-five aircraft were landed on the FIDO system [out of a total of 228 landings], requiring a great deal more work than normally experienced by FIDO crews. This section has never been up to establishment and is now being depleted more than ever by overseas postings. During a full burn we now have only nineteen men to operate sixty control pits. Should an aircraft swing to the burners after landing, it is laid down that a man should be there to turn off the valve. In practice this cannot be done. We take the risk but we do not accept the responsibility. The inner lines of FIDO have exceeded their lives by 100 per cent.

During the last week, owing to severe weather conditions, there has been an inch of ice on the runway almost every morning. On six occasions there were more than twenty-five aircraft parked on the edge of the runway as the loop was full. Fog badly interfered with the transfer of crews, and on one occasion, to reach accommodation at Lissett, all available transport was formed into a convoy which, led by the station commander in person in his car, took an hour and a half to cover the three and a half miles between the two stations.

Altogether in December 1944 there were 228 emergency landings at Carnaby including sixty-five by FIDO. Petrol consumption was just on 1,700,000 gallons.

On into January, but changing the calendar to 1945 did nothing for the weather which was exceptionally bad: 'The frequent rains of the autumn were followed by many days of persistent fog, some of the worst this century, which gave way to freezing conditions and several weeks of snow, thaw and snow again during the New Year. The lot of the ground crews was miserable and the whole effort to sustain operations made extremely difficult.'

New Year's Day saw no respite for the FIDO crews. The system had earlier been damaged by an aircraft swinging off the runway during an emergency landing, putting a whole 40 yd section out of action, and to make matters worse only twenty-eight men were available to operate and service the double rows of burners. Shortage of crew meant that the inner rows of Haigill IVs, the most frequently used, could not be repaired and cleaned in time for the next operation. They 'have exceeded their life by 100 per cent and will take four weeks to replace. Should anything happen to the outer pipes the airfield will be u/s.'

Despite the dire situation, FIDO crews stood by at first light on 1 January when six 38 Group Stirlings were diverted from their own fogbound airfields. As visibility decreased through the morning, fog mixed with smoke 50 ft deep necessitated the light-up of the installation. A number of aircraft lacking SBA were brought safely in: Halifaxes O-Orange and C-Charlie, Lancaster R-Robert and an Oxford. More aircraft were to come, but fortunately the visibility which FIDO established stabilized naturally and the five Halifaxes, five Mosquitos and three Lancasters which subsequently landed had only the gloamin' to contend with. Even so, FIDO was burning intermittently for three and a half hours and used up over 200,000 gallons of petrol.

The four weeks which the FIDO team reckoned to be necessary to replace the worn-out burners had not expired when the system was next required. On 22/23 January, 107 Halifaxes of 4 Group were part of a force of 152 aircraft carrying out a raid on Gelsenkirchen. About midnight a shallow layer of smoke drifted across the East Riding at not much more than chimney height. This was one of those in-between conditions which obscured airfield lighting when viewed obliquely. Some diversions were expected and the cross-burners and two-thirds of the outer lines of burners were lit; sufficient to burn off the mist from the approach end of the runway. Altogether, the system was alight for two and a half hours, though the landings by 4 Group Halifaxes took place between 00.47 and 01.20. In that half hour Z-Zebra landed with hydraulics u/s; J-Johnnie came in with no brake pressure and had to fish-tail his way to the far end of the runway; Q-Queenie's air speed indicator was u/s, and O-Orange had only three engines working. FIDO used 136,000 gallons of petrol, but it is certain that twenty-eight crewmen considered it well spent.

A raid by 219 Liberators and 112 Fortresses of the USAF's 2nd Air Division took place on 31 January 1945. The intention was to attack Brunswick and Hallensdorf, but 'doubtful weather conditions for return to bases necessitated the recall of the mission'. After more than a week of little activity warning was received at Carnaby of a large diversion. Ground crews were hastily organized to clear snow from the enormous runway, which was shrouded in a thick mist. It was only necessary for the approach markers to be lit, but the persistence of the mist and of an extremely low cloud base meant that the burners were on the go from 09.55 until 15.50 hours. During that time no fewer than sixty-five Liberators were landed, together with six non-operational Halifaxes caught out on exercises. Although many of the aircraft had mechanical faults, all that reached the threshold landed safely. FIDO consumed 114,000 gallons of petrol. The station's ops record book comments, 'Considering the fog and extremely low cloud, we did well to land all the aircraft without incident.'

James Wilkie, Chief Technical Officer at Carnaby, recalls that: ' . . . the Liberators did not wait for landing instructions, but came down in droves. Frequently there were two or three aircraft completing landings at the same time, once the crews had heard or seen other successful landings.' Sadly, he recalled, as did Dorien Freeman, that some of the crews would not fly over the marker flames: 'As a result, a number of them ran out of fuel and subsequently crashed on the moors north of Scarborough, and we had the unenviable job of spending about three days locating the wrecks and recovering the bodies in atrocious weather conditions.' At least seventy-nine aircraft were landed at Carnaby with the aid of FIDO in January, out of nearly 300 diversions.

The night of 2/3 February was one of intense activity for Bomber Command, 1,253 sorties being flown at a cost of twenty-one machines and their crews. 4 Group aircraft were part of a force of 323 bombers carrying out an attack on Wanne-Eickel. Battle damage and bad weather caused many diversions upon their return, some of them to Carnaby. FIDO was lit at 00.29 and over the succeeding hour or so the extra-wide, extra-long runway received a

Halifax with undercarriage trouble and faulty R/T, followed by two more without brakes, one of which had no tail-wheel either. Bringing up the rear came another Halifax, R-Roger of 10 Squadron from Melbourne, also with no brakes. Aboard was Roy Jarvis:

> We were hit by flak over the target and lost our hydraulics, so had no means of lowering the flaps or brake pressure for landing. We were diverted to the emergency landing strip at Carnaby, near Bridlington. It was thick fog, with a low cloud base, and FIDO was in operation. This was the first time I had landed with FIDO and it was an awe-inspiring experience to land between two lanes of flames. . . . It was amazing how effective FIDO was to clear the fog; two pipes with holes through which fuel was pumped and ignited. It was of course essential that you did not swing on landing.

Bomber Command mounted a heavy raid on Pforzheim on the night of 23/24 February. The town was attacked by 367 aircraft of 1 and 6 Groups and thirteen Pathfinder Mosquitos which were covered by RCM aircraft from 100 Group. During the raid itself ten aeroplanes were lost and widespread fog on the return flight caused many diversions, with FIDO being lit on at least four airfields. No fog dispersal report for Carnaby has survived, but we know from other sources that throughout the night a series of diversionary landings was made at the base. First, a 'successful Darkie landing by a lost Liberator and another which was diverted'. Towards midnight 'the diversions continued'; three Halifaxes, three Liberators, a Lancaster and four Flying Fortresses. Exactly how many of them needed the services of FIDO is not certain, but ten or eleven is the likely figure. Fortress GB-H of 214 Squadron from Oulton in Norfolk certainly did. New Zealand tail-gunner L.A. Budge recalled the diversion. His pilot, Flt Lt Liles, made a tentative approach but felt the turbulent effect of FIDO when still some 200 ft up, from which height they made contact with terra firma 'with one hell of a splash!' After their rough arrival the skipper was considerate enough to enquire via the intercom if brother Budge was still there!

A total of 140 emergency landings were made at Carnaby during February 1945. As far as can be ascertained twenty-seven were with the aid of FIDO.

The first three weeks of March were quiet as far as FIDO was concerned, although emergency and general diversions caused the station to be as busy as it had been in February. Part of the system only was lit for a long period on the 12th, however, to aid the landings of a number of aircraft with mechanical trouble. There was some industrial haze about, sufficient to mask the sodium lights, but not enough to justify a full burn. Marker burners were lit and a single 20 yd burner on each side of the approach end of the runway, so that pilots could establish its location and heading. Their arrivals were well spread out over a seven-hour period from noon. First came a Lancaster with undercarriage trouble, followed by one on only three engines. These were followed by two brakeless Halifaxes and another with aileron controls u/s. All put down safely at a total cost, calculated to a nicety, of 15,488 gallons of petrol. A total of 1,108 bombers had taken part in operations, chiefly against Dortmund on that date, but whether those which landed at Carnaby were part of that force is not recorded.

With the force's return in the early hours, warning had already been received at Carnaby of the likelihood of widespread diversions and FIDO was lit at 01.10 in conditions of 600 yd visibility, which the marker burners increased to 1200 yd. Fred Swain was air-gunner aboard Halifax W-Willie of 640 Squadron based at Leconfield in Yorkshire. On the evening of 8 April 1945 a force of 440 planes of 4, 6 and 8 Groups attacked the shipyard area of Hamburg.

> I remember flying over Carnaby and seeing those large jets of flame and thought that something was on fire. We circled for a little while until it was our turn to land. From the rear turret looking backwards it was a great surprise when the large jets of flame passed underneath. I swear I felt the heat, and then there were more jets down each side of the runway. We taxied to the far end, into a huge circular dispersal and stopped when our nose was almost touching the tail of the plane in front. There must have been about 100 Halifaxes there that night.

Another airgunner with a remarkable tale to tell was Flt Sgt John Francis Smith of 58 Squadron, who scraped in while Fred was queuing for a bed. The *Emergency Landing Bulletin* records that:

> At 05.45 on 9 April, Carnaby was informed that a Coastal Command Halifax in trouble and short of fuel was approaching from the sea. Carnaby was then in fog, with visibility down to 60 yd, but attempts to re-divert the aircraft north had been abortive and it was thought that E-Easy was heading for Carnaby to make a forced landing. FIDO was ordered and lit immediately, sodium and contact lighting also being switched on.
>
> R/T contact was established almost as soon as the aircraft's plots began to appear some 50 miles out. At 06.06 a fair clearance of fog had been obtained and E-Easy, then plotted at about thirty-five miles out, reported that the glare was visible and that they were heading for the runway.

At 06.15 E-Easy was overhead. The pilot could see the lights of the runway but reported that without FIDO, landing would be impossible and that fuel was insufficient to reach another division airfield. All was cleared for him and:

> E-Easy made a good flapless landing. It was then seen that the aircraft had sustained extensive damage, and when the marshalling party approached, the mid-upper gunner was found to be hanging below the fuselage, his parachute harness having caught up in a projection at the rear of the shattered bomb bay.
>
> In the course of a successful anti-shipping patrol off Norway, a photo-flash had accidentally detonated in the bomb bay, blowing out the rear end. Other damage included the mid-upper turret blown off, leading edges blown off the tail-planes, extensive damage to the fuselage floor frames and skin, and port and starboard flaps rendered unserviceable. The mid-upper gunner had fallen out through the gap blown in the bottom of the fuselage and the crew had believed him lost. The gunner had been caught up close to the underside of the aircraft and, apart from shock and exposure sustained in the three-and-a-half-hours flight home from the target, he was not injured in the course of landing, although his oxygen mask and goggles were found to have been scraped by the runway surface!

So FIDO at Carnaby ended its wartime story with an incident every bit as exciting as its early days.

It is not possible to give an exact figure of the total number of landings made with the aid of FIDO. A Bomber Command report refers to a figure of 1,580 emergency landings from April 1944 until the end of the war. Of these, we estimate that more than 250 were made with the use of FIDO. Lack of documentary confirmation prevents a more accurate estimate. Even so, that figure represents more than 1,700 aircrew who might not otherwise have been able to collect their war service medals – even though a Bomber Command medal might not be one of them! Nowadays most of the airfield site is an industrial estate. One link with the past has been retained in that the road which runs along what was the southern edge of the runway is called Lancaster Road.

SEVEN

Downham Market

. . . a vast flame-lined grave

Gp Capt H.G. Davis, pilot, 195 Squadron

Official records might refer to Downham Market, but as far as local inhabitants were and are concerned it has always been Bexwell aerodrome. The airfield lies to the north of the road running through the village and the main runway was parallel to it. Most of the land in the area lies about the 100-ft contour. Within a few miles of Downham the land drops away noticeably into the Fens.

RAF Downham Market opened as a satellite of Marham in October 1942. On 1 December it was transferred from 2 Group to 3 Group and in March 1944 to the Pathfinders, as the

Plate 34 Downham Market aerial. Runway 27. FIDO burners just discernible at first runway intersection. Storage tanks by road south-east of touchdown. See Fig. 14 (Crown/MoD)

home of 635 Lancaster Squadron and the Mosquitos of 608 Squadron. At this time the FIDO installation at Graveley had just been completed and Pathfinder AOC Donald Bennett was anxious to have another airfield as an alternative. On 4 March it was agreed that the PWD should install 1,200 yd of what became called Haigill Mark III burners (see Fig. 4), and the airfield should be designated station IV. Progress was not very swift, for the development of the FIDO burners on airfield scale was undertaken at Graveley and work at Downham Market of necessity lagged behind.

Eric Basford remembered an incident on the night of 27 August 1943, before FIDO had even been used operationally:

> Stirling O-Oboe was one of 218 Squadron's aircraft taking off with a full bomb load in a raid on Nuremburg. As the aircraft gathered speed along the runway, the pilot lifted the tail, thereby putting the full weight upon the main wheels. The tyre on its port wheel then burst with a loud bang. The Stirling immediately slewed to port and left the runway, finishing up on the grass between the runway and the perimeter track. The crew were shaken, but they all got out safely.
>
> The crashed aircraft being well clear of the runway, the rest of the squadron continued to take off. The pilot, Sgt Bennett, explained afterwards that he had inadvertently run off the perimeter track as he approached the runway and the port wheel had run over the FIDO pipes. His flight engineer had got out and examined the wheel and undercarriage as best he could with a torch. When he declared it to be undamaged, Sgt Bennett had then moved on to the end of the runway and begun take-off procedure.

Nevertheless, contractors William Press reported on 20 September that the installation 'was now ready for filling with petrol and preliminary trials. Should be operational by the end of the present month.' The initial FIDO layout, as depicted in Fig. 13, had an approach box of 500 yd, 160 yd wide, followed by 700 yd of burners on each side of the E–W runway. This meant that the system crossed the eastern perimeter track but did not extend as far as the first intersecting runway.

The system was a mystery to Bill Overton in the beginning, but:

> Later on when FIDO was lit up and used, its purpose became obvious, but such was security during its installation that I don't think we even speculated what it was all about. To get to our place of

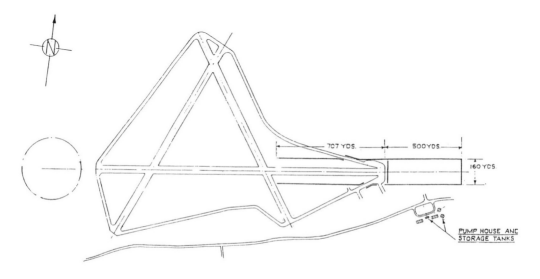

BURNERS INDICATED THUS: ———

Fig. 13 Downham Market, original FIDO layout

work at the aircraft dispersals, my colleagues and I had to pass the end of the runway and often stopped to wait for aircraft to land before crossing. During those waits, one could hardly avoid seeing the pits where the controls for FIDO were located. These contained the control wheels and instruments for operation of the system, which was reminiscent of the footplate of a steam locomotive – masses of gleaming brass gauges, large handwheels, etc, all maintained in spotless condition.

The first trial landings with FIDO took place on 11 October 1943. Without the advantage of a landing or two in clear weather to experience the effect of the installation on touchdown, Sqn Ldr K.F. Jolly and Gp Capt L.J. Crosbie bravely took off from Feltwell in Oxford HN478 at 05.55 in the dark with practically nil visibility, with fog 1,000 ft deep. They picked up Downham's beacon almost immediately, and soon after saw the glow of FIDO from about five miles out. Making a normal beam approach, they dropped into the fog when about 600 ft up. At about 300 ft a reddish glow became visible and at about 150–200 ft the runway burners and cross-line came clearly into view, permitting a normal touchdown. Some turbulence was experienced as the aircraft passed over the cross-line burners, but not during the touchdown itself. Sqn Ldr Jolly reported that dividing one's attention between the instrument panel and the runway could cause drifting in a cross-wind, and emphasized the need for experience in beam approach work on particular aircraft types. Four landings and take-offs were subsequently made and station commander Gp Capt Downs, who joined them for the last one, expressed himself well pleased.

'Then it was time to top up the storage tanks again,' recalled Ron Dill. He and his colleagues were supposed to clamber up on to catwalks over the petrol storage tanks and take dipstick readings through the filling caps to establish the 'fuel remaining' state. This could be a bit of a chore if it was carried out in the dark with only the aid of a torch, so, like any servicemen worth their salt, they quickly devised a method of their own. A sharp condensation line appeared on the outside of the tanks in cold weather, which showed where the level of petrol inside the tank had reached, and by keeping an eye on it as fuel was pumped in its contents could be gauged; this method was not in the manual but was nonetheless very effective.

FIDO was lit twice on 21 November for practice and trials. Sqn Ldr Jolly flew over from Feltwell with PWD's liaison officer Wg Cdr Wooldridge in their Oxford, solely on instruments. They were in 300–400 ft of fog, above which were about 300 ft of clear air, surmounted by interminable cloud. They felt like a very tiny piece of meat in a foggy sandwich. As they approached Downham Market the SBA instruments failed. With outside visibility practically nil they were able to detect only a column of black smoke piercing the ground fog. Flying directly through this they caught a momentary glimpse of the burner lines alight, but it proved impossible to land visually without guidance from the SBA beforehand and the trial was abandoned.

Changing to Oxford DF456, which was getting to know its way to Downham, Sqn Ldr Jolly and Wg Cdr Wooldridge tried again, though conditions were, if anything, worse than before. This time they picked up the Downham beacon without difficulty, though they did not spot the burners until they were about 900 yd from the airfield. Visibility was still bad, however, and though they saw the lines of fire they were not sure whether they were to the right or the left of the runway. However, the 900 yd gave them a brief moment to establish their line and make the necessary alteration in course prior to making a safe landing.

The reports of Sqn Ldr Jolly and Gp Capt Crosbie resulted in a rethink about the layout of the FIDO system at Downham Market. The length of runway covered by the burners was increased to 1,362 yd, bringing FIDO almost to the second intersecting runway. Such work involved the installation of special intersecting runway burners (IRBs), with surface vaporizers but with the burner lines sunk into trenches and protected by a grating where the main runway was crossed by runway 33/15. On only the second aerodrome to be equipped

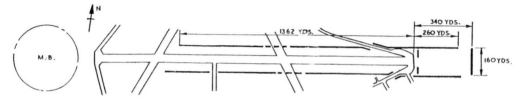

Fig. 14 Downham Market, eventual FIDO layout. See Plate 34

with FIDO, this delayed the operational use of the system by many weeks. The eventual FIDO layout at Downham Market required the construction of over eighty Mk IV burners each 40 yd long and in excess of 16,000 yd of various diameter piping to supply them from the storage tanks (Fig. 14).

Carol Holt, a meteorologist at Downham Market in FIDO's early days, brought to mind that it:

> . . . caused quite a commotion when it was first proposed, with 'conferences' held in the Met Office by the forecasters and so-called experts, a strange collection of people with bees in their bonnets. Fog was not a great problem in summer, but we suffered a lot from North Sea stratus, which meant the diversion of returning aircraft, as the stratus was often as bad as fog.
>
> FIDO is by no means my abiding memory of Downham; rather it is of crashing kites, Stirlings having a nasty habit of swinging to port on take-off, which often meant ploughing through the FIDO pipes and heading for Control and the Met Office. The worst one I saw was in daylight, when a Stirling cartwheeled from wing tip to wing tip, sending FIDO pipes, repairs only just finished after an earlier crash, in all directions.

Making runway observations during test burns and some of the trial landings in late 1943 was one of the duties into which Carol was pressed:

> I remember being dumped near the caravan at the end of the runway and walking along part of it, to do my best with cloud-cum-lifted fog base and with slowly improving visibility along the runway. It was a strange experience; roaring pipes on either hand, black runway between, fog enveloping everything, and *very* lonely.
>
> On two, perhaps three occasions, I nearly jumped out of my skin as an aircraft whistled by my ear, unheard before its sudden appearance due to the din from the FIDO pipes. I do not recall that they were operational burns, but presume that they must have been, for I remember very well a collection of utterly unprintable opinions from aircrew the following morning!

The night of 16/17 December 1943 was disastrous for Bomber Command, when a heavy raid was carried out on Berlin by 483 Lancasters. There was strong opposition on the way to and over the target and twenty-five Lancasters were shot down. A further twenty-nine subsequently crashed en route for home. Harry Darby was a 514 Squadron air bomber on that raid. His pilot was Plt Off D.C.C. Crombie, RAAF. Their long return flight over Denmark and the North Sea was made more perilous by the loss of one of their port engines:

> We approached our home base at Waterbeach, to learn that the whole of East Anglia lay under dense fog, and we were diverted to Downham Market, one of the few airfields in those parts equipped with FIDO.
>
> On approaching Downham Crombie called up Flying Control and asked for permission to 'pancake'. The reply came back, 'You are turn 36. Circle the beacon at 18,000 ft.' This meant that thirty-five other aircraft, stacked at intervals of 500 ft, were waiting to land before us. Crombie asked for priority on the grounds that we only had three engines working, but the answer was that others below us had bigger problems.
>
> It seemed an eternity before our turn came round to make a blind approach, and all our nerves were on edge as Crombie gently eased the kite down. I stayed in the nose in case he needed any last-

minute guidance. Gradually the total gloom gave way to a diffused glow ahead, and then I suddenly saw the FIDO flares along both sides of the runway. We were beautifully in line, but I could see that we were far too high. I shouted to Crombie to this effect, but he yelled back, 'I'm buggered if I'm going to overshoot on a night like this!' We landed with a heavy bump and ran right off the end of the runway, into what looked like a cabbage field, but Crombie swung the kite round on to the perimeter track. We were safely down after being in the air for more than nine and a half hours and according to our flight engineer, with just about enough fuel to fill a cigarette lighter.

Following this event no records survive referring to FIDO's use for another ten months. A possible explanation for this is that Downham Market was originally equipped with Mk III burners (see Fig. 5), which were subsequently replaced by Mk IVs (see Fig. 6). Unfortunately, though simpler to construct, they did not have a very long working life under continuous operational conditions, and were replaced at station after station by Mk Vs (see Fig. 7) as skilled labour and materials became available.

Record or no record, 218 Squadron wireless operator Tom Mankelow recalls being very glad of FIDO on 28 January 1944. The night was one of a heavy raid during the Battle of Berlin, which had cost Bomber Command forty-six planes. Part of a force of sixty-three Stirlings which were mine-laying in Kiel Bay on the same occasion was provided by 218 Squadron. As midnight approached, visibility had decreased, and in Stirling EF133:

It was a case of all eyes looking out for any airfield lights. We saw a flare go up, I believe to aid an aircraft before us to pinpoint the beginning of the runway. We made an approach keeping the point of the flare in mind, but when we saw the runway with FIDO on each side we were too high to make a landing and had to overshoot. We were advised to have another try rather than be diverted to yet another airfield. Another flare gave us a clue to the beginning of the runway. This time we came in lower and found the runway for the pilot to put down and stop before we got to the end of it. We found it comforting to see the orange flames with the black smoke coming from them, slowing down as we went past and knowing that we were safely down without running out of runway.

In March 1944 218 Squadron departed when Downham Market became part of 8 Group, being replaced by the Lancasters of 635 Squadron. During the succeeding months 635 Squadron was heavily engaged. James Stewart was a petrol tanker driver at Downham Market: 'We had to go to the King's Lynn depot to get loaded, and it took ten tankers each doing five runs [at about 3,000 gallons a time], whenever FIDO was topped up.' This sometimes coincided with operational landings when FIDO was ablaze:

If you were the first to arrive at the base, you couldn't see your hand in front of you. Then the world seemed to light up as you saw a sheet of flame tearing down each side of the runway. As you stood there and watched it seemed as if the flames were never going to stop and you wondered what was going to happen. As you watched, the fog started to rise; slowly at first, but then it got higher and higher until it was like looking down a great long tunnel . . . the heat was terrific . . . they burned thousands of gallons an hour . . . sometimes there was the roar of aircraft overhead, and even as you watched, way up in the sky you suddenly saw two wheels appear, followed by the whole body of the aircraft. It was nothing short of a miracle!

Fog dispersal records begin again on 23/24 October 1944, albeit not in the detail we would have liked. A force of 1,055 bombers carried out a heavy raid on the Ruhr town of Essen, with additional attacks on Berlin by Mosquitos of the Light Night Striking Force (LNSF). Fourteen of the Lancasters involved were from 635 Squadron, and twelve of the Mosquitos were of 608 Squadron. The weather deteriorated considerably during their absence, until at Downham Market visibility was only 80 yd in a shallow fog. As the aircraft from Downham crossed the coast, the possibility of a trouble-free landing decreased and accordingly FIDO was lit at 10 o'clock. Within a quarter of an hour a good clearance had been obtained – 1,800 yd horizontally and clear up to the sky. During the next two hours eleven Lancasters and eleven Mosquitos landed without hazard. The CO, Sqn Ldr Ovenden, was very pleased, as it saved diverting both of Downham's squadrons to goodness knows where, whence it might take days to reassemble them. An idea of FIDO's thirst can be obtained from the fact that the burn consumed 105,840 gallons of petrol. After which, as many a ground crew had occasion to complain, it was topping up time for the tanks and pricking out time for the burners.

Ten Lancasters of Downham's 635 Squadron formed part of a force of 485 bombers of 1, 5 and 8 Groups which took part in the daylight raid on Düren on 16 November 1944. The raiders suffered few losses, but as the force made its way home the weather deteriorated in the form of radiation fog aggravated by industrial pollution carried by an 8-knot wind from the south-west. By 4 o'clock surface visibility was below 1,300 yd and the fog was estimated to be 700 ft deep. Instructions were given for FIDO to be lit at 16.30 for Downham's own aircraft and any others which might be diverted there. Though two preheaters (the top pipe in the triangle of three) burst, causing excessive smoke to begin with, the whole ground operation earned the commendation of Flying Control and enabled all ten home-based Lancasters to land safely (A, B, C, D, J, K, M, N, V and Y) along with C and N of 156 Squadron diverted from Upwood. The last plane landed on only three engines, without hydraulics and with a 1,000-lb bomb hung up in the bomb bay. Pilots reported that they could pick up the glow of FIDO anything from 5 to 20 miles away, but that neither the angle of approach indicators (AAIs) nor the contact strip was visible. It is not recorded how long FIDO remained alight, but 148,600 gallons of petrol were used.

When the Mosquitos of Bomber Command were not accompanying main force raids over Germany, many were engaged in attacks by the Light Night Striking Force on Berlin and other major cities. Jack Bailey, navigator with 608 Squadron, recalls taking part in a raid by fifty-six Mosquitos of the LNSF which attacked Berlin on the night of 24/25 November. 608 Squadron supplied thirteen of the aircraft. The operation was carried out without loss, but Downham's ops record book notes, 'Base conditions very bad on return and all aircraft had to land with FIDO.' 'The uplift of air was tremendous' was the lasting impression of Jack, 'but when the Mosquitos came in the system pressure was reduced as the uplift was too great for our light wooden construction'.

On 27/28 November 1944 fourteen Lancasters of 635 Squadron and twelve Mosquitos of 608 Squadron took part in raids on Neuss and Berlin respectively. Weather conditions were expected to improve for the homeward flight, but although it did so in some areas, Downham's weather remained poor. Visibility was only 400 yd, due to shallow radiation fog, 40 ft deep, which a slight wind was blowing across the runway. To avoid large-scale diversions, FIDO was brought into operation at 20.38. 'Despite some of the control pits being partially flooded, all drills were promptly carried out.' Visibility was raised to 2,500 yd and over the next two and a half hours all twenty-six of Downham's machines plus two strays landed safely. The burn could be seen up to 200 miles away and one captain thought that the glow was from an aircraft burning in the sea. The two strangers that had joined the circus were Halifax Q-Queenie of 415 Squadron, short of petrol, and a Barracuda of 827 Fleet Air Arm Squadron, lost and without wireless aids, whose pilot, with Senior Service reticence admitted, 'Very good indeed.'

As November moved into December the weather deteriorated, though any hopes that fogbound aerodromes would be allied to a merry Christmas were shattered halfway through the month. On 16 December Field Marshal Runstedt mounted his famous Ardennes offensive but not until 21 December were Pathfinder aircraft able to take part.

With only 600 yd visibility Plt Off Pickard, Flg Off Green and Flg Off Barson in Mosquitos F-Fox, G-George and Q-Queenie of 608 Squadron took off as part of a force of ninety-seven aircraft, attacking the railway yards at Bonn, while Lancasters A, J, L, Z, C, M, N, E and S raided those at Nippes, Cologne. No aircraft were lost on either of these raids, but decreasing visibility hazarded their return with radiation fog 700 ft deep swirling over the airfield, aggravated by a 9-knot wind. FIDO was lit at 18.46, but smoke from the north burner line reduced its effectiveness. Nevertheless, the glow through the fog was visible from 40 miles out.

Before any Downham aircraft arrived, however, the pilot of Mosquito N-Nan of 85 Squadron from Swannington, without R/T or W/T and whose base was closed in, began to circle overhead, attracted by the glow. He circled until the smoke cleared and then swooped over the airfield at 200 ft, flashing his navigation lights. He was given a green which he did not see and continued to orbit for nearly half an hour before chancing his arm and making a safe landing from the western end of the runway, with a following wind. The pilot said that he thoroughly enjoyed his experience and thought FIDO was a wonderful aid.

Fortunately, Flying Control kept Downham's own planes out of the way while he was performing, and after patiently waiting their turn, all twelve put down without mishap – the right way round! They were nearly all using FIDO for the second or third time and were just as enthusiastic as before. The system was alight for approximately two hours, during which time 113,920 gallons of petrol were burned.

On his 63rd operation, Gordon Webb was pilot of Lancaster P-Peter of 405 Squadron which raided Bingen on 22/23 December. Departure was unusually early, 15.00, with the idea of ensuring all aircraft a safe landing before the onset of fog, forecast to set in about midnight:

> The operation went off quite well but as always we were glad to set course away from the target area and return home. We held 18,000 ft almost to the enemy coast, then pushed the nose down so that we could not only pick up speed but also get rid of our oxygen masks, which, after a few hours, became very uncomfortable
>
> By the time we were coming up to Gransden Lodge we were flying at 3,000 ft, on top of a very solid-looking cloud cover. The fact that we had no glimpse of the ground came as no surprise, for as we were crossing the Channel, wireless operator George Biva had received a message from Group advising that the fog had arrived earlier than expected and that not only was our home base zero-zero but also every other base that our remaining fuel supply would let us reach.

On receipt of Group's message Gordon immediately reduced power to gain maximum endurance, for fuel supply had now become a critical factor. It was not, however, the only problem. Navigator Vic Painter had long since given up on GEE and his H2S was giving only a blurred return. Much more serious was the loss of SBA and ADF:

> I contacted Gransden as soon as possible and was advised that George had got it exactly right. Visibility was zero and so was the ceiling, with no possibility of landing there. I passed them our serviceability state and I believe that our lack of SBA may have given them cause for thought. Shortly, they came through and told us to proceed to Downham Market. This we did with a growing concern about our fuel state which seemed to be moving to 'empty' at an alarming rate.
>
> As we approached Downham Market I held 3,000 ft, watching the fuel gauges moving inexorably down. I eased the throttles back a little more and re-trimmed to get the most out of the engines. Johnny Whitehouse, our flight engineer, was working away at the crossfeed arrangements so that we got every last pint of fuel out of our auxiliary tanks.
>
> Vic, who had been working furiously with his grassy H2S, advised that Downham should be straight ahead. I knew he was right on, because I actually saw a faint glow through the clouds that I perceived to be FIDO. I contacted Downham Market and was advised that the weather conditions on the ground were zero ceiling and visibility, but that FIDO was in operation and that we were to hold our position and wait our turn to make an approach.
>
> Since we had no other means of carrying out a controlled approach, I decided, while holding on top of the fog, that I would assume the light spot to be the runway and to fly, as nearly as I could, a normal circuit and hope that at the end of it there would be a runway. I explained this to the crew, and although I wasn't going to order them to bale out, I gave them the choice and strongly recommended it. Ed Scarffe, our rear-gunner, seemed to sum it up by saying, 'We've come this far together and we've done it before – we stay!' They stayed.

With the number of operations they had flown together, the crew had developed a practice of saying nothing unless necessary. Each contemplated the situation in his own way, but kept his thoughts to himself, and Gordon Webb was grateful. At moments like that a pilot was very much alone:

> It was now 21.30. As I sat above the dense fog, it was almost peaceful, with no turbulence. . . . All I could do was watch the fuel gauges and wait for my instructions to leave this rather peaceful altitude, stick the nose down and be enveloped in the dark cold cloud. 'Downham Market to P-Peter; do you read? . . . You are cleared to make an approach. FIDO is in operation. Surface wind zero, visibility zero, ceiling zero.'
>
> I tried to sound matter of fact; wouldn't do to let anyone know how I really felt. Frankly, I hated to enter that cloud. . . . The problem was to descend low enough in the fog at the right place so as to see the runway and to take advantage of the visibility afforded by FIDO.
>
> It is true that the glow from FIDO may penetrate vertically through the fog, depending on its thickness, as in our case. However, there is quite a difference between vertical and horizontal visibility through fog. Many a pilot has learned this fact the hard way. Very often, when landing in foggy conditions, he can look vertically down and see the runway lights, only to find that on final approach he can no longer see them and has no forward visibility either.

Finally, the Control Tower cleared them for an approach and landing. Following a timed approach procedure from 1,200 ft, three minutes later Gordon estimated that he was on his final runway heading, descending at some 300–500 ft per minute:

> At 100 ft I tried to hold the aircraft level. Altimeters can have a ±50 ft error. We could easily be only 50 ft above the ground and who knows what? A Lancaster has a tendency to float during landing . . . and I not only had to get P-Peter over the end of the runway, but once there I had to execute a landing so as to be able to walk away from it and not go roaring off into the wilds at the end of the runway. . . .
>
> I don't know who saw what first. I think both Johnny and I saw a wall of flame at the same moment to the left. I wheeled P-Peter over, pushed the nose down, corrected the air speed, chose a point which I thought centred us between the two walls of flame and cut the engines. We were on the runway. We made it . . . a white moment that I shall never forget.

Lancaster W-Willie on the same raid was the aircraft of Sqn Ldr Marcou. His WOp/AG was Don Vockins who also recalled being unable to land at Gransden Lodge and diverting to Downham Market, albeit with a different conclusion. Having landed they were directed around the perimeter track to a hardstanding. When everything was shut down, the crew clambered out of the aircraft and, as was their custom, lined up near the tail wheel to relieve themselves, to talk about the trip and, on this occasion, to talk about FIDO:

> All of a sudden there were rumblings and loud explosions, with large lumps of concrete and great clods of grass flying all around us and the Lancaster. We didn't know if it was Jerry unloading on the drome or what it was. There was a good old fire roaring away near us too. Finally, an ambulance turned up, presumably in case we were injured, and took us to de-briefing. We were then told what had happened. Apparently fuel from the FIDO lines had leaked into a drainage ditch where we were and had ignited and exploded with all the consequent fireworks. I am not sure whether it was a common occurrence, but it was one which we could have done without!

An amusing (at this distance) postscript to the raid was that there were no civilian casualties in Bingen but that the citizens complained that 'the town wine store was hit'. When we told Don Vockins of this he replied, 'I'm sorry about the wine store now, but in those days we were a little unsociable!'

Six of 405 Squadron's Lancasters (A, B, O, P, U and W) made completely successful landings. A seventh, J-Jig, piloted by Flg Off Woods was already an engine short when he tried twice to land at Graveley before being diverted to Downham Market by R/T:

'Unfortunately, during his second attempt to land here he hit an obstruction, making his third engine u/s, and he arrived over this airfield on only two engines. He was immediately given permission to land, but again bad luck dogged him, for his undercarriage would not come down. He decided to belly-land, not on the runway between the burner lines but on a well-chosen position in the overshoot area, conveniently illuminated by FIDO. The crew were unhurt.' All was not yet over, however, for Sgt Zapaznik, skipper of Lancaster X-X-ray of 300 (Polish) Squadron with only fifteen minutes petrol to spare was also attracted by FIDO's welcoming glow. Eschewing the niceties of landing procedure, he descended post haste, quite successfully: 'All eight pilots were very enthusiastic about FIDO, especially as their crews were spared the unpleasant task of baling out.'

The impression of FIDO alight at night was a constant theme of personal reminiscences of Downham Market and elsewhere. Bill Overton, who worked on Stirlings in the early days of FIDO, recalled:

I was invited into a pit one night while FIDO was alight. I knew a bloke on the FIDO team. The operators were in communication by field telephone to the officer i/c who gave the operating instructions. The flames seemed to be turned up high for the first stages of the burn – I'm desperately trying not to exaggerate but they must have been at least 12–15 ft high. The noise of the vaporized fuel burning was considerable and the heat of course quite intense. When aircraft were landing, that obviously would be when sufficient fog had been dispersed to enable the field to accept aircraft, the flame was turned down to a height of 1–2 ft, but even at that setting considerable heat was still generated. In full blast, when viewed from the end of the runway, looking along the tunnel of flame, FIDO was quite an awesome spectacle, and of course would be seen for miles around.

Christmas Eve 1944 was the busiest day for FIDO during the whole time that it was installed at Downham Market. Thirteen of 635 Squadron's Lancasters under Wg Cdr Sydney Baker, already with over 100 ops under his belt, led a raid on Lohausen (now Dusseldorf) aerodrome. As they prepared for take-off thick fog descended over the airfield, threatening to put paid to the operation. But the FIDO crew rose to the occasion and had FIDO lit within 12 minutes of stand-by – even though it was dinnertime. As soon as the runway was clear Wg Cdr Baker opened the throttles of Lancaster N-Nan at 12.28 and accelerated down the runway:

After about two-thirds of the take-off run, my port outer engine cut out, which of course initiated a violent swing to port. I managed to control this without leaving the runway by applying full opposite rudder and throttling back the starboard outer engine. As I was now running out of FIDO I decided to attempt a take-off rather than abort. I slammed fully open the throttles of the three good engines and we just made it. From memory the FIDO burners extended down the runway for 1,000 yd, which meant that on take-off you ran out of it before becoming airborne. The transition from flaming murky visual to foggy blankness on instruments was not at all pleasant and I was relieved when I broke through into the clear above. It was very hairy, but once airborne and through the fog my crew and I decided to press on to the target which we reached on time. We were slightly lower than the other bombers but sustained no damage, though we attracted some attention from the German flak.

Fred Sherwood recalled:

After the Lancasters had gone, a dense fog descended on the airfield, reducing visibility to nil. Then at approximately 15.30 FIDO alongside the main runway was lit again. The heat was scorching, the smell was terrible. It burned with heavy smoke and everybody and everything within 100 yd was covered in soot. However, eventually it lifted the fog to about 50 ft, and after circling the airfield all of the Lancasters landed back safely.

As Fred said, the installation was re-lit with the fog clamping down to only 50 yd, but visibility was cleared by FIDO to two miles in the space of 40 minutes. Just after 16.00 two of 608 Squadron's Mosquitos took off for an attack on Munster. During the next hour and a half all thirteen of 635 Squadron's Lancasters returned without mishap, intermingled with a gaggle of three Lancasters, two Dakotas, a Fortress and a Norseman, lost and attracted to FIDO's glow as moths to a candle. Wg Cdr Baker reflected:

> Landing was not easy. The FIDO could easily be seen from above the fog, so that positioning downwind, across wind and, while still above the fog, into wind, was straightforward. However, upon entering the fog on let-down, all you could see was an orange, smoky glare. We had no aids to line up the runway or keep track of height relative to the glide path, so we relied on our blind flying instruments and our own skill; but with eyeballs on the windscreen, hoping to see the runway, it was not difficult to wander off the landing direction and get the rate of descent wrong. This would result in violent changes of height and direction near the ground, and, if too far out of line, throttles open and round again. It was like landing in a fiery inferno!

FIDO was turned off again just after 17.00, but at 18.31 was lit for the third time, in marginally better visibility but with the hazard of night landing to contend with. By its light, one of the Munster Mosquitos returned early, the other electing to divert. The latter was Mosquito KB273 flown by Ted Durnford. The raid of 24 December was, to Ted, an odd incident:

> It was to have been a spoof diversion to draw enemy fighters away from a heavy operation, and to have comprised six Mosquitos, with three stations each supplying two aircraft carrying target indicators and four 500-lb bombs.
> Approaching the target area, my navigator and I were surprised that the target was not being marked, so we flew round and round in brilliant moonlight. Then we turned south and dropped our bombs into the fires of a raid just finishing. Much later I learned that the Munster raid had been cancelled. The other two squadrons had received their recalls, but not 608. So, only the two Mosquitos from Downham Market set out. One had engine failure on the way and, with a barometrically fused target indicator aboard, had to drop his load in the sea and return. Thus, I was the only one to reach Munster – and even then I finished up bombing somewhere else!

Lastly, five Mosquitos from 8 Group, diverted from stations under the weather, two Dakotas and another Lancaster made their way safely down; a total of forty-five movements, consuming 240,000 gallons of petrol. None of the visiting aircraft had any difficulty, although for most of them it was their first experience of FIDO. However, one American pilot was heard to say, 'Gee, it sure was tough landing among them flames!'

On Boxing Day 1944 Bomber Command had its first opportunity to intervene directly in the Ardennes offensive. A force of 294 aircraft from all groups except 100 set out to attack German troop movements near St Vith. In the van were seven Lancasters of 635 Squadron. Many 8 Group airfields were out of action due to the bad weather and Downham Market's visibility was only 100 yd.

FIDO was lit at 12.10 so that the seven Lancasters and two of 608 Squadron's Mosquitos could take off. S.F. Jackson, a navigator of 635 Squadron, recalled the 'Long Stop' operation. Thick fog at the station made him doubt the possibility of any take-off at all. The aircraft crept round the perimeter and its crew surveyed the drifting fog and smoke from the as yet improperly heated FIDO. Visibility was nearly nil. The skipper opened his window when they eventually found the end of the runway. Ultimately FIDO cleared the air to a distance of 800 yd. With head half in and half out and steering on a compass course they took off, finding clear air at about 500 ft.

Wg Cdr 'Tubby' Baker led the 635 Squadron Lancasters into the air. His no. 2 was Alex Thorne and crew in D-Dog. A graphic description of getting airborne is to be found in Alex's book *Lancaster at War 4: Pathfinder Squadron* which he has written in the third person:

> . . . When all the checks had been completed and without any snags being encountered, there was still more than an hour before take-off, and the uncertainty of the whole business was beginning to generate an atmosphere almost of resentment. 'Why the hell can't they tell us what's happening?'

was the general feeling among the crew. They stood kicking their heels outside the ground crew's hut, too unsettled to stay inside in the warmth, when they heard the scuffling of feet coming towards them through the fog. Simultaneously, a reddish-yellow glow appeared, spreading in an east-west direction. 'They've activated FIDO. Some poor so-and-so is up there trying to get down.' No sooner had he spoken than Tubby Baker materialized out of the fog followed by his car driven by a WAAF. He was wearing flying boots which accounted for the characteristic scuffling noise which preceded his appearance. The crew will never forget his words in what was a short and hurried conversation with Thorne.

'Do you think you can take off on FIDO, Alex?'

'Gawd knows, I've never tried.'

'Well, here's our chance. The fog is clearing from the north, just about enough for main force to take off, so somehow we have got to get airborne. You will be No. 2 for take-off after me at 13.17 hours. I'll go and find the others now. Best of luck. See you later.'

With that he went to the front of his car which had been manoeuvred to a few feet away, waved his arms for the driver to follow him back to the perimeter track and disappeared into the murk to carry the glad tidings to the five other crews.

. . . FIDO was essentially a landing aid, and without being too dramatic, it would be a case of venturing into the unknown to attempt a take-off with it. When the final approach to a landing was being made, the pilot could see the two lines of fire stretching below and ahead, so he simply followed the normal procedures and landed between them. The aircraft did tend to hold off and float more than in a normal landing due to the heat produced by the lines of burning petrol, but, once the wheels touched down, control of the aircraft was no more difficult than in normal visibility. The unknown factors in the present situation were take-off with the extra weights of over 11,000-lb bomb load and 2,000 gallons of petrol. And how would the heat and glare from the FIDO installation affect the take-off with the aircraft gathering speed, as opposed to reducing it to a standstill on a landing? No one could say, so Thorne and Harry agreed that they would take it as it came and act accordingly – or words to that effect.

. . . The main problem, as it appeared to them, might be the possibility of FIDO becoming a massed red glare reflected in the fog to the front as well as on both sides as the aircraft speed increased from a standstill up to and beyond the lift-off at around 110 mph. In that case he would have to depend on his reading of the instruments in order to keep a straight course until the glare became lost behind them. But then, Thorne thought, why should that be difficult? After all, he would be climbing entirely on instruments until they were in the clear at 3,000 ft or so, if the Met boys were correct in their forecast.

One thing he had decided with the crew was that they should allow plenty of time for the half mile or so journey around the perimeter track in the fog to the end of the east–west runway for take-off. There was time for a chat with the ground crew who told them that some of their colleagues – they did not know how many – from the aircraft not flying, would be on each side of the perimeter track, with torches to help guide them to the take-off point. Then, after the last cigarette for at least the next five hours, Thorne led the way to the bottom of the ladder into D-Dog. The time was 12.50 hrs when everyone was in position and settled down with intercoms switched on for him to start making the individual crew checks, starting at the back: 'Okay Jim?' 'Okay Skipper.' 'Okay Jock?' 'Okay Skipper.' . . . and so on, until he said, 'Right, so am I. We'll get cracking.'

Sliding his window back, he put his head out and shouted, 'All ready down there?' to the airman standing down below with the trolley accumulator plugged in to the port inner engine. In a few seconds the propeller turned slowly and gathered speed until the fog was swirling backwards above and below the wings. The revs were then reduced and when the other three engines had received similar treatment to Thorne's and Harry's satisfaction, it was 'Chocks away!' and the slow trundle through the fog commenced.

. . . Sure enough there was an airman with a torch light just visible on the port side. There was no difficulty making the short distance from the aircraft's hardstanding to the perimeter track, where they turned left and were picked up by a succession of airmen on the port side. It was slow going, but it worked well, and Thorne turned D-Dog round on to the approach to the standpoint at a right angle to the runway, which was somewhere in the middle of the reflected glare of FIDO, now appearing as a vast orange-red curtain of fog on the starboard side. He moved tentatively forward until a red light was waved and he could just discern the blurred outline of another Lancaster at a standstill in front.

'That must be Tubby,' said Reg Keary, who had been keeping a look out from the bomb aimer's compartment in the nose of D-Dog. 'And we've got another behind us,' came the voice of Jim Rayment over the intercom. 'Good,' replied Thorne. 'Let's hope the other three have made it. Keep listening and I'll tell you when Tubby moves, so that you'll be ready for the off.' It was a fidgetty, eye-straining wait, until Reg called 'He's moving.' A split second later, the sound of Tubby's engines revving up indicated that the CO was turning right on to the runway, unseen by those in the fog behind him who would follow.

There was silence for perhaps two minutes, and at exactly 13.17 hrs came the – at first – gentle roar of the four Merlin engines increasing to a straining crescendo as the Baker crew headed between the flaming burners towards lift-off. Then everything seemed to happen in rapid succession. A torch-light, green this time, was waved in a forward motion in front of D-Dog, followed by another, white now, swinging to the right. Almost immediately came another red and Thorne brought D-Dog to a stop. Now he could distinguish the flames from the burners stretching ahead at the bottom of the glare on each side as he waited for the final green. With the speed increasing as the throttles were advanced, Thorne found that the flames maintained their identity within the glare and there was no more difficulty in keeping a straight course than on a normal take-off. The tricky bit came when the burner flames were suddenly left behind, and immediate attention had to be concentrated on the compass and air-speed indicators.

At 120 mph Thorne and Harry went through the routine of throttling back the engines to climbing power, wheels up and locked, flaps up, at the end of which Graham Rose came through with the course for the first turning point over The Naze on the coast six miles south of Harwich.

Air movements continued to be hampered during the remainder of December, but on the 29th Downham's aircraft were able to take part in a raid on Troisdorf railyards as spearhead of a force of 197 planes from 6 and 8 Groups. Fifteen Lancasters were detailed for the marshalling yards and three of 608 Squadron's Mosquitos set off for Gelsenkirchen. Conditions were poor and the raid was not regarded as successful, but no aircraft were lost. The weather closed in as the squadrons returned home, however, and threatened to achieve what the enemy had failed to do. It was a bitterly cold day with the air temperature 2° below freezing point and a heavy ground frost which had persisted for days. Visibility on the airfield was below 900 yd and fog was moving diagonally across the runway in a 5 knot wind.

The order to light FIDO was given at 19.30 as the home aircraft neared base, and a clear pathway 2,000 yd long awaited Flg Off Sheppardson, the first man home in Mosquito F-Fox at 20.03. During the next hour and a half the other two Mosquitos and fourteen of the Lancasters landed safely (U, S, H, L, D, J, X, A, E, B, Z, N, T,) with Flg Off Parks bringing up the rear in F-Fox at 21.36. The fifteenth Lancaster diverted elsewhere. FIDO was extinguished at 21.44, having consumed 123,000 gallons of fuel. This brought December to an end as far as FIDO was concerned, during which PWD records estimate that twenty-three aircraft took off and sixty-six landed at a cost of 670,000 gallons of petrol.

FIDO was required on 6 January 1945, following a raid on Hanau, near Frankfurt: 482 aircraft of 1, 4, 6 and 8 Groups were involved and another 147 Lancasters of 1 and 3 Groups took part in an attack on the railyards at Neuss. Together with Spoof, RCM and mine-laying operations, 788 sorties were flown, eleven aircraft being lost. As the machines from the main force streamed home, fog descended over many of their aerodromes and FIDO was lit at 19.47 in radiation fog, with less than 1,000 yd visibility, against the homecoming of Downham's twelve Lancasters and two Mosquitos from Hanau.

Within a short time the home-based aircraft began to arrive and circuit the fire-fringed runway. First, Mosquitos E-Easy and U-Uncle landed, followed by Lancasters U, B, A, E, L, T, F, S, X, J, C and W. All made good approaches and landings born of experience; a total for the night of eighteen, apart from any which may have come in before the fog clamped down. Downham was 'crammed with aircraft of all types'. A 2-hour 20-minute burn consumed 113,400 gallons of petrol.

During the next weeks the weather in East Anglia became worse, so much so that it was impossible for FIDO to deal with the dense fog which shrouded it. In fact, there are no further operational records for FIDO until the night of 19/20 February when 254 Lancasters of 5 Group made a heavy attack on the town of Böhlen, with a substantial diversion by eighty-two Mosquitos to Erfurt. Twelve of the Mosquitos were from Downham's 608 Squadron. Take-off was in the clear and they bombed at about 20.00, but by the time the aircraft were due home conditions were poor. There was 10/10 cloud down to 1,000 ft and below that the best of visibility was no more than 700 yd in a thick smoke haze. The burner lines were not fully operational due to arrears in maintenance, but the haze was penetrated sufficiently to enable pilots to line up with the runway without difficulty. Mosquitos C, Q, K, P, D, M, F, Z, G, R, J and U landed safely in just over an hour, one of them navigated by Jack Bailey. Apart from his relief for a safe return Jack recalled: 'After sustained periods of operation, the FIDO system had to be drained of petrol so that the necessary repairs could be carried out. As soon as it was known that this was to be done, those who were fortunate enough to own a car went dashing down to the runway in the hope of collecting any stray petrol being drained!'

Gp Capt H.G. Davis, then of 195 Squadron, based at Wratting Common, remembered a training flight on 20 February 1945 when he was advised that his base was closed due to fog and was instructed to land at Downham Market:

> It was the first time I had ever seen FIDO in operation and as it was lit while we were still 40 miles away the whole sky was illuminated. As we neared the airfield, there appeared to be one enormous fire. We were cleared to land, and the lasting impression I have always held was that we were about to descend into a vast flame-lined grave! The reflected moon on top of the fog – probably about 500 ft deep – made the fog look like the ground and the runway with its flaming outline appeared to be subterranean! Apart from the turbulence on the approach, and a prayer from all of the crew that I would not swing off the runway, the rest of the landing was uneventful.

On 22/23 February a force of 367 Lancasters and thirteen Mosquitos of 1, 6 and 8 Groups carried out a heavy raid on Pforzheim and, among 'minor' operations, seventy Mosquitos attacked Berlin. A total of 666 sorties were flown during the night, from which seventeen aircraft failed to return. Eleven of 635 Squadron's Lancasters, led by Wg Cdr Baker, were part of the PFF and twelve of 608's Mosquitos went to Berlin. No fog dispersal report for the night has survived, but 'Tubby' Baker recalls a take-off in clear conditions. Larry Melling, a 635 Squadron pilot, remembered another incident from about the same time. It was during daylight and everything had been brought to a standstill by the fog:

> Even the birds were walking. All airfields in the vicinity were in the same condition and nothing was flying. We were all hanging round wondering what to do, when suddenly we heard aircraft engines. The sound passed over the field and shortly afterwards returned from the opposite direction. This continued for quite a long period, and then, much to our surprise, there was a flurry of activity and FIDO was started up.
>
> Some time later a USAF B-17 landed and taxied up to the Control Tower behind the 'follow me' van. It transpired that the B-17 was on a flight from the Azores to Lakenheath and somehow had got lost. He was running low on fuel and couldn't find any place to land. Luckily for him he was in our area and we were equipped with FIDO. Apparently the delay in landing was caused by trying to explain to the American crew what FIDO was, as they had never heard of it.

There are no further references to the use of FIDO at Downham Market. A Bomber Command document lists the following FIDO movements from the time it was fully tested on 1 October 1943: 173 landings and 43 take-offs, at a total consumption of 2,145,000 gallons of petrol. One hundred and fifty-nine landings were operational and fourteen were from training flights. Of the operational landings, there were ninety-eight Lancasters, fifty Mosquitos, four Dakotas, three Halifaxes, one Fortress, one Wellington, one Norseman and one Barracuda. The grand total of 216 FIDO movements does not tally exactly with our estimate, and with the possibility that some occasions may have been omitted, it is likely that the figure could be as many as a dozen higher. Instructions for the dismantling of the FIDO system were issued on 25 September 1945.

EIGHT

Fiskerton

... the airship clearly before us, flanked by walls of fire

Bill Spence, air bomber, 44 Squadron

RAF Fiskerton occupied a site between the villages of Fiskerton and Reepham in the vale of the River Witham, about 5 miles east of Lincoln. The airfield sat on a plateau about 50 ft above sea level, overlooking Fiskerton and the Delph stream to its south. Although reasonably well drained into the Delph, gumboots were a wintertime necessity, and folk who worked on the airfield said that it sometimes 'felt as if you had a breeze block on each foot'.

Plate 35 Fiskerton aerial. Runway 26, approach box. Storage tanks south of touchdown. See Fig. 15 (Crown/MoD)

Fiskerton was opened as a sub-station to RAF Scampton within 5 Group in January 1943, its operations record book dating from 10 May, and it first appears in PWD records in April 1943, designated station XIII (Plate 35). This did not prove to be an unlucky number when installation of FIDO began in August 1943, for the airfield benefitted from the experience gained at Graveley and Downham Market and did not have its system revised almost as soon as it was laid down. The east–west layout of the main runway 26 favoured the construction of a straightforward system of Haigill Mk IV burners (see Fig. 5). It was not necessary to uproot trees and hedges for the approach box. The perimeter track at the eastern end of the runway acted as a Bird gap. The first runway intersection was over 1,300 yd down the line, avoiding the necessity for intersecting runway burners as at other airfields. The last third of a mile of the runway was covered by a staggered series of burners (Fig. 15).

The overall FIDO contract was taken on by Messrs A. Monk, and the on-site assembly work by the Strong-Arc Welding Co., operating from Lincoln. Their supervisor George Gillam recalled that construction was undertaken in sections of about 200 ft at a time and that: . . . together with anchor blocks and guides, holding down bolts, bringing all materials from the contractor's compound, laying out on site, lining up drilled pipework, etc. would take approximately twenty-one 12-hour working days. This would require a tractor driver, four pipe fitters, four labourers, two electric-arc welders for the cutting, fitting, tack-welding, etc., and a foreman fitter/welder.

As their HQ, the workforce had a small shed, which had to serve as drawing office, canteen and drying room. All construction work was exposed to the elements. George supervised the work at Sturgate, Metheringham and Ludford Magna as well as at Fiskerton, and considered the operations very similar, 'except that maybe one site was boggier than another!' He was very proud of the work undertaken by his firm and said: 'I speak truthfully about this; in all our welds on all stations we never had a weld which broke, though sometimes the fierce heat of burning FIDO distorted the pipes out of all recognition and fractured the iron retaining brackets, causing petrol to spray out all over the place.'

For the first month work went ahead without hold-up, but on 20 September the airfield progress report commented, 'Work slightly delayed due to low-lying country and flying. No

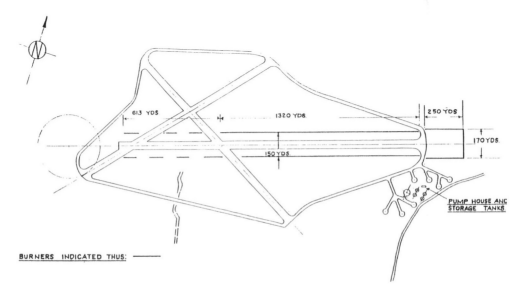

Fig. 15 Fiskerton FIDO layout. See Plate 35

other difficulty, and this site should be operational on schedule,' namely, 20 October. During the later stages of FIDO's installation Fiskerton's 49 Squadron aircraft were temporarily transferred to Dunholme Lodge and operated from there.

On 27 October Denys Fox, PWD's resident engineer from Staines, visited Fiskerton to iron out teething troubles in the system, spending hours inspecting progress on the south line of burners which had been giving trouble due to, among other things, mud in the pipelines. Flying Control officers had to be trained as well as the RAF crews, following their introductory course at Staines. Later in the day Technical Director A.C. Hartley and Bomber Command Liaison Officer Wg Cdr John Wooldridge visited Fiskerton to observe the first test burn of the installation. Considerable local flying was in progress and weather conditions were extremely unfavourable. There was a heavy haze, with the sun low behind it, with the result that pilots were having to land into a glaring sheet of light. The aircraft were using one of the shorter runways which was into wind, but the crews had nothing on which to line up their aircraft, so that when the runway appeared they were as much as 50° off line. One Lancaster had made no less than seven attempts to land.

Although FIDO was not yet complete, the burners on the left-hand side of the main runway were operable and the order to light them was given at 15.15. Gradually they were coaxed into life until eventually two-thirds were working. The burners gave off thick smoke at first due to wet grass and a strong cross-wind, but on average were burning cleanly within 7 minutes of lighting. As soon as the line was burning strongly the aircraft switched runways and the machine which had been in difficulties landed within three minutes. After that six others put down in quick succession and more were arriving when Mr Hartley and Wg Cdr Wooldridge departed.

One of the participants was Lancaster E-Easy with J.S. Mason aboard as flight engineer. They had received a recall during an exercise flight from Dunholme Lodge and were directed to Fiskerton:

> On arriving, the runway seemed to be in flames from end to end, but instructions over the R/T were to carry out a normal approach and landing. Looking down at the funnel end we could see bars of flame running across the entry, and thought 'this can't be right'; so we made our approach from the other end.
>
> When we landed it was quite eerie, as all you could see were flames shooting up on either side. We taxied to dispersal and were met by the CO and some boffins who were keen to get our reactions, as we were the first to land with the new installation. It was also pointed out that we had come in the wrong way round!

PWD's Denys Fox recorded two full burns in the presence of A.C. Hartley and Air Ministry officials on 4 November – 'effect was ok'. Even so things were not quite right, for it was discovered that the storage tanks had been built too near the hardstandings and a number of the latter had to be re-positioned. No sooner had this been carried out than, on 11 November, the station commander received a complaint from the clerk to the Welton Rural District Council. Apparently, when sections of FIDO were completed they were tested under pressure, and some ingenious soul in the contractor's party decided that it would be extravagant to use petrol for this purpose. He therefore connected the pump to the main water supply and proceeded with the tests. Unfortunately FIDO was a very thirsty animal and householders for miles around found their taps gurgling forth nothing but rusty dregs!

FIDO was lit again at Fiskerton, this time for night landing trials, on 21 November. Visibility on the ground was estimated at only 120 yd and advection fog was anything from 50 to 900 ft deep. Sid Finds was a ground crew member of 49 Squadron at the time and recalled that first night when FIDO was lit:

> We were on stand-down but the emergency services were not warned what to expect. I was cycling towards Lincoln, fog or no fog, when I met the entire fire brigade heading for the airfield. It

Plate 36 Test burn at Fiskerton, 3 November 1943. Furthest burners placed alternately. See Plate 37 (RAF Museum)

appeared that the local inhabitants got so scared at being enveloped in the thick black smoke that the fire brigade was inundated with 999 calls. By the time they arrived FIDO had been turned off. The firemen's thirsts were subsequently quenched in the NAAFI!

On the night of 26/27 November 1943, fourteen of 49 Squadron's Lancasters formed part of a force of 450 aircraft in a raid on Berlin. The raiders suffered heavy casualties: twenty-eight were destroyed and fourteen more crashed in Britain. Of Fiskerton's machines, that of Plt Off Ratcliffe was forced to return early and WO Brunt's was shot down. Plt Off Clive Roantree recalled in his book *To Fly Lancasters*:

> The long homeward haul was uneventful but below, the cloud density had increased so that we could not see the enemy coast that showed so clearly on H2S as we passed over. Power was reduced for the descent towards the English coast, and as we came down, Ken's turret, hitherto immobile, slowly thawed and could be moved again. The wireless operator reported that, as predicted before we left, there was fog over Lincolnshire and though other squadrons were being diverted, Fiskerton would be using FIDO operationally for the first time.

Conditions at Fiskerton as midnight approached were quite severe, with radiation fog 1200 ft deep and visibility down to 450 yd. FIDO was lit at 00.15 for its first, serious operational use, and 10 minutes later the first aircraft approached. 'The pilot reported no difficulty in seeing the installation, landing, or taxiing clear afterwards,' said the fog dispersal report. It was half an hour later that Clive Roantree in Lancaster A-Able crossed the coast, from where he and his crew could see:

. . . the reflection of our FIDO installation through what could now be seen as heavy fog. As we reached Fiskerton we heard Control give permission to land to D-Dog, being flown by another Australian, Sgt Richardson, who was on his first trip. . . . We were to position ourselves to land immediately after D-Dog. He would turn into the approach to the runway – the funnel – while we were on the downwind leg and should be just clear of the runway as we were coming in to touch down.

The two parallel lines of fire, one on each side of the runway, could be clearly seen, with bars of flame at each end to stop the fog rolling into the cleared area. On our practice landings we had found that after we turned into the funnel at 600 ft and lined up with the runway, the fire on the crossbar reflected on the perspex windshield, so that it was impossible for the pilot to see out. For the inexperienced pilot it could be frightening.

To overcome this Jack Grimshaw, Clive's flight engineer recalled: 'Having had a couple of practice landings on FIDO my pilot and I had already adopted the practice, on our own initiative, of me calling airspeed and height all through the approach, right through to touchdown. I believe that this later became standard practice.' Subsequently, the cross-line was shielded to avoid the glare:

On this night [continued Clive], with wheels down, pitch in fully fine and about twenty degrees of flap, we were at the end of the downwind leg, ready to make our turn across wind before entering the funnel, when there was a dull flash on the ground right at the beginning of the funnel. I knew that an aircraft had crashed and to my horror realized that it must be Sgt Richardson in D-Dog. I continued the landing procedure, turning across wind and there, right below us, was an aircraft on fire.

Giving the crew the order that we were to overshoot I called Flying Control: 'Hello Passout; Bandlaw Able overshooting. An aircraft has crashed and is on fire in the funnel. I say again, an aircraft has crashed and is on fire in the funnel.' There was a short pause before we were called again by Flying Control to repeat the message. Because of the flames from FIDO and the position of the Control Tower, they could not see the burning aircraft.

After completing our overshoot procedure we continued around the circuit and this time, as we were completing the downwind leg, there was a flash of flame as D-Dog's petrol tanks exploded. We called again for permission to land, and commenced our circuit again as the other squadron aircraft waiting for landing instructions were called in. Nerves and senses were now tuned to the dangers as we carefully made our approach in copybook style. There was a slight lift as we crossed the heat rising from the crossbar and then A-Able sat down smoothly in a three-point landing.

At de-briefing Clive Roantree reported on the raid, and then gave an accident report on D-Dog. It could only be assumed that due to the glare from the cross-line Sgt Richardson had entered the funnel too low and had insufficient power to correct the fault before striking the ground. 'It was bad enough when crews were missing over enemy territory, but there was an awful accentuation of loss when a crew had completed its mission and disaster struck so close to home and safety,' concluded Clive.

On the night of 1/2 December 1943, fourteen of 49 Squadron's Lancasters were among those detailed to attack Leipzig. Fiskerton's station ops book records, however: '22.45, all ops cancelled owing to slow clearance of fog from northern bases'. The airfield's fog dispersal report for that date records that a 900-ft deep smoke fog had reduced visibility to only 500 yd by about five o'clock in the afternoon and that: ' . . . the installation was lit to take in an aircraft which had been diverted from Swinderby owing to poor visibility there, and that the aircraft in question did not have enough petrol to be diverted again to an airfield 100 miles away.'

Seen from a crewman's point of view the story went like this, from Doug Tritton, flight engineer of the Lancaster:

We were detailed to deliver one of our cast-off Lancasters to the HC Unit at Swinderby some 12 miles distant. Swinderby was distinctive in layout and adjacent to an easily followed road system, so we decided that helmets and parachutes were the only accessories we would need, and we boarded the aircraft so equipped. As we climbed aboard, our Flight Commander approached with another officer, bidding us drop the latter off at Wrexham!'

Not daring to let the flight commander know that they had planned to take off with no navigational equipment, the crew was fortunate enough to lay hands on a map, and pursued a somewhat erratic course to Wrexham. It was late in the day when they eventually set off for their original destination:

Some while before we reached Swinderby we realized that the ground was more difficult to see than we expected. We could see but dimly vertically downwards, and not at all obliquely. No cause for concern yet, for Swinderby would appear underneath us shortly – and indeed so it did. . . . Confident that we could effect a trouble-free landing, we called up for permission, only to be advised that we were to proceed to Silloth, in Cumberland!

With an unknown amount of fuel remaining, no navigational equipment, darkness rapidly setting in and a hazardous destination, they felt that the risk of losing the aircraft and possibly their lives was not justified, and advised Control that they intended to attempt a landing back at their home base of Fiskerton. This brought the Swinderby Flying Control Officer to the microphone, who repeated his previous instruction, adding, 'This is an order!'

Our reply [continued Doug Tritton] had to be simple. 'Message received, understood and refused.' Whereupon we returned to Fiskerton and requested a landing there with FIDO. This was quickly lit and permission to land granted.
Completing our circuit we turned into the funnel and settled down, committed to land, when suddenly the rear-gunner's voice broke in, tinged with incredulity, advising us that there was an Oxford behind us! 'I'm looking straight at the pilot a few yards away,' he said. The Oxford then dropped back a little and we touched down. Almost immediately the gunner reported, 'The Oxford's down too. Keep going!'

Having taxied in and shut down, the Lancaster crew stepped out into the full blast of their flight commander's wrath. He bundled the skipper into his van and their raised voices were clearly heard as they drove off. Doug does not recall any subsequent action on the affair, but remembers the question:

Where did the Oxford fit in? In fact it belonged to Station Flight and had been returning from a test flight when overtaken by fog and unable to see anything. Having no functioning radio, they were unable to contact anyone to advise them of their plight. The navigator had completed his log and pocketed it, packed up his bag and donned his parachute. While discussing at what instant they should jump for it, they saw FIDO flicker into life and then a Lancaster, us, silhouetted against the flames. Nose down they made a hair-raising dive to catch the Lancaster before it landed and the flames were extinguished. That afternoon FIDO certainly saved an Oxford and almost certainly a Lancaster too.

Fourteen 49 Squadron Lancasters took part in a raid by 458 bombers on Berlin on the night of 2/3 December 1943, continuing a series of attacks on the German capital. Incorrectly forecast winds resulted in the force becoming scattering, particularly on the homeward flight, and night fighters brought down many of the forty machines which were lost. The weather deteriorated during their absence and by 22.00 visibility was down to about 800 yd, with a shallow radiation fog 60–100 ft deep.
    The order to light FIDO was given at 22.50. The system was not 100 per cent effective, and the fog dispersal report speaks of faulty assembly, leaking unions under pressure, five burners bursting and choking in the feed-line. Nevertheless, Fiskerton landed twelve of their own aircraft at an average time of 3½ minutes each. One machine with a punctured tyre had to be diverted elsewhere, lest it should block the runway, and another had to be landed out of sequence, with only three engines running. Four other aircraft, diverted from Waddington,

Skellingthorpe and Bardney were also taken in without difficulty, apart from the last one, which held off at 20 ft and dropped in from that height. Fortunately both the Lancaster's undercarriage and the runway survived the impact. In the midst of this a stranger arrived unannounced, like a cat among the pigeons. He had originally been given permission to land at Waddington, but was diverted, lost his way and joined the Fiskerton circuit. The machine could well have been a Lancaster of 61 Squadron flown by Sgt Martin, with Leslie Cromarty in his crew:

> We were running out of fuel [recalled Leslie], and had received diversion instructions soon after crossing the Dutch coast. As we approached the English shore we saw the glow of fire reflected on the base of the low cloud in the distance. We thought that we were running into an enemy air raid. As we flew nearer we could see a huge rectangle of fire and we realised that it was at the same position as our diversion. We circled the airfield, using its call sign. We got an immediate answer, 'Starlight aircraft, pancake'. We made a normal approach and tried to land, but as soon as we touched the hot air we soared and then dropped like a stone, hit the runway and bounced 30 ft or more. We bounced and ballooned several times until Sgt Martin regained control and we taxied to a halt.

It was not until they reached dispersal that the crew realized they had landed at the wrong aerodrome. This was not an unknown event and cases are recorded of aircraft from Ludford Magna, which also had FIDO, homing in on Fiskerton while tuned in to Ludford on VHF/RT! Shortly after landing, the crew were summoned to the Control Tower, continued Leslie:

> . . . where everyone was sitting in a darkened room looking out through a huge window on to the runway. The only light was provided by FIDO. Everyone was interested to find out what we thought of FIDO, because until then only the crews who had been instructed and trained had landed on it. Armchairs were found for us and when we realised that we were not going to be court-martialled we began to relax and enjoy our new-found fame. Until, that is, a voice from behind me said, 'Would you like a cigarette, Flight?' I replied, 'Thanks,' and reached back for the cigarette. An arm came over my shoulder, a lighter flared and I almost swallowed the cigarette as I counted the rings on the sleeve. A quiet voice said, 'Carry on, Flight.' It was Air Marshal Ludlow-Hewitt, Inspector General of the RAF, who had come over to watch a demonstration, and had witnessed our unscheduled landing instead.

Sir Edgar recalled the occasion shortly afterwards, although he missed out the bit about offering Leslie a light:

> On that night visibility was about 700 yd at first and I was struck by the fact that standing on the runway one could see the whole length in one direction with no sign of fog. Looking the other way, however, the runway was obscured much too much by thick smoke, and the Fiskerton layout gave me the impression that the central burners sent out too much smoke which might be very embarrassing when making a landing. It cleared in time, however, and later, when most of the smoke had cleared, fourteen or fifteen aircraft returning from operations landed with the help of the apparatus. At that time visibility might have been 800 to 1,000 yd and landing without the apparatus would have been difficult, but not impossible.
>
> My personal opinion is that on that night, the apparatus was useful, did help the crews to get down, and if they had to land without it there might have been at least a minor crash or so. Pilots found no difficulty in using it, except that the amount of light tended to dazzle them, making it difficult to read their instruments.

The confusion over landing instructions is well illustrated in the FIDO report and station ops record book for 16 January 1944. During that afternoon ten Dakota aircraft were on exercise from RAF Fulbeck, about 12 miles south-west of Fiskerton, when visibility closed in and Fiskerton were ordered to land them with the aid of FIDO. None of the aircraft subsequently arrived, due to a combination of poor navigation and disregard of diversion instructions.

However, an eleventh Dakota, piloted by USAF Lt Jacobi did put in an appearance – though with visibility at 50 yd 'appearance' might not be the best word. The PWD crew had great difficulty in obtaining an effective burn, for several burners burst and permitted fog to be blown across the runway. Eventually, a 100-ft-high arch was cleared and Lt Jacobi was briefed on the landing procedure. He did not seem to get the hang of things, and when he made his first approach he tried to land *across* the runway.

Conditions could hardly have been worse for the American's initiation, but after further briefing, two more tries (including a pass over the storage tanks at 50 ft) and 25 nail-biting minutes, he came in to make a good landing some 600 yd down the runway, the first American to use FIDO. With a strong cross-wind constantly hampering efforts to maintain a reasonable clearance the compiler of the station ops record book felt justified in saying that 'this effort must rank as our best to date', adding that if the burn had been ordered by CFC direct, some at least of the 120,084 gallons of petrol consumed that month might have been saved. It was subsequently determined on 27 January 1944 that authority for lighting FIDO should rest with: 1) for a FIDO equipped airfield's own aircraft: The station commander; 2) for aircraft from other airfields within a group: The Group Commander; 3) for aircraft from outside a given group: Central Flying Control.

Flt Lt Michael Beetham (later Marshal of the Royal Air Force, Sir Michael) recalls his return from a raid on 9/10 March 1944 when forty-four Lancasters of 5 Group attacked an aircraft factory at Marignane, near Marseilles: 'I felt the system at Fiskerton highly effective in enabling one to line up the runway, but a bit frightening once on the ground with the flames on either side – I would not have liked to have swung off the runway!'

By this time the FIDO installation had clocked up quite a few hours of burning and was showing great signs of wear. The Mk IV burners (see Fig. 5) were of simple design and easy to erect, but their service life was short. As materials and labour became available they were replaced by Mk Vs (see Fig. 6), twenty of which were delivered on 12 March.

FIDO at Fiskerton was lit at 02.49 on 17 March 1944 as two squadrons of Lancasters were arriving back over their bases at Metheringham and Woodhall Spa after a bombing raid on the Michelin tyre factory at Clermont Ferrand. Twenty-one aircraft of 106 and 617 Squadrons were homeward bound in deteriorating weather, and Flying Control were anxious. Visibility was down to 200 yd and there was 700 ft of radiation fog. John Richards, on his 26th op with 106 Squadron, remembers that his aircraft had been promised support from the main stream of bombers on the way out, but that it had not materialized and they did the trip 'on their Tod'. The raid was uneventful, but the predicted fog closed in as they returned and they were diverted to 617's base at Woodhall Spa. Several aircraft in front of his landed safely, but after two unsuccessful attempts John was warned off on his final approach, after nearly landing on a hangar roof. By now fuel was very low, and he and four others were diverted again, to Fiskerton. FIDO was very slow in clearing, with three burst burners emitting far more smoke than usual, but eventually visibility on the runway was raised to 1,000 yd.

As the last of the gaggle John spent an anxious time circuiting the airfield, but finally made a tail-up landing well down the runway. When FIDO was extinguished, the fog returned so thickly that the dispersal van could not find them and they spent ages seeking somewhere to rest their weary heads. There were only 100 gallons of fuel remaining in the tanks when C-Charlie was shut down.

Flight engineer Robert McCullough was on his first operation with 617 Squadron on 17 March, after twenty-six with 50 Squadron. His aircraft too was diverted to Fiskerton. As U-Uncle approached:

> . . . a glow was seen through the fog and we entered a tunnel of clearness for landing with a wall of flame extending the length of the runway. My position in the cockpit was to the pilot's right, with a good all-round view and up into the astrodome. On the night in question the fog came very quickly indeed and the situation became very dicey. I didn't pay particular attention to Flying Control

transmissions as I was engaged in taking readings of revs, fuel, etc., and listening for orders from my pilot Flt Lt J.A. Edwards.

FIDO's light was seen from above as a dull glow, and as we descended on final approach we could see the runway quite clearly in front of us. At touch-down, throttle-back and braking we passed walls of flame to port and starboard. Then, as we turned off the runway we gradually lost vision until we came to a standstill.

Whoever thought FIDO up and engineered its use has my undying gratitude and those of thirty-four other aircrew, and also Gp Capt Grindell who guided us to terra firma that night.

A copy of the Group Captain's report sent to Winston Churchill commented that 'the fog was so thick that the air crews could not be taken to the dispersal sleeping huts one and a half miles away and they slept in the mess.'

On 24/25 March Bomber Command mounted a major raid on Berlin. It was a night of particularly strong winds, which drove many aircraft off-course and impeded their progress so that they fell victim to anti-aircraft gunfire and night fighters, seventy-two of the 818 aircraft taking part being lost. As if that were not bad enough, widespread fog formed over Lincolnshire in their absence. Fiskerton was ordered to light FIDO in order to receive its own machines and such aircraft as could not be landed back at their own bases. The installation was fired just after 01.00, and by 01.20 was ready for its first visitors. So far, so good. Gp Capt Grindell reported:

There was no difficulty in landing the first three aircraft, and everything was set to take in the remainder. On receipt of the third aircraft, however, a major snag occurred; in fact, one of a highly dangerous nature, in that aircraft from Ludford Magna, the home of 101 Squadron, seeing the installation from many miles distant, concluded at once that it was their own installation and made for it. [Ludford and Fiskerton are only about 10 miles apart.] They orbited our airfield and called up Ludford on their frequency, and as Ludford were having good two-way communication with their aircraft when orbiting this airfield they received 'Pancake' from Ludford and came in to land here, thinking it was their own station. The ensuing results were highly dangerous in that we were not receiving these aircraft on our R/T and they were not receiving Fiskerton on theirs, and on two occasions, only by the vigilance of our own crews was a collision avoided.

Luck held out until the ninth machine, which was from Ludford, made its approach. Doug Tritton of 49 Squadron was in the circuit at the time when:

. . . suddenly an Australian voice (one of our own pilots) came over the R/T. 'Hey up! There's someone in the funnel with me!' Immediately the Tower responded with 'Overshoot!' which he did. On hearing that call we looked down and saw two Lancasters close together in the funnel. One overshot and the other continued in and we saw its undercarriage collapse. Those of us who were in the stack, including the baulked aircraft, were then directed to Waddington.

So far as could be ascertained, the cause of the Ludford aircraft's crash, fortunately without casualties, was that the pilot held off too high, stalled and dropped the aircraft on to the runway when a tyre burst, causing a violent swing. The undercarriage then collapsed and the Lancaster finally came to rest across the edge of the runway, blocking it for any further landings.

Seven of 49 Squadron's machines landed safely and so did two of 101's, including the casualty, and ten of 49's were diverted to Waddington. The difficulties did not end there, however, for when the runway became blocked FIDO was extinguished until the wreckage could be cleared away. Unfortunately, as soon as that happened, visibility, which had risen to 2,000 yd during the burn, immediately clamped down to less than 50 yd, and not only were the aircraft seeking dispersal stranded in the murk, but the salvage vehicles could not find the wrecked aircraft to remove it.

As would be expected, the call for FIDO's services lessened during the spring and summer months. Early on 20 May, however, as a force of Lancasters was homeward bound from raids on Amiens and Tours railyards, visibility decreased quite sharply and 100 ft of radiation fog made it impossible to see more than 600 yd near the ground. FIDO was lit and quickly burned off the fog over the runway so that it was possible to see the sky above, and for aircrew to see a clear rectangle down below. Fog often created its own wind conditions when operating, in this case veering 60° to the runway and increasing to 10 mph as it burned. Four Lancasters, M and E of 44 Squadron (Flt Lt Hildred and Plt Off Ibbotson) and M and Z of 619 Squadron (Flt Sgt Paterson and Flt Lt Buttar) 'made perfectly successful landings at five minute intervals and only one experienced difficulty when taxiing to dispersal outside FIDO's influence'.

Not all FIDO landings were operational or even in foggy conditions. Leslie Hay's was on a daylight cross-country exercise on 29 July 1944, when with 49 Squadron:

> As far as I can remember we returned to base in the late afternoon, to find FIDO being tried out although visibility was clear. After the usual circuit drill, our final approach was somewhat like that of a flare path at night. As we reached the funnel position the runway became a shimmering area of dancing heat. Crossing the perimeter at the usual height, I became aware of the uplift caused by the heat, which made the aircraft float on and on and on, drifting as the turbulence took effect.
>
> The further we floated towards the centre of the conflagration, the more we rose on the thermal caused. I was desperately trying to stall it, but the aircraft just wallowed on, until, to my intense relief, I was able to touch down halfway along the runway. My navigator, Paul Smith, vividly remembers being decidedly alarmed that the Lancaster drifted towards the flames and that our height actually increased as we went along. My lasting impression is of the aircraft wallowing on with sloppy controls while I was looking for the crucial point at which I must open up and go round again before doing any damage to the far boundary fence!

The night of 26/27 August began with clear weather conditions. Eight of 49 Squadron's Lancasters, part of a force of 174 bombers from 5 Group, were briefed to attack Konigsberg, an important supply port for the German Eastern Front, involving a round trip of about 2,000 miles. Unfortunately, widespread fog covered eastern England by the time they and aircraft raiding other targets returned, and many machines had to be diverted. Although not much of the night remained, neither did reasonable visibility and from about 05.00 FIDO systems at Fiskerton, Graveley, Ludford Magna, Metheringham and Tuddenham were lit. No fog dispersal report for Fiskerton has survived, but R.E. Paul recollected:

> I was a Flying Officer bomb-aimer and on 26 August 1944 [43 years to the day, when he wrote] I went on my first operation as a replacement bomb-aimer in Flt Lt Jock Blair's crew in Lancaster EA-R of 49 Squadron. The target was Konigsberg (now Kaliningrad) and we were told that it was to help the Russians to capture it. We bombed but some aircraft laid mines. As far as I know only 5 Group was flying that night because of the weather, and for me it was the longest flight of the war. My logbook shows that we took off at 20.30 hours and landed back again 10 hrs 35 mins later.
>
> When we returned to Lincolnshire there was 10/10 deep fog. As we flew towards Fiskerton (or where we thought it was), we saw a bright glow in the fog some distance away to starboard. We circled and then dropped slowly through the fog towards the glow. Eventually we saw the runway, with alarming flames rising on either side, and touched down. As far as I remember, we then swerved off the runway, through the flames and came to rest on the grass beyond them! We were safe, but I believe the Group lost a lot of aircraft to fighters on the way back over the Baltic.

On the night of 29/30 August, 403 Bomber Command aircraft carried out a heavy raid on the Baltic seaport of Stettin, in which twenty-three Lancasters were lost. On the same night 189 Lancasters of 5 Group attacked Konigsberg for the second night in a week. Carried out at extreme range, because of heavy cloud the bombardment had to be delayed until the marker aircraft could find a gap in the overcast. This and heavy fighter opposition over the target made it a difficult though successful raid which cost the force fifteen aircraft and their crews.

By the time the 5 Group Lancasters were approaching home it was daylight, but much of Lincolnshire was wreathed in fog and numerous diversions were ordered. Among them were the machines of 44 Squadron, based at Dunholme Lodge, which were instructed to put down at Fiskerton. Bill Spence was air-bomber aboard U-Uncle. After a flight which totalled 11¾ hours, the entire crew were relieved at the thought that a landing would be possible before their fuel tanks were empty:

> The first impression was from a distance, seeing this glow, a diffusion of light marking the airfield, a welcoming sight, for here was a help to getting down safely. Then, as we passed over the flames at the end of the runway, we were suddenly in clear space, with the airstrip clearly before us, flanked by walls of fire. The suddenness of this change has remained with me. With it, of course, came an enormous relief that the system really worked and that we were safely home. It never entered our heads that the landing might go wrong, for we had complete faith in our pilot – a faith which was justified throughout our tour.

A total of nine of Dunholme's Lancasters put down at Fiskerton with the aid of FIDO, plus numerous others critically short of fuel. We know that all eight of Fiskerton's aircraft landed safely back at base too. At some point during the early dawn Fiskerton's FIDO welcomed its hundredth guest.

Major Nicky Knilans, USAF retired, then a sergeant pilot with the RCAF, recalled a similar experience flying with 619 Squadron. Operating from Dunholme Lodge, he too had been diverted to Fiskerton:

> We were guided to the general area by a WAAF controller. The air was clear at 1,500 ft. I had to aim at the glow while on a certain heading and let down into the thick cloud/mist. It was a bit breath-stopping for my crew and myself. We had hit the ground on a previous landing approach due to a faulty altimeter which registered too high. We broke into the clear at a bar of fire close to the beginning of the runway. It looked like a scene from hell with huge spouts of flame on both sides of my Lancaster. The black smoke billowed and mixed with the swirling white fog as we hurtled down the runway.

The autumn of 1944 saw some turmoil at Fiskerton. The station was closed while the runways were re-surfaced from 10 to 24 October, and flying operations were carried out from Dunholme Lodge. It is also likely that the Mk IV burners which had been in use for nearly a year were removed at the same time. During the closure Fiskerton was transferred from 5 Group to 1 Group as a satellite for Scampton; 49 Squadron was relocated at Fulbeck and its place at Fiskerton taken by 576 Squadron from Elsham Wolds and, for a short time, by 150 Squadron on its return from the Mediterranean. Both squadrons flew Lancasters.

Of the return to operational use runway controller Les Robinson recalled:

> It must have been mid-October 1944 when I arrived at RAF Fiskerton, which was then the home of 576 Lancaster Squadron, and so to my introduction to FIDO. . . . The normal position of the runway caravan was 50 ft to the left of the runway with the FIDO burners another 25 ft out. We just had a field telephone to the control tower, red and green Aldis lamps, and a Verey pistol with red and green cartridges. As you know, for the first 15 to 20 minutes after FIDO was lit the resulting smoke actually made things worse, but gradually the fuel seemed to vaporise more easily, and when it was burning fully it really was an awesome sight, cutting a huge oblong out of the fog. At Fiskerton the runway controller had no R/T to tell him of landing aircraft, so it was a case of keeping a very sharp eye on the approach to make sure that an aircraft's undercarriage was down okay. It always seemed to me that pilots favoured the left-hand row of burners and in consequence you had to move over a bit, which took you towards the considerable flames.
>
> Subsequently, the caravan was moved outside the burner lines altogether when FIDO was alight. Fortunately, the FIDO lines at Fiskerton extended into the approach box, which helped to pick up the aircraft visually, and I never saw one aircraft fail to land from a FIDO approach.

On 16 November 1944 British and American bombers took part in raids to support the American 1st and 9th Armies on the continent. Bomber Command flew 1,188 sorties and the USAF another 1,239, plus escort fighters to the tune of 250 Mustangs. Of this air armada,

485 Lancasters attacked Duren, including twenty-one from Fiskerton's 576 and 150 squadrons. Visibility was poor all day, and as the crews returned in the late afternoon they experienced great difficulty in locating their runways in thick haze rather than fog. So many aircraft were involved that diversions ran into hundreds and FIDO was lit at eight airfields. At Fiskerton, conditions were 'very bad, night fog and frost very severe'. Visibility was about 1,500 yd, but a westerly breeze of about 4 mph kept the mist steadily rolling in as aircraft stacked up for their turn to land. Oblique vision was poor and the angle of approach indicators indistinct. Only a few burners on each side of the runway were lit, to mark its limits rather than to disperse the fog. In the space of about an hour and a quarter, all twenty-one Lancasters put down safely after what is termed in the station ops record book 'a highly successful attack'. Among them was Lancaster T2 of 576 Squadron piloted by Flg Off Ridge at 1715 hours. Aboard her was air-gunner Vic Mattocks, completing his twenty-fifth op. He recalled that:

> . . . because of the near impenetrable fog, the problem of marauding enemy fighters did not arise and I was able to vacate the rear turret for the landing and witness the event from the cockpit. The experience of landing on FIDO was breathtaking. It was as though a big knife had sliced a perfectly rectangular chunk out of the fog to form a tunnel over the runway and at the same time provide near daylight conditions for landing.

FIDO was used again at dusk on 29 November 1944 when seventeen 576 Squadron Lancasters were homeward bound following a raid by 1 Group aircraft on Dortmund. As on the 16th, haze rather than fog was the problem, affecting oblique vision, and replenished over the airfield by a 10 mph south-westerly wind. By now quite a few 576 crews had gained experience of landing with FIDO and once the runway had been defined, circuiting presented no problem. Including the initial warm-up, the system was alight for barely an hour, in which time all seventeen machines made safe landings.

On 16 December, 235 Flying Fortresses were detailed for a raid on the railyards at Stuttgart. The weather was poor right from the start and many aircraft abandoned the mission while still over England. A large number were diverted and Fiskerton was warned to expect thirty-eight Fortresses for lunch. Visibility was low, with cloud base to match at only 300 ft, and the fog dispersal report says that 'conditions made it impossible for aircraft to land without FIDO'. Only five burners were lit (three on the north side and two on the south), but the welds on three others burst, although they were supposed to have been repaired three days previously. Nevertheless, the runway was sufficiently marked to accept the visitors by 11.30. Unfortunately, only six of them had arrived by 13.47, the remainder having chosen to divert elsewhere. Later on, a Lancaster of 576 Squadron and two Oxfords on training flights lobbed down, so the burn was not entirely wasted. Les Robinson was on duty in the runway caravan that day:

> The reason this sticks in my mind is that one of the Fortresses landed the wrong way! When FIDO was burning fully it made a lot of noise (almost like a Lancaster running its engines up) and above this noise I thought I could hear aircraft engines approaching, but could not see anything on the approach. I nearly died when I turned round and saw that Fortress on the runway finishing its landing run. Fortunately as it turned out, it was the last one to land so no awful accident happened.

The weather approaching Christmas 1944 was particularly bad from every point of view, civilian or military, and the Germans took full advantage of it to launch their Ardennes offensive. Attempts to stem the advance by aerial bombardment were thwarted by persistent fog for days on end and not until 21 December were squadrons able to take part in concerted attacks against opposing ground forces, airfields and communications centres. Fiskerton's squadrons were not operating that day, but twenty-four Lancasters from 625 Squadron based at Kelstern were aloft in a raid over Bonn. Poor weather conditions caused diversions to be called for on their return. FIDO was lit at Ludford Magna, Sturgate and Fiskerton. Radiation fog more than 700 ft deep lay over the latter and although surface visibility was nearly half a mile, the angle of approach indicators (AAIs) could not be distinguished. FIDO was lit just after 19.30 and in the space of an hour and a half, nine of 625 Squadron's aircraft (Z, S, T, C, J, W, J2, C2 and D2) had come safely to roost. Of these, Lancaster W- (ostensibly Willie, but dubbed Wally Wallaby, because of youthful connections of its pilot Keith 'Bill' Bailey), landed at about 21.00. Of its 'five nations' crew Desmond Lush was air-bomber. He: '. . . seemed to remember staying in the bomb-aimer's position for the landing, and it was most impressive on entering the funnel to see the enormous banks of flame on both sides of the runway. I expect I made a silent prayer that my skipper would not do a ground loop. Since he was an excellent pilot, no problems were encountered and we flew back to Kelstern next day.'

Despite the poor conditions, over 500 bombers were abroad the same night, 21/22 December 1944, attacking targets as far afield as Bonn, Cologne and the synthetic-oil refinery at Politz, near Stettin on the Baltic coast. Lancasters of 5 Group which took part in the Politz raid were not expected back until after 01.00. At the midnight meteorological conference it became apparent that only Coningsby and East Kirby would be safe for landing and at 01.00 all except Coningsby and East Kirkby aircraft were diverted to aerodromes in Scotland. 'The FIDO airfields at Metheringham, Fiskerton, Ludford Magna, Carnaby and Woodbridge were ordered to stand by.'

FIDO was lit at 02.30 when there was fog 700 ft deep and visibility was down to 400 yd. The burners were able to achieve very little clearance, but the glow was sufficient to give pilots an indication of the runway's location, which with fuel running low they were thankful to take. Between 02.30 and 04.00 seven Lancasters were able to land, N, S and Y of 9 Squadron, E and P of 61 Squadron, B and Q of 467 Squadron. Ray Lushey was the pilot of E-Easy:

> For some reason (listening on the wrong frequency I think) the W/Op missed the diversion message and we arrived in the circuit area over Skellingthorpe with the weather clamped in, and were refused permission to land. Skellingthorpe diverted us to Grimsby, but the same thing happened there; by which time fuel was running critically short. I then resorted to 'Mayday' and Fiskerton replied immediately. They must have been keeping a listening watch on the distress frequency and told us that it would take 15 minutes to light FIDO, but it seemed less, for in a short time the two rows of fire were plainly visible at about 5 miles.

Ray's WOp/AG, Harry Parsons, remembered: '. . . the fog below turning red and then we were coming down through it to land, which was like flying into your fire in the grate at home. We saw the lines of fire each side of the runway and landed, racing down between them.' 'The aircraft entered clear air at about 150 ft [resumed Ray Lushey], after which I continued into a visual landing. The landing roll had not finished before FIDO was turned off – the consequent darkness was unbelievable. I think the craft's engines cut from fuel starvation and that it had to be towed from the end of the runway to dispersal.'

After the ten-and-a-half-hour flight from Politz, another aircrewman who was glad to see FIDO at Fiskerton was Brian Booth, a 9 Squadron air-gunner:

> Our aircraft on that occasion was N-Nan. At briefing we were told that we might be diverted on our return, but that if we hadn't received any message by a given point on our long leg back across the North Sea it would be clear to come to our own base at Bardney. By the time we reached Lincolnshire it was a 'pea-souper'. After what seemed to be utter confusion with so many aircraft milling around, we were told to go to Fiskerton, which isn't far from Bardney, and to land there.
>
> After contacting the tower we were given permission to land. There could be no hesitation; it was just a case of funnel on to the runway and get off as quickly as possible. It was just like flying into the middle of a great bonfire. It scared us. I don't think the skipper had to turn the engines off; they just stopped – no fuel!

A great deal of credit must go to the flying control staff in getting so many aircraft safely down, and I think they had a shock in the morning when they counted the aircraft they had landed, including some they didn't know about.

When they talk about near-misses nowadays, I wonder how they would have coped with over 250 Lancasters milling around Lincolnshire on a foggy night!

Despite the worst weather for several years, Bomber Command and the US 8th Air Force maintained their pressure on the German forces in the Ardennes salient and their supply lines whenever weather conditions permitted. Two hundred Lancasters attacked the railyards at Rheydt in daylight on 27 December. Conditions were poor throughout and Gilbert Hampson of 170 Squadron based at Dunholme Lodge recalls being diverted to Fiskerton at the end of a 6-hour flight. Visibility had dropped from 1,000 to below 600 yd within a very short time and there was haze up to a height of 1,500 ft. It was decidedly murky when FIDO was lit at 15.45: 'I was glad to have the opportunity to use the FIDO landing facilities at Fiskerton when I was diverted there, for all the other reachable airfields were fogbound. The glow of the flames through the top of the fog was a very welcome sight, and apart from the turbulence, the approach and landing were quite straightforward. Without FIDO, who knows what might have been our fate!'

Ten homeward-bound Lancasters landed at Fiskerton that afternoon. This day's 'bag' of eighteen brought December's use of FIDO to a close. During the month a total of 43 machines landed, at a cost of 188,000 gallons of petrol, and the estimated number of landings since its installation was well on the way to the 200 mark.

'From the flying point of view,' records Martin R. Cook, 'the New Year at Fiskerton started off badly, with glazed frost on the first two nights of January – and then got steadily worse!' There were only five days in the whole month with favourable flying conditions. Snow, mainly in the form of showers, persisted from the 6th to the 11th, by which time it lay 6 in deep. Even when a rapid thaw set in, the snow was replaced by heavy rain and low cloud. On 18 January, continued Martin: '. . . very stormy conditions developed, with widespread gales, severe squalls, heavy rain and local hail and thunder. This was followed by an influx of extremely cold air of Arctic origin which continued to dominate until 30 January. During this period, air temperatures showed nearly 20° of frost quite often and it was not to exceed freezing point for twelve days. Jim Owen recalls one night when there was a sudden very heavy snowfall over Lincolnshire:

> FIDO was put into action, and with the help of all available personnel on the station the runway was kept clear, giving a safe landing for our planes on their return. Apart from planes of the home station, others from airfields which could not cope were diverted here. When daylight came, it was an amazing sight. Lancasters were stacked nose to tail all round the perimeter and late arrivals were actually parked at the far end of the runway, thus reducing the landing distance for the last to land. All landed safely and it was a great achievement; another step towards victory.

Moving on through the early spring of 1945 there is a dearth of evidence of FIDO's use until 12 March. On that date sixteen of 576 Squadron's Lancasters were detailed as part of a force of 1,108 aircraft in a daylight raid on Dortmund; the largest number to attack a single target throughout the war. Of this enormous force, only two were lost. The Fiskerton crews approached home in late afternoon to find hazy conditions and the sun's glare in their eyes. FIDO was lit at 17.55 to enable them to line up with the runway, and within the hour, at a cost of less than 5,000 gallons of petrol, all were safely gathered in. This appears to have been the last occasion when FIDO was used during the war, at Fiskerton.

An exact tally of landings with the aid of FIDO is difficult to establish. The writer's best estimate is 220; but bearing in mind the words of Walter Reid, who compiled the PWD general survey, that: '. . . in a great many cases records were incomplete, many landings being made without official returns thereon, especially when only a limited number of

Plate 37 Fiskerton oblique in 1987. Compare with Plate 36 (Leroy Keeping)

burners were used,' the number is likely to be higher. Fiskerton closed as an active bomber station in September 1945, and was reduced to care and maintenance in December of that year. Since then the area has been progressively handed back to agriculture. Concluded Bruce Halpenny, 'It was from this airfield that the bombers took off for Germany, but now all is silent – the heavy roar of engines as they struggled to get airborne under their heavy loads is just a whisper in the night breeze.'

NINE

Foulsham

... dug a huge trench out of the clouds and fog

Bill Walsh, rear-gunner, 214 Squadron

RAF Foulsham, pronounced Foalsham as any local will tell you, lies centrally between the Norfolk villages of Hindolveston, Foulsham, Wood Norton and Guestwick. In fact, Foulsham's main north–south runway (190°) was exactly in line with Hindolveston church tower to the north.

In those days three of the four villages had their own railway station, and when the aerodrome was built they were the supply points for the huge quantities of materials required. Thousands of bags of cement came by lorry from Hindolveston station; hangar girders, storage tank cladding, etc., from Melton Constable; personnel via Guestwick and smaller items via Foulsham, through whose streets trundled hundreds of lorries loaded with sand and gravel. This left the villages running with mud for months on end.

Foulsham opened as a station within 2 Group in May 1942, but it was some months before it operated its Mitchell bombers. It was the first station to do so. On 1 September 1943 Foulsham became part of 3 Group, flying 514 Squadron Lancasters. When 100 Group was formed in December 1943 Foulsham, together with a clutch of neighbouring airfields, came under its command (Plate 38).

In that month Bomber Command asked for the eight FIDO airfields in operation or under construction to be increased to twelve. Foulsham was earmarked as one of them, and was designated Station XXII, some earlier proposed installations not being proceeded with. As such, Foulsham became 100 Group's own, as it were. The airfield plan (Fig. 16) shows that it was intended that a mile of the main runway should be lined with a series of Haigill Mk IV burners (see Fig. 5). The runway was crossed shortly after touchdown by runway 26 and about 1,000 yd further on by runway 32. To avoid these runways being obstructed by the main lines of burners, the latter were replaced by intersecting runway burners (IRBs; see Plate 22) set in trenches at these points. Any aircraft landing should be safely down and under control before the junction with runway 32 was reached, and the last quarter mile of the main runway was lined with a series of burners placed on alternate sides. Initially, an approach box of only 100 yd was planned, but this was increased to 220 yd by extending the perimeter at this point.

To fuel the burners, three gasometer-like steel storage tanks encased in brickwork were built in the grounds of Low Farm. Filling and replenishing the storage tanks by road, along the narrow lanes of Norfolk, was out of the question, so a single-track siding was constructed alongside the railway line near Foulsham station. This could accommodate up to about twenty-five wagons at a time. Their contents were pumped out through a 6–in main by a stationary engine in a nearby pumphouse and then drawn across the intervening 2 miles to the airfield by the main pumps. This is an assumption based on the set-up at Manston which was a similar distance from the railway line (see Fig. 19 and Plates 49–52).

Plate 38 Foulsham aerial, runway 18. Burner scorch marks on each side of N–S runway. Storage tanks top left of photograph. See Fig. 16 (Crown/MoD)

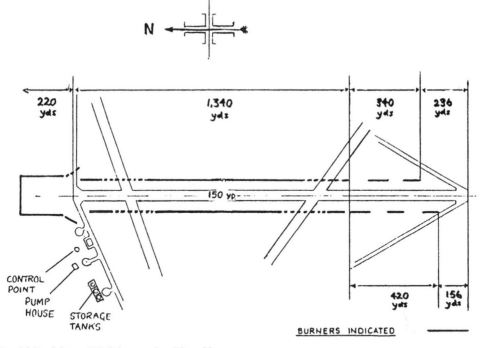

N ◄━━━

220
yds

1,340
yds

340
yds

236
yds

150 yp.

CONTROL
POINT

PUMP
HOUSE

STORAGE
TANKS

420
yds

156
yds

BURNERS INDICATED ━━━

Fig. 16 Foulsham, FIDO layout. See Plate 38

William Press were the FIDO contractors and Percy Turzig was their site agent. He recalls a workforce of about 100. A few were locals, but the majority were bussed in from Norwich. With the great demand for artisans such as welders on war work, skilled labour was at a premium and by the time the ranks of the unskilled were reached, the standard was of a very indifferent quality. Work on the installation began early in 1944. By 20 January, according to a PWD progress report, little more than the completion of drawings and ordering of materials had been covered, but by 8 February construction was considered to be ahead of schedule although nothing had been done about the railway siding. Things fell behind again in March: '. . . due to the alterations the Air Ministry required to fall in with their safety distance of 125 ft from the perimeter track for all buildings. The position of the tanks and control house had to be shifted, but a suitable layout has now been agreed and work on the tank and pumphouse foundations is well in hand.'

By 20 April progress had improved and the first IRB crossing had been completed, the tank and pumphouse sites were well under way, the first tank was almost ready for testing and the railway siding was under construction. An anticipated completion date of 27 May was put forward. We do not know if this target was met but records show that five test burns of the system were carried out in July, consuming 16,250 gallons of pool petrol.

Use or no use, crews had to be trained and ready to operate the system whenever it should be required. Fred (Lofty) Pond was a member of the FIDO crew at Foulsham for the last year of the war. The gang consisted of one mechanically minded sergeant and two corporals to operate and maintain the pumps, one M/T driver for the section's lorry and twelve erks to do everything else. To judge from the establishment at other stations they were very much under strength:

We lived on the 'drome near the perimeter, in one Nissen hut for the erks and another for the NCOs. Living and working so far from the main built-up station, bicycles were a must for meals, pay and clothing parades, etc. We had very little to do with the main base or with Foulsham village socially, being so far from both of them. The village of Guestwick was only a field away and its pub was as good as any.

FIDO section was on duty day and night even when ops were cancelled, because FIDO was for all. All duties were performed in 24 hour shifts. 'On duty' meant cleaning burners, situated on both sides of the runway, during the day, and staying within the hutted area at other times. 'Stand by' meant being suitably dressed and ready to mount bicycles with a box of matches in each pocket. 'To your pits' did not mean 'get back into bed', but was most difficult at night. The so-called 'pits' were indentations in the ground about 9 in deep which housed the burner controls. Finding a pit at night in thick mist or fog was no easy task, and it had to be your own pit. The usual allocation was three or four pits per man, about 50 yd apart. The 'Light up' came over the pit Tannoy speaker and meant that the pumps were operating and petrol was flowing through the system. No pumps, no petrol, which was a safety factor when the system was not in use.

Every pit served two burners, a control valve to each. The operator would open the valves, allowing petrol to pour from the burner holes. He would then find the other pits under his control and do likewise. Returning to the first pit, the operator would shut off the valves and then paddle through pools of petrol to close the other control valves in turn.

Then came the frightening part; igniting the petrol. This was done by returning to the first burner, throwing a lighted match at the spewed petrol and running like the wind to the pit. You threw yourself down on your stomach and tried to flatten yourself within the 9–in indent, while smoke and flames bellowed over your head; soot too if you were unlucky windwise.

The operator then started 'playing' with the valves, opening and closing them as necessary until the pre-heater pipe above the burners became hot enough to turn the petrol into gas, thus getting rid of the smoke. When this was achieved and a clean double flame was shooting several feet into the air, he then went to the next pit and repeated the process, and so on.

With the clearing of the smoke came an increase in noise as the petrol vapour was forced through the small holes, barely one-tenth of an inch in diameter, in the burner pipes. When the whole system was burning correctly on both sides of the runway and a fog-free tunnel was achieved, the operator could relax a little but must stay near a pit Tannoy for further instructions. The man was now in a hot, noisy world of his own, unable to hear or see what was going on around him or on the runway. He could not hear because of the roar of the gas and could not see because of weather conditions and the wall of flames. Fred goes on:

'Shut down' was the signal to close all valves, and, if it was light enough, to actually watch the pipework contract as it cooled; and have a feeling of great satisfaction that all had worked well and that maybe lives had been saved. After a turn, operators were either black or brown according to the wind direction.

Within a few hours of shutdown, petrol bowsers would arrive from the railhead to top up our storage. Road deliveries were unloaded straight into the tanks on the 'drome. Rail supplies were pumped by the same engines which pushed the petrol through the burners. This meant that several bods had to be at Foulsham station coupling and uncoupling the connections.

Another must after use was cleaning the burners. The supply pipework of the burners were holed every 4 in for petrol vapour to pass. These holes had to be cleared of carbon build-up. There were 1,000 yd of burners, two runs of supply pipe to each, on both sides of the runway. [Approximately 2,000 yd of approach box and runway x 2 pipes each side x 9 jet holes per yd = 72,000 holes.] Nothing stopped the cleaning, not even the taking off and landing of bombers. Both the topping up of supplies and the cleaning had to be completed before half the section was allowed off-duty status.

Apart from a number of test burns during the autumn, there are no records of FIDO's further operational use until December 1944. This was to be the busiest month of the war for FIDO airfields, over 800 aircraft landing or taking off in conditions varying from mist to dense fog. The night of 18/19 December 1944 was the occasion of a concerted raid on the Polish port of

Gdynia. Accompanying the main force were numerous 100 Group aircraft: Mosquitos, Halifaxes and Fortresses on RCM patrols, including a number from 192 Squadron, Foulsham's own, and 214 Squadron based at Oulton. A Halifax and a Mosquito on Special Duty patrols and three Halifaxes on Window patrol were provided by 192 Squadron. Howie Wing, rear-gunner of Fortress R-Roger of 214 Squadron recorded in his logbook that the raid was: 'an attack on the remainder of the German battle fleet. Heavy, medium and light flak was encountered from *Prinz Eugen, Lutzow* and several *Hipper* class cruisers, who resented our intrusion. Flak ships opened up at us over the Danish coast on our return. A diving turn was necessary and we levelled out at 500 ft.'

The weather closed in as the force neared home, and widespread diversions were ordered, as many as six FIDO airfields were alerted. Some 100 Group aircraft were instructed to head for Foulsham instead of their own bases. FIDO was lit at 02.02 in preparation for the station's first operational fog landings. Lack of crew and expertise meant that it took twenty-five minutes before the installation was burning clearly, aggravated by two whole sections of burners being waterlogged and creating clouds of steam and smoke before being doused. During that time visibility decreased from 500 down to only 100 yd outside the system, and there was much intrusion 'up' the runway and through the gap left by the faulty burners. FIDO also created its own peculiar wind conditions, for although the general wind direction was from the SSE at 5 mph before light-up, once the burners got going it increased to 14 mph outside the system and 12 mph from the SSW over the runway. This stirring-up of the airflow caused the actual clearance of fog to take place well to one side of the installation, and although no less than 300 ft of wet fog was lifted, a sharp course correction was necessary the moment the threshold came into sight. Despite this, Wg Cdr D.W. Donaldson in Foulsham's S-Sugar led the way in at 02.33, using SBA to make the first FIDO landing at the station.

Still some 20 minutes flying time away, Flt Lt Eric Morrison in Fortress R-Roger was ploughing into trouble. Howie Wing recalled:

. . . extremes of bad weather, severe icing, the rattle of hailstones, together with some of the worst cumulo-nimbus we had ever experienced. We couldn't get above it nor go round it, so we were forced to fly through it – all a little frightening. Our arrival over this country was greeted by fog. We called our base at Oulton and were advised to make our way to Foulsham where they would land us on FIDO. It seemed that everybody was trying to get in, many of whom, like ourselves, were desperately short of fuel due to the bad weather previously encountered. [The machines had already been airborne for over 9 hours.] When we were given permission to land our skipper told us that it would have to be now or never; we just hadn't enough fuel to go round again. So we took up our crash positions in the wireless compartment, facing aft, with our hands locked behind our necks.

Jim Mitchell was R-Roger's navigator on that occasion. His log book entry reads much the same as Howie Wing's, but concludes: 'Diverted to Foulsham – landed on FIDO necessitated by appalling fog – visibility 100–150 yards – shaky do!' He then elaborated:

The 'shaky do' refers to our FIDO landing. I set up the GEE co-ordinates and homed in to the field, which first appeared as a large fire with no definite outlines. I confirmed the position with a check fix, then we called up and received permission to land. We had no SBA and the ILS needles did not appear to be activated. I then moved from my position in the nose and stood immediately behind the captain, just forward of the top turret.

We descended, making a normal circuit in the clear, and making the final approach on the heading of the runway in use towards the centre of the blaze. The speed on finals was 10 mph faster than standard in accordance with FIDO procedure. At 150 ft the sodium funnel lights were seen but the glare prevented sight of the glide path indicators. Flare-out was commenced at about 50 ft, when turbulence was encountered and the starboard wing dropped by about 30°. Correcting aileron was applied and before the controls could be centred the column was hauled back and the aircraft touched down . . . To summarize; it was a very good landing, achieved by conditioned reflex.

Flt Sgt Tugham, piloting Fortress L-Lion, was not so lucky. He had no SBA either, and came in to port of the runway as Flt Lt Morrison had, but bogged down on the grass some 300 yd from the end of the runway, fortunately without damaging his crew or the FIDO pipes. Visibility was so bad that Flying Control could not see the aircraft once they had passed the runway intersection and there was a hold-up before the fourth aeroplane could be accepted.

Things were becoming somewhat desperate for Plt Off Cosbie's Fortress H-Henry. He was flying on only three engines and fuel was running low. Plt Off Goodyear in Mosquito G-George from Coltishall had become aware of Cosbie's predicament some miles out over the North Sea and had shepherded him to the approaches to the airfield. Despite the lack of telephone links with the far end of the runway, Plt Off Cosbie was informed of the position, and after a nail-biting 20 minutes, touching down short and keeping well to the right of the runway, he landed safely at 03.23, expressing himself well pleased with FIDO.

Plt Off Goodyear landed with no difficulty a few minutes later. Foulsham's first operational burn had taken approximately 2 hours from light-up to shut-down, consuming 170,000 gallons of petrol, with five aircraft landing safely. So dense was the fog that within half an hour of extinguishing, visibility over the whole airfield was down to 100 yd again – time for Lofty Pond and crew to feel their way back to billets, snatch a quick snooze and then begin pricking out the burner pipes once again.

Two days later, on 21 December, FIDO was required once more for an evening landing. At this time the German counter-offensive in the Ardennes was at its height. Lancasters of 3 Group attacked the railyards at Trier by day, and night raids were made on the marshalling yards at Nippes and Bonn. These were covered by numerous RCM and Mosquito patrols. Two of 192 Squadron's aircraft were to have undertaken Window patrols, but failed to take off due to engine trouble, and it appears that the only Foulsham machine to join fifteen RCM patrols carried out by 100 Group was Mosquito M-Mother. The Mosquitos patrolled to the south-east of the target area from which night fighter opposition was expected, but no contacts were made.

By the time of their return visibility had deteriorated. At ground level it was possible to see for 1,500 yd, but mist and haze made angular vision very poor, and the homecoming aircraft were offered the choice of diversion to distant, fog-free aerodromes or to put down at Foulsham where FIDO would be awaiting them. Six Mosquitos elected to take this option: C and K from West Raynham, D, V and O from Swannington, about 8 miles distant and, last but not least, M-Mother, the home-based machine, piloted by E.R. Taylor:

> We were returning from an operation to Cologne and Bonn, and on crossing the Dutch coast, from an altitude of 29,000 ft, could see a huge red glare over the English coast. On nearing base we were informed that FIDO was in use and that we could either make a landing or be diverted to another airfield free of fog.
>
>   I chose to land by FIDO and made the usual approach and was told to touch down in the box at the beginning of the runway. I was about 40 ft above it, just about to touch down, when a motor car shot underneath me across the runway. I can remember shouting over the R/T, 'Some silly fool has just driven underneath me!' We eventually made a good landing and were amazed at the height of the flames shooting up on either side of us. We had to taxi the full length of the runway before turning off and being led to dispersal. Once out of the aircraft, the roar of the fire was deafening and could be heard quite a distance from the airfield.
>
>   After de-briefing we learned that the 'fool' who had driven across the runway was a flight commander from a neighbouring airfield, whose planes had been diverted to ours during the emergency.

Lofty Pond recalls an occasion which does not find a place in official records. He and the FIDO crew were in action on Christmas Eve when the apparatus:

> made it possible for several returning bombers to land safely. The system was alight for well over an hour and a great deal of petrol was used. Sure enough, on Christmas morning Foulsham railway

station was packed with petrol bowsers waiting to refuel the storage tanks. At breakfast time the station CO had all the FIDO section in his office, saying 'All station ops are off, but you must work. You'll get your Christmas dinner later.'

As usual, half the section began hole clearing and the other half went down to the railway station. I was with the latter. Late that evening we emptied the last lot of wagons. Not only were we very tired and filthy from train soot – we were also very merry from the pints and pints of beer passed to us from the nearby local by air crew who had used our tunnel the previous night!

According to PWD records, fifteen aircraft landed at Foulsham during December 1944 and 361,854 gallons of petrol were used. This figure includes trial burns, but the great majority was for operational use. Poor weather throughout the month meant that many operations were curtailed and 192 Squadron completed only 128 sorties. As this figure is almost a quarter of 100 Group's RCM operations for the month, it is quite a respectable number; and Mandrel, Window and Spoof raids accompanied every one of the twenty-seven targets attacked in December.

To many of the villagers nearby, FIDO had been a bit of a mystery and was the subject of many tales until it was actually put into use. Len Bartram recalled his family being indoors at about 8 p.m. around the end of the year when an ever-increasing roar filled the air. Looking out, they saw the sky 'as if everything was on fire'. As one, they hastened to the bike shed, 'mother and all,' and pedalled furiously to the aerodrome perimeter to witness this most impressive phenomenon.

It was important that all Bomber Command raids, by day or night, should be covered by RCM patrols to reduce the chances of interception by German radar-carrying fighters. To this end, 462 (RAAF) Squadron, operating Halifax IIIs, arrived at Foulsham from 4 Group at the end of December 1944 to join with 192 Squadron. On 16 January 1945 over 1,200 aircraft were abroad, attacking targets in central Germany, and these included fifty-two Mosquito and fifty-five RCM patrols. At Foulsham eleven Halifaxes were detailed for Window patrols, though two had to be withdrawn, while 192 Squadron briefed five Halifaxes and four Mosquitos for Special Duty and two Halifaxes for Window patrols. Our source of information is the station ops record book which tells us that: 'owing to bad weather at the time of take-off, FIDO was brought into operation and made it possible for all the aircraft [presumably twenty] to take off under conditions which would normally have caused a cancellation of the effort'. Although the countermeasures worked well, twenty-seven bombers were lost. Seventeen of these were shot down around Magdeburg, although it is thought that the night fighters which engaged them were actually en route to a different interception.

To cover a main force raid on the Ruhr oil targets of Bruckhausen and Gelsenkirchen on the night of 22/23 January, 192 Squadron detailed two Halifaxes for Window patrols and three Halifaxes and three Mosquitos for Special Duties. At the same time twelve Halifaxes of 462 Squadron were also to drop Window. Of the last, one machine bogged down before take-off and three had to return early with equipment failure. The remaining eight, with the 192 Squadron aircraft, successfully completed their missions.

As they returned home towards midnight visibility decreased dramatically, with radiation fog and thick smoke haze, probably from the industrial parts of Norwich. FIDO was lit and with its aid all the Halifaxes and a Mosquito landed safely at Foulsham. It is likely that the other two Mosquitos had returned before FIDO was lit. The station ops record book comments: 'Owing to very poor visibility FIDO was brought into operation and once again proved its worth in making possible the landing of thirteen Halifaxes and a Mosquito which would otherwise have been diverted.' To this night's tally Len Bartram adds that: 'Mosquito (USAF) overshot and crashed when landing at Foulsham using FIDO. Pilot, Lt Geary, was injured.'

There are no records of the further use of FIDO during January, but this is not surprising in view of the limited number of operations possible during the month. The station record book's summary reads: 'Weather conditions were the worst for many years and operations were possible on only thirteen nights.' Even so, FIDO assisted to the tune of at least twenty take-offs and fourteen landings.

FIDO was next called for on 18 February. Five Halifaxes and two Mosquitos of 192 Squadron were engaged on RCM patrols, while six Halifaxes of 462 Squadron went Windowing. Visibility dwindled to only 400 yd during their absence and the order was given for FIDO to be lit on full burn at 21.30. Within a short time the fog was cleared from the full length of the runway and beyond. We do not know the circumstances under which all the machines returned; some may have landed before visibility grew too bad and others may have chosen to divert, but it is recorded that during a forty-five minute burn, five Halifaxes landed in safety at a cost of 57,000 gallons of petrol. Within half an hour of shutdown the fog became even thicker, reducing visibility below 300 yd.

The following night 260 aircraft of 5 Group took part in a raid on Bohlen, near Leipzig. The attack was covered by 34 RCM and 18 Mosquito patrols, of which 192 Squadron supplied six Halifaxes and three Mosquitos for Special Duties. Other 100 Group bomber support aircraft included Fortress HB785 from Oulton, flown by Flg Off Mark. His rear-gunner was Bill Walsh who recalls:

> We had flown over to Foulsham during the late afternoon as fog had been forecast. It took us twenty-five minutes, but most of that time was spent waiting our turn to land as there seemed to be whole squadrons trying to get in and find a parking space.
>
> By the time we got down and parked, it was dark. We went to get a meal, which meant queuing up – first come, first served; rank meant nothing. When we had eaten our meal, we just parked ourselves in a corner, and some of the lads got the cards out. We smoked and chatted and managed not to mention the evening's target.
>
> Everywhere was packed with crews from different squadrons. What sticks in my mind was the sheer number of men crowded into every inch of space. It was the same if you wanted to go to the toilet – you just joined the queue and waited your turn. Everybody had their flying kit on and was much bulkier with padded arms and legs. Quite a few crews went back and sat out the waiting time in their aircraft, but we stayed in the sergeants' mess, crowded but warm . . . As we left Foulsham what sticks in my mind was that FIDO had cleared the fog and it looked just as if someone had dug a huge trench out of the clouds and fog.

FIDO was lit at 22.27 on 23 February 1945 to receive any aircraft in difficulties following a major raid on Pforzheim. Eight Halifaxes and three Mosquitos of 192 Squadron covered the raid with RCM sorties. Two returned early, two failed to return and the four remaining Halifaxes were diverted to Carnaby because the apparatus at Foulsham was not functioning satisfactorily. At the same time, 462 Squadron sent nine Halifaxes out on Window patrols, six over Neuss and three to Dusseldorf. By the time of their return, fog had reduced visibility to less than 400 yd. FIDO provided 'an unsatisfactory burn, in that fog drifted across the runway up to a height of 50 ft, making landing dangerous, and could be used in extreme emergency only'. Five of the burner pipes burst, which would have added smoke to the fog. A 100 Group Mosquito attempted to land without permission before the smoke had cleared and crashed at the end of the runway. Ken Spriggs, a Special operator/air-gunner with 462 Squadron recalled this sad occasion. He was under the impression that the machine came in to land downwind, ran off the runway and collided with some parked Halifaxes. Len Bartram records the incident: 'Mosquito NT354 of 239 Squadron overshot and hit parked Halifax LW174 of 192 Squadron and crashed just beyond Foulsham airfield boundary. The pilot was killed and the navigator injured. Subsequently a lone Halifax landed safely at its second attempt. The others were diverted.'

The last recorded occasion when FIDO was lit at Foulsham during the war was on 18/19 April 1945. A force of 5 Group Lancasters carried out a raid on the railway yards in the Czechoslovakian town of Komotau. Thirty-five RCM and thirty-three Mosquito patrols were flown to cover the raid, 192 Squadron providing nine Halifaxes and three Mosquitos for Window and Special Duty patrols, while 462 Squadron sent four Halifaxes a-Windowing. Visibility as they came home was very poor. Details are lacking and the fog dispersal report records only that, 'Eleven Halifaxes and two Mosquitos landed 06.16–07.50'.

No further use of FIDO is recorded before the end of the war. The tanks were drained and dismantled following authorization dated 25 August 1945. So far as records and recollections can tell us, a minimum of thirty aircraft took off and over fifty landed during the eight months of its operation; though we incline to the view that the overall figure might well be as high as ninety.

TEN

Graveley

. . . a great illuminated Fox's glacier mint

John Slater, wireless operator, 44 Squadron

Reference to the initial installation of FIDO at Graveley has already been made (p. 10). When the Pathfinder Force was formed, 35 Squadron and its Halifaxes moved in from Linton-on-Ouse on 15 August 1942. Less than two months later Graveley was earmarked for the installation of FIDO and designated Station II. It was transferred to 8 Group in January 1943. As the first operational aerodrome to receive FIDO, Graveley was very much the guinea-pig, and it was there that full-scale trials of the various installations had to be carried out, without interfering with flying. Contractors William Press were often hard put to it to avoid disaster, especially as the main FIDO runway was crossed by runway 20 very soon after touchdown. Fortunately, they succeeded. The first system to be installed was fitted with the Four-oaks type of burner (see Plate 1), but within a short time they were replaced by the Haigas or Mk I burner (see Plate 11). Mk Is were difficult to build and progress was slow, but they were the type in use when Air Cdre Bennett made his first successful landing on 18 February 1943 (p. 19). Modification of Mk I burners into Mk IIs (Plate 15) took place in May 1943.

A problem which faced the FIDO engineers was the gap in the line of burners where the first intersection of runways occurred. It was overcome initially by mounting the burners on a gate, but subsequently the burner line was built into a trench at the junction. The appearance of the layout was as in Fig. 17. To fuel the burners, two banks of eight horizontal cylindrical steel storage tanks were erected to the rear of Rectory Farm. Each tank was 30 ft long and 9 ft in diameter and capable of holding 12,000 gallons, supplied by a fleet of road tankers. Pressure was provided from a pumphouse between the tanks which accommodated five pumps driven by Coventry Climax engines, any three of which were sufficient to feed the system.

The approach box extended beyond the camp bounds and into an orchard, as John Archbold, a navigator with 692 Squadron, recalled:

> The storage tanks for petrol used for the burners were sited in a little dip or hollow just outside the village of Graveley. Many of the pipes and connections leaked. Not all of these leakages fell to the ground. In one officers' living quarters there was a floor made of concrete slabs which had a constant strong smell of petrol (how they could sleep there is beyond me), and of course, smoking was actively discouraged. But the reward was fuel for elderly motor cars to make sorties to some of the more remote pubs in the area, like the Ferryboat and the Pike and Eel. Thus, FIDO befriended those on the ground as well as those in the air. These losses were put down to evaporation!

A number of people have vivid recollections of the early days – or nights – of FIDO at Graveley. For example, L.J. Newman brought to mind that:

> The ignition of the petrol in the starting-up period caused a terrific black pall of smoke over its whole length, just like a tanker on fire at sea. This lasted quite five to ten minutes before the flames

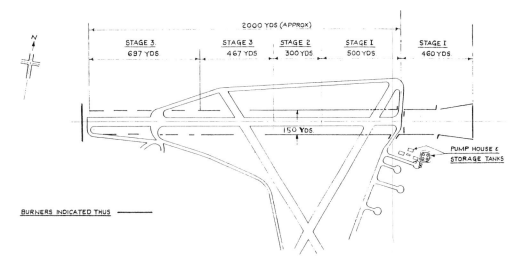

Fig. 17 Graveley, FIDO layout, showing sequence of burner completions. See also Fig. 2 and Plate 39

Plate 39 Graveley aerial. Runway 26. Scorch marks visible around approach box and alongside runway. Storage tanks, two types, to south of approach box. See Fig. 17. Twenty-six aircraft are visible at various dispersals (Crown/MoD)

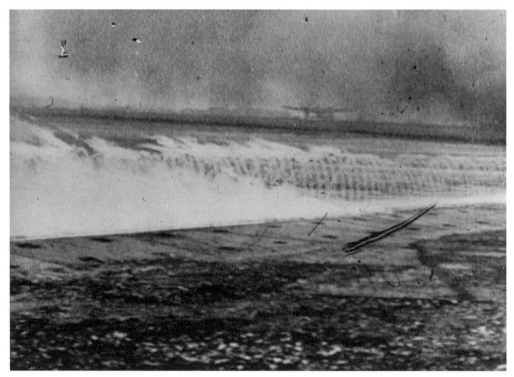

Plate 40 FIDO burner being lit in the fog at Graveley. Petrol jets ignited by hand from left. Flames flash to right (IWM)

Plate 41 Graveley oblique. Test burn of FIDO 1943, when only stages 1 and 2 completed. See Fig. 3 (PWD)

settled down and heated up, rather like a blowlamp getting hot. FIDO was nothing to look at (I saw it close enough when working on the runway) – a mile or so of pipework less than a foot high, with drilled holes from which piped petrol sprayed out. I know the villagers were wondering what on earth was going on when that thick pall went up (and so did quite a few airmen) when it was first used.

Air Cdre Bennett's successful landing on 19 February was not by any means the end of the line as far as the PWD was concerned. Other airfields came under consideration as likely sites, and developments at Graveley were watched so that the most efficient systems available could be installed at them. The changeover from the Mk I to the Mk II took place while Graveley was still operational; and since this was a Pathfinder station busily engaged in the Battle of the Ruhr, it was not the easiest of tasks to carry out the modifications without interfering with aircraft movements. It was months before the system was completed and on several occasions emergencies arose which neither the installation in its transient state, nor its limited crew of operators, could cope with. One of these occurred on the night of 4/5 May 1943.

Air Cdre Bennett reported to Petroleum Minister Geoffrey Lloyd:

> The installation at Graveley suffered a sad disappointment a few nights ago. We had urgent necessity to use it but unfortunately an aircraft damaged by enemy action crashed slightly on the runway and very effectively prevented further landings. We were therefore unable to use FIDO on an occasion when it was urgently needed. I am afraid that we lost two aircraft. I feel sure that if we had not been so unfortunate as to have the runway blocked, the installation would have been most useful.

Geoffrey Lloyd relayed the report on this disaster to Lord Cherwell, concluding his letter with the sentence: 'Now, having recently seen some of the wounded and burnt men from fog crashes, who are in Dr McIndoe's hospital, I am keener than ever to bring this job through to success if it is humanly possible.'

Successful trials in foggy weather were held on 16/17 July 1943. Geoffrey Lloyd submitted a report on this experiment to Winston Churchill, taking the opportunity to commend Lord Cherwell for his persistence in backing FIDO when it was not considered likely to be a viable system. Lloyd sent Cherwell a copy of the minute, adding the note 'This successful experiment would never have taken place but for you.' He also referred Winston Churchill to his minute of 10 April suggesting half a dozen additional FIDO-equipped airfields, commenting, 'Your own endorsement of the urgency of the requirement would be of the greatest assistance.' This was swiftly forthcoming. Churchill's reply was brief and positive: 'Yes. Press on and refer to me as may be necessary.' The Chief of Air Staff also took the opportunity to add his appreciation of Lord Cherwell's persistence and 'insistence on the possibility of achieving success in spite of the dismal prognostications and fallacious calculations of the so-called experts.' A series of trial burns took place during the summer as the system at Graveley was gradually updated, and aeroplanes landed on nine occasions. Pat Moorhead, a navigator with 35 Squadron, flew on one of the tests from Graveley:

> As I remember it – whenever it was – there was a very heavy mist, and once airborne we could see very little of the ground, and circled round waiting for someone to strike a match. When they finally did, very little seemed to happen at first; and then gradually, the elongated rectangle of the runway began to show more clearly, with belching yellow flames and rolling swirling fog all around and above. The worst part was coming in over the flames at the end of the runway, and I remember wondering whether the undercart wold melt or buckle or go up in flames – like entering the jaws of hell, and certainly different from a normal landing.

Every unit has its characters. There is always a camp comic, a barrack-room lawyer, a Pilot Officer Prune and so on. As far as FIDO at Graveley was concerned it was Sqn Ldr H. Hemming. Gp Capt Deacon recalls that he would have things exactly as they should be and

Plate 42 Lancaster landing during test burn of FIDO at Graveley. Note low cloud in suspense (PWD)

was a bit of a martinet. Mrs M. Brittan remembers: 'He was quite a character, an old RFC man with a patch over one eye. He regarded FIDO as his baby and if ever it failed to light he would tear up and down the lines in his jeep to get it going.' Alan J. Card of 35 Squadron also brought him to mind: 'He was a jolly man, an observer from the Great War, with only one eye. There was a standard joke in the mess. Someone would call out "FIDO!" and he would whip out a large cigarette lighter with a great flame to it and hold it above his head. Like the others with first-war medals, he seemed incredibly old to us!' Alan Vial referred to him as 'Popeye' and said that aircrew blamed him for the prangs which the station suffered.

Following an abortive burn on 9/10 October when aircraft had to be turned away, AVM Bennett reported that the time to light up was about twenty-five minutes and inexperienced handling caused smoke to persist from burning petrol spilt on the ground. Some of the holes had not been serviced properly and were blocked, and pipes had twisted so that flames from the burners were not playing on to the vaporizing pipes. Bennett recommended that the corrugated iron shields be repositioned to give greater protection to the flames in a cross-wind.

When Geoffrey Lloyd read this report, he was furious:

> I cannot escape the conclusion that it is a humiliating document and that the night's operations constitute a blot on the otherwise fine record of the department on FIDO work. The plain fact is that we missed our first opportunity to help six Mosquitos returning from Berlin. A fiasco of this kind, which might have been tragic, demands careful enquiry, strong disciplinary action and effective arrangements to make sure that it never recurs.

The 'careful enquiry' revealed that part of the trouble was caused by the leaded petrol introduced in the middle of the year. This had caused fouling of the jets and reduction in the burners' efficiency, and such reaming tools as were available could hardly touch the tough deposits. When Lord Cherwell heard of Geoffrey Lloyd's annoyance, he wondered whether some means of identifying the position of the landing strip or the line of approach from above the fog might be achieved by some sort of fireworks discharged from the ground, or even by small balloons carrying lights. When this was put to the pilots who had landed with the aid of FIDO, they were unanimously against any such innovation. They pointed out that: 'the trouble arises when the fog is fairly deep and the aircraft has to dive down into it. For a time the pilot is wholly dependent upon the beam and . . . inexperienced pilots may come in off-line and find it difficult to recover their direction before overshooting the runway.'

The Professor concluded his pep talk to Geoffrey Lloyd by saying: 'The most hopeful development is the adoption of the "talk down" system which will relieve the pilot of any need for the use of beam landing technique. A number of "talk down" sets are now becoming available and the Director of Air Safety is arranging to have these installed at our fog dispersal stations.'

One of AVM Bennett's right-hand men at Pathfinder HQ was Hamish Mahaddie. He recalled making a flight to test FIDO at Graveley on 19 November 1943 and later set his recollections down in Alan Bramson's *Master Airman*. Taking off from Wyton in a wooden, light aircraft, Hamish was less than enthusiastic about the occasion as the flames from FIDO pierced the fog:

> . . . and this glow gets redder and redder and redder. We are getting lower and I am watching that altimeter until we seem to be almost on the ground – 60 ft or something like that. Then we burst through and there are these flames burning away as far as the eye can see. He [Bennett] lands, then he does a roller, takes off and comes around, flying under the cloud this time. We flew back to Wyton where there was no FIDO and a cloud base of only a few hundred feet. And it doesn't bother Bennett at all. But by xxxx it bothered me!

On the night that this flight was made, FIDO made aviation history. Seven of 35 Squadron's Halifaxes took part in a raid by 266 bombers on Leverkusen. Equipment failure of OBOE caused twenty-seven towns to share the bombs intended for the target area, where records show only one HE in the town. Only four aircraft were lost in the raid, but many of the machines returning from the operation encountered fog conditions on reaching England and two Halifaxes and a Stirling crashed.

Some of Graveley's aircraft were diverted to other airfields, but four of them headed for home where they found the aerodrome still covered by the fog which had put the wind up Hamish. It was only about 50 ft deep, but so thick that at ground level visibility was down to 100 yd. The order to light up was given at 21.26 and within 10 minutes had cleared a lane along the runway through to the sky, so that the stars could be seen overhead.

Flt Lt Muller in A-Apple touched down at 21.56, followed by Lt Ghovertad of the Royal Norwegian Air Force in G-George, Flg Off R.V. Jones in Q-Queenie and Flt Lt D. Rowe in U-Uncle, within a period of nineteen minutes. Flt Lt Rowe said, 'When about 12 miles from base I saw two strips of fire which the navigator said was the fog dispersal apparatus.' Flg Off Jones commented, 'I could see the fog dispersal apparatus burning 30 miles away from a height of 3,000 ft.' Lt Ghovertad reported: 'After crossing the coast I could see a few searchlights and aerodrome beacons when south of Reading. I saw a big red fire to the north-east on approaching base and realized that the fog dispersal installation was in operation . . . The lines of burners showed up so clearly that I had no difficulty in lining up with the runway and found everything completely normal.'

Despite this promising beginning, as often happens, things got worse before they got better. The night of 16/17 December 1943 was a grim occasion for Bomber Command as a whole and for the Pathfinder Force and 1 Group in particular. 1 Group's Lancasters were part of a force of 483 Lancasters and ten Mosquitos from 1, 6 and 8 Groups. Many German fighters were encountered en route and twenty-five Lancasters were lost, sixteen more crashing on their return. Wg Cdr John Northrop of 83 Squadron remembers:

> Black Thursday . . . as pilots tried to get down using a combination of SBA, angle of glide indicators and FIDO. Contributory factors to the crashes could have been the relative inexperience of the pilots and the fact that the angle of glide indicators were set at the steeper angle used by the Halifaxes of 35 Squadron which were then based at Graveley; certainly at least one Lancaster crashed through overshooting the runway.
>
> That night, I was flying a Lancaster of 83 Squadron, and as things turned out was the last of the Group to land safely with SBA at Wyton. On my first approach, cleared to land by flying control, I was over the inner marker beacon at 150–200 ft, when a rogue aircraft almost collided with me as he carried out a steep turn across my bows, trying to land visually. I had to drop below him, carrying with me the branches of some big trees, and then carry out an emergency overshoot to safety above the overcast, where I stayed for the next half hour recovering my composure. Sad to say, the rogue aircraft crashed nearby.

FIDO was operational at only three Bomber Command bases at that time: Fiskerton, Downham Market and Graveley. The part played by the first two is not clear, as no official record survives. This only leaves Graveley. Its own 35 Squadron aircraft were not flying on the night of 16/17 December and the station was under a complete stand-down. But here also conditions were appalling. According to the fog dispersal report, advection fog polluted by smoke drifted slowly across the airfield. The fog was 500 ft deep and, as if that was not bad enough, on top of it was 3,000 ft of stratus cloud. FIDO was lit, but due to a shortage of crew lighting up was slow. Eventually the fog on the runway was cleared so that horizontal visibility improved to 1,600 yd. Unfortunately there was no way the apparatus could shift 3,000 ft of stratus, nor could the glow from the burners penetrate the blanket, so that pilots attempting an approach had only a vague idea where the runway lay.

Just after midnight, four aircraft were heard overhead and shortly afterwards one of them crashed north-east of the airfield. By 00.16 aircraft J, D, R, H and O (squadrons unknown) were stacked overhead. They were given permission to land, but communication with them abruptly ceased. FIDO was lit at 00.39 and during light-up H-Henry landed safely. Several other machines sought permission to land, but were diverted to Wyton or Warboys. One of them, P-Peter, soon radioed: 'There's no future at Wyton, can I have a crack at your FIDO?' He approached, but almost at right angles to the runway. Just when it looked as if he was going to touch down he opened up again, but then his engines cut and P-Peter crashed into the bomb dump and burst into flames. Thanks to the efficiency and indifference to danger of the fire party and the armaments crew the fire was brought under control and no bombs went off. Shortly afterwards two more aircraft crashed to the north of Graveley.

Mrs Isabel Burton, then a WAAF M/T driver, recalled:

> I shall never forget that night. I was walking back to the WAAF site after duty. There was a nasty, eerie reddish glow all around. Many aircraft crashed near the airfield and in the neighbourhood. It was said that they were dazzled by FIDO. This was of course in its early days. The WAAF drivers on duty that night had the unenviable duty of driving medical orderlies around to pick up injured and dying aircrew, although some managed to bale out – one actually landed in the WAAF quarters!

Sadly, Sir Archibald Sinclair had to report to Winston Churchill:

> Last night 482 Lancasters and fifteen Mosquitos took part in a raid on Berlin. The Germans refused to be spoofed and Pathfinders, consisting of the Mosquitos and ninety Lancasters, found fighter flare paths already lit over the approaches to the city. As a result, six PFF Lancasters were lost. Losses from the main force of 392 were nineteen, but exceptionally bad weather conditions with drifting masses of very low cloud developed at base, some 20 minutes before the bombers returned, resulting in thirty-four crashes. Fortunately, from these, sixteen entire crews are safe and also a number of individuals.

Air Marshal Sir Edgar Ludlow-Hewitt, Inspector-General of the Royal Air Force, summed up the causes of the heavy losses by saying that they were:

> . . . partly caused due to the lack of any pre-planning and practice of a scheme for homing in bad weather and neglect of SBA. The system should not be regarded as obsolete because it is to be replaced by GCA. The night was ideal for SBA, but many stations ordered aircraft to break cloud over the sea and try to come in under the low cloud, which resulted in accidents due to aircraft flying into high ground and congestion over airfields at low altitudes.

This was a tragic phase in FIDO's career after a promising start. The system worked, but the task set was too great for the equipment at that stage of its development. But, as the story-books say, help was at hand. When fog dispersal systems were installed at the later batch of airfields approved in July 1943, that at Graveley was enlarged and improved as well by the installation of Mk IV burners in place of the Mk IIIs. A trial burn of the system brought Geoffrey Lloyd to attend a demonstration on 15 January 1944. It was not an unqualified success.

The system was lit at 09.45 when there was radiation fog 200–300 ft thick, and visibility was limited to 100 yd. A gentle breeze was blowing up the runway. Due to a shortage of operating crew the light-up was slow and uneven and much smoke developed during the hour and ten minutes of the burn. A great deal of petrol, thought to be from the feed-pipes buried alongside the burners, leaked into the airfield drainage ditches. There, perhaps irritated by the poor show that FIDO was making, it ignited, nearly setting fire to the main transformer. The minister departed, his comments unrecorded.

Almost the same thing happened five days later (20 January) when FIDO was lit just after midday to aid a lost Lancaster, G-George of 97 Squadron. There was radiation fog 400 ft deep and surface visibility of only 150 yd when light-up was ordered. Owing to a strong cross-wind, which the pilot estimated at up to 20 knots, numbers of jets actually blew out and had to be re-lit. In the interim the unburned fuel again found its way across the field before igniting, where, burning as brightly as FIDO itself, it destroyed the airfield lighting cables and caused the entire system to be declared temporarily u/s. With this gratuitous conflagration it is perhaps not surprising that it took G-George's pilot four attempts to land.

Fortunately, all had been restored by 10 February when HM King George VI and Queen Elizabeth visited Graveley where they spent a brief time. Mrs Isabel Burton recalls: 'We WAAFs were lined up at the camp gates to welcome them. All edging blocks were freshly painted white for the occasion. The king and queen stood on the Control Tower steps watching FIDO blazing away – burning 48,000 gallons of fuel in a very short time.'

At the beginning of February 1944 the first Mosquitos of 692 Squadron joined Graveley, and on the 4th carried the first 4,000 lb to be flown by Mosquitos. It was noted that:

> . . . during the whole of their operating period they always took off from the main runway though at times there were cross-winds of 20–25 mph. This was considered necessary owing to the tendency of a fully laden Mosquito to swing to port. On several occasions the FIDO pipes were cut by aircraft swinging, but fortunately no serious damage was done, though the incidents caused a tense atmosphere in Flying Control. On one occasion the Mosquitos were taking off from the west end when one swung off the runway and headed for Control. Fortunately the pilot was able to get back on line and take off safely.

A force of twelve Mosquitos from Graveley's 692 Squadron raided Hamburg on 6/7 April 1944. John Gover recalls:

> Visibility at the target had been excellent, but it was anything but back at base just after midnight. However, when I got there, lo and behold! there was FIDO burning merrily away. I believe the idea was that FIDO would be seen miles away in poor visibility. This was not so, but it was marvellous on the circuit once you were home.

Having got home, the next problem was to get down. I made a normal circuit and approached and, as I came over the airfield boundary, felt the heat. The Mossie was liable to swing viciously to port on take-off and landing if the pilot wasn't careful, and I had no wish to go through a burning fiery furnace. I did not find it easy to judge my height from the ground, but no doubt that was because I had not landed with FIDO before. However, the landing was quite okay, so all was well.

The airfield was full of aircraft, as other squadrons had been diverted there, and I did not find any pilot who had trouble using FIDO. The experience was not without its curious side. I was flying a Mosquito XVI equipped with VHF. When I first called up to identify myself some 50 miles from the English coast I got no reply. However, when I got back to base I could hear perfectly clearly, which meant that the fault was its limited range. When I saw FIDO alight I thought that there had been a diversion order which I had not received and that FIDO had been lit especially for my benefit. I then thought that nobody would believe what I said about the VHF and would say that I had ignored the diversion order so that this enormously expensive piece of equipment had to be used just to get me down in one piece. I was greatly relieved to find that this was not the case and I was not in trouble.

Flying Control was very pleased with the performance of FIDO and the Mosquito crews. A radiation mist had gathered with a light wind of about 5–10 mph blowing at an angle to the runway:

Twelve Mosquitos made satisfactory landings [A, B, G, J, K, L, N, O, P, R and S of 692 Squadron and N-Nan of 139 Squadron], at a good average touchdown rate. The pilots' reports indicated that stratus cloud had been encountered over the runway and some of them found that the light from the apparatus penetrated this cloud and helped them to align their aircraft correctly for the approach. They all agreed that FIDO was of considerable assistance to them.

Later, Graveley's runway became unique among standard FIDO installations, in that the fourth side of the rectangle was closed by a Rapex burner as described on p. 31. But even though it could be extinguished in less than half a minute, and lay in a trench so as not to be an obstruction, pilots were most chary about charging straight for it, no matter how quickly it might (or might not) go out. On more than one occasion pilots considered a swift bump over the side-burners to be a safer alternative. Eventually it was found that intrusion of fog at the 'far' end of the runway could be reduced by extending the length of the side-burners, but staggering them so that exit was possible at numerous points. The use of the Rapex was subsequently discontinued.

It was not always necessary to have FIDO at full burn. On 30 July 1944, for example, by which time 35 Squadron's Halifaxes had been replaced by Lancaster IIIs, three Lancasters were detailed to attack Caen, and ten to a morning raid on 'the battle area' covering the Caen break-out. When they returned there was 10/10 cloud right down to 500 ft with mist at ground level. It was considered sufficient to light the 460 yd funnel only, so that once down low, pilots could line up on the runway where visibility was nearly a mile. For the consumption of about 8,000 gallons of petrol, nine Lancasters were landed within the hour.

Ten of 35 Squadron's Lancasters carried out a raid on Forêt de Nieppe on the night of 31 July/1 August. At midnight horizontal visibility at Graveley was 2,500–3,000 yd but the base of low stratus cloud was only 300 ft. There was a slight following wind from the ENE. The order to light FIDO was given, and within an hour nine of the station's aircraft touched down with an average of 5 minutes between machines. The station commander, Gp Capt S.W.B. Menaul, said that conditions could hardly have been worse, especially as none of the pilots had ever used FIDO before. Flt Lt Knobloch commented: 'FIDO appeared to have burnt a hole through the cloud over the airfield, though there was much smoke to leeward.' The only incident was damage to the cross-burner at the west end of the runway whose control valve and Tannoy loudspeaker were destroyed by an aircraft running over them. Damage to and by FIDO occasionally kept ground crews scuttling to and fro. Alfred Wray brought to mind:

I drove a Lorraine crane, and if an aircraft ran off the runway, it very often ran on to the FIDO installation, and had to be lifted off so that FIDO could be repaired. When FIDO was in full flame and aircraft were landing thick and fast, our WAAF drivers did a remarkable job, and the men too deserved the highest praise. It was said by many to be like Dante's 'Inferno' trying to get crews to the dispersal points as quickly as possible, and it took a lot of nerve to dodge aircraft on the perimeter track.

On 26/27 August a force of 372 Lancasters and ten Mosquitos raided the German port of Kiel and 174 Lancasters of 5 Group attacked the Baltic seaport of Konigsberg, the supply port for the German Eastern Front – 950 miles from English bases. At about 05.00 the situation was becoming critical, for the Konigsberg raiders were approaching the coast with fuel running low and visibility deteriorating fast. Widespread diversions were ordered and five FIDO stations alerted. The system at Graveley was lit at 05.46, and the radiation fog gradually dispersed over the runway. After nearly 10 hours airborne, tired eyes sought a clearly defined flare path – and found it. Eleven Lancasters of 44 Squadron and one of 619 Squadron landed safely in thirty-nine minutes. Seventeen others were diverted to Wyton.

Rum-laced coffee is the abiding memory of John Slater, WOp/AG to Flg Off Anning that night. On crossing the Swedish coast they were assisted on their way by coordinated Swedish searchlights. They ran down to the target area and laid their mines with German flak firing down on them from the surrounding hills. Three crews were lost from 44 Squadron but the others survived and turned for the home run across the North Sea.

> Halfway home I vacated the front turret which I usually occupied during an attack and returned to my W/T equipment. . . .To my surprise, instructions were passed for us to divert to Graveley as fog had clamped down over the Lincolnshire bases. I passed the instructions to our captain and navigator who plotted a new course to bring us in over the Wash and across to Graveley. As we approached the English coast we could see the fog-banks stretching away in front and to starboard.
>
> Suddenly, at about 15 miles range a strange apparition appeared before us, dead on the nose. I can only describe it as like a giant illuminated Fox's glacier mint, for that is what it looked like from the astrodome. As we started our run in for the landing, we began to pick out the flames of the burning fuel on either side of the runway. We eventually motored in over the threshold with flaps fully down, but, due to the hot air, we floated and floated and floated. I thought the wheels were never going to touch, but finally they did, and we were able to brake to a stop before reaching the end of the runway but only just.
>
> At the debriefing we were given rum-laced coffee, a common practice on PFF stations, but our first experience of it – and it went down well.

Not until 22 October was FIDO again used operationally at Graveley, probably while the storage tanks were being changed. Initially the station had quite a battery of horizontal cylindrical tanks, 30 ft long and 8 ft in diameter, but later, four vertical tanks with a combined capacity of over half a million gallons were erected adjacent to them.

Concerning the incident on 22 October Ron Vere and John Archbold, pilot and navigator respectively of Mosquito M-Mother of 692 Squadron jointly recall, Ron first: 'Mosquito MM176 took off from Graveley at 16.55. It was our ninth operation and the target was Hamburg. Forty-five Mosquitos were detailed for the sortie. There were no losses. However, there was dense fog over the eastern counties and Graveley being one of the few stations equipped with FIDO we were able to land at our home base after 3 hours 45 minutes.'

John Archbold's diary records:

> Sunday 22 October 1944. On again tonight in M-Mother. No air test as clouds too low. Target was Hamburg again. I'm getting tired of going to this place [this was the third time on the trot that we had been sent there]. Flak was a bit hot too; I was quite glad to get away from it. When we got over the coast we could see a glow in the distance under the clouds. It turned out to be FIDO, an amazing sight. Two parallel lines of fire underneath us, between which we could see faintly the lights of the flare-path. We landed okay; no trouble at all. It was like daylight. So now we tell the boys to get some FIDO landings in!

Ron Vere's memories of the last few miles home were:

> . . . that as we approached Graveley, the fog which lay ahead and below parted like the Red Sea. But it was not the hand of God. It was man's ingenuity – a brilliant yet fearful concept which forced a safety path down to our base.

The stacking and circuit procedure was uneventful but on the final approach, in concentrating on keeping M-Mother between the blazing lines of fire, I did not see the flarepath lights until almost the last moment. Then, dead ahead, the runway appeared, so narrow that it seemed impossible that the high wing-span of the Mosquito could settle down between those twinkling lights. We touched down, and as we sped between those soldiers of fire a silent prayer passed my lips, and gently we were led to safety along the perimeter track away from the ferocity of FIDO.

Warning was given that three Fortresses of 482 Bomb Group at Great Ashfield were in difficulty on an operational training exercise just after 22.20 on 24 October and FIDO was lit to guide them in. The three Fortresses landed safely in the worst conditions of low stratus yet seen. The aircraft did not have the advantage of beam equipment, but nevertheless they executed excellent landings. Pilots expressed appreciation; one of them was heard to remark, 'Well, it saved our lives.'

Aboard one of the Fortresses was Truman Smith (later Lt Col USAF). He takes up the story some time before the landing, when they had already been diverted from their home base to Alconbury:

On this particular night I was flying co-pilot, because Francis J. Hartel and I alternated daily from left-seat to right-seat . . . Well, Francis screwed it up. He missed the Alconbury runway on the approach. I knew this as soon as we dropped beneath the very low cloud and saw that there was no runway beneath us, and were about to stick the wheels of a 30-ton airplane into the sod at 135 mph. 'Go on around!' I said, proceeding with my co-pilot duties of getting the wheels up and making ready for a go-round. I also turned on the landing lights and they shone straight through the vacant windows of an abandoned storehouse that was at a normally safe distance from the runway . . .

But Hartel was good – and we avoided our end for the moment – and quickly took us back up into the soup. I turned the lights off again, because lights in a cloud or fog only serve to blind you and destroy your night vision.

The Fortress's abrupt arrival and departure had considerably disconcerted the Control Tower staff at Alconbury, but presently they contacted Hartel and Smith again, instructing them to tune in to another frequency, which they did:

Very shortly a female voice said, 'X-X-ray, this is FIDO. Do you read?'

Well, that was a shocker. I'd never had a female call me on the radio before, and I must say it got my attention. I mean; what twenty-year-old male could ignore the call of a female? I would have heard it through static and/or panic.

Hartel and I responded to the instructions of the siren called FIDO . . . We complied with her request and flew the heading she gave, in absolute blind faith that it would lead us to wherever she might be.

The darkness through which we flew began to glow from a vague pinkish colour into a rose-red. The closer we got to wherever it was, the more orange it became. From time to time FIDO directed us to change headings and altitude, bringing us closer and closer to the mystery. Except for the absence of music it was the Disney world of *Fantasia* as we descended into – what? It was beginning to look like the very gates of hell, and the cockpit was charged with tension.

Lt Hartel was mesmerized. As Truman Smith prepared power, wheels and flaps for a landing, and read off the air speed to him, Hartel kept pushing the nose of the aircraft down and they had quite a tussle over the throttle controls. Flying Control had told them to approach at 5 mph faster than their normal speed, but Lt Hartel seemed intent on putting down as fast as possible. Continued Truman Smith:

Boom! We broke out into what appeared to be a Nissen hut of fire, pulling large wisps of cloud with us. There was a runway under us but we were going too fast. 'Go on around!' I said, and we thundered forward between the walls of flame that paralleled the runway. So this was FIDO.

Obviously we finally got down. It was on our second attempt, after we learned what to expect. Although still a hot landing, we ran off the far end of the runway, but without any damage. All in all we did a good job of it, being able to walk away from it and having no idea what we had gotten into.

An extremely active day for the United States 8th Airforce and Bomber Command and also for FIDO countrywide was 16 November 1944. Over 2,400 aircraft were detailed to attack towns in the path of the American 1st and 9th Armies between Aachen and the Rhine. The weather was poor throughout the day and widespread diversions were ordered as they returned. Twelve of Graveley's Lancasters had taken part in a raid on Düren, and it was deemed advisable to light the approach funnel to enable them to line up with the runway as they came in. This was sufficient to penetrate the thick haze, and for a consumption of only 12,000 gallons of petrol, all twelve landed safely, plus two 'cuckoos' diverted from elsewhere. The station FIDO report said that 'the pilots were unanimous in their decision that landing without FIDO would have been very hazardous'.

AVM Bennett had occasion to drop in on FIDO on 13 December. He recalled:

I had been visiting some other aerodrome, and came back to my own Group to find that things were completely fogged in and that most of England was closing down rapidly. At Graveley they announced that although FIDO was going full bore, a substantial cross-wind was blowing the fog across the runway so rapidly that it was quite impossible to land. I was in the Beaufighter [V8214] which I used as a hack in those days – not the most pleasant aircraft for blind approaches, but one which I had fully equipped with SBA and with pilot-operated GEE. When I got to Graveley I called up and told them I was coming in to land. I did my approach on SBA and having had a full description of the direction of the wind, I deliberately swung out to starboard, since the wind was from port to starboard of the runway.

Conditions for the light-up had been appalling. The shut-off valves were frozen stiff and petrol had to be poured over them and ignited before the system could be primed. To light the burners pressurized goose-necked flares (like overgrown watering cans with a wick sticking out of the spout) had to be used. The IRBs were inoperative, aggravating the intrusion of fog.

As expected, I found the chasm cut in the fog exactly as planned, but instead of the walls being vertical they were sloping very sharply over to the right at about 50° from the vertical. When, however, I entered the chasm, I simply did a slanting approach on to the runway and landed quite normally.

I had informed Flying Control of my movements and as I ran out of the fog-cleared area into the thick fog beyond, I stopped and asked them to provide assistance. This apparently left them completely speechless, and they asked me to report my position. I told them that if I knew that I would be able to taxi in on my own. . . .

Finally, I realized that they thought I was still in the air and I had to make it quite clear that I was firmly on the ground – after which I got the assistance I needed.

David Saward records that:

When on 16 December 1944 Field Marshal von Runstedt launched his famous counter-attack against the Allies through the Ardennes in weather that completely hampered all air operations, an urgent call went out from General Eisenhower's HQ for tactical support. Due to thick and extensive fog which was spreading not only over the battle area but over the bases in France, Belgium and England, the Allied Air Forces were unable to respond – with the sole exception of Bomber Command.

As part of this attempt to hinder the supply of war materials to the German front, a force of 136 aircraft attacked the Nippes marshalling yards near Cologne on 21 December. Included in this number were just four of 35 Squadron's Lancasters, while three of 692 Squadron's Mosquitos took part in a raid on Bonn. As the aircraft streamed back towards 19.00 in the evening, visibility, which had been poor all day, deteriorated still further and aircraft attracted by the light-up of FIDO for Graveley's own aircraft joined in the circuit, like the proverbial moths around a candle.

The three home Mosquitos set down safely within 4½ minutes, to be followed by two of 142 Squadron from Gransden Lodge. Then came the four 35 Squadron Lancasters which picked up one from 405 Squadron en route. Its captain said that he had seen the glow of FIDO from a hundred miles out and that it gave him great confidence, but the station commander Gp Capt S.W.B. Menaul pointed out that it was necessary 'to erase the idea prevalent at some stations that pilots had to pass through a wall of flames'.

The poor weather persisted for days on end, and aerial operations were severely handicapped, but attacks were made on communications at Koblenz and Bingen on 22 December. Five Pathfinder Lancasters of 35 Squadron were detailed to lead the raid on Koblenz. Base was covered with a mixture of fog which restricted visibility to 200 yd, and the clouds were at 1,000 ft. FIDO was lit at 15.49, but before the Lancasters could take off Group told the station to stand by to receive two Fortresses reported to be in distress. When, after a while, no further news of them was received, the home aircraft were allowed to proceed, and all disappeared into the fog within the space of eight minutes, following which FIDO was extinguished.

At 20.40, word came through to re-light FIDO, and visibility which had come down to only 100 yd in the planes' absence gradually improved. Things were made difficult because a slight following wind caused an extra build-up of fog at the approach end of the runway. Nevertheless, Graveley's five Lancasters homed in to land safely, followed by a Lancaster from each of 103, 106 and 405 Squadrons.

The persistently bad weather continued to restrict all Allied air support for the American ground forces, but every effort was made to get the Pathfinders away whenever possible. Ten ops into his second tour, John Whitworth was posted to the re-formed 162 Pathfinder Squadron at Bourn. On 23/24 December he flew Mosquito F-Freddie, along with fifty-one others, to attack the railway marshalling yards at Limburg:

> We returned about 02.00 to find Bourn shrouded in fog. We were second in the queue, came in on SBA and had just 'found' the flare-path at about 100 ft when I was sent round again as the first aircraft in had become stuck in the mud at the end of the runway. After some airfield circling we were all (about a dozen I think) sent to Graveley to land on FIDO.
>
> We knew all about it from previous briefings, but had never seen it before. What a wonderful sight on a foggy night! An absolutely clear hole in the fog and with a slight cross-wind a large part of the airfield on the port side also clear.
>
> Easy approach, slight bump as we crossed the perimeter, about which we had been warned, plenty of power and an easy 'wheeler'. The Mossie was a wonderful aircraft; no float even in nil wind, but I would not have liked to swing into those flames! Rapidly marshalled off the runway and to bed after de-briefing.

A daylight attack on the German airfields at Lohausen and Mülheim was mounted on 24 December 1944. FIDO was being operated under great difficulty by now according to the fog dispersal report: 'It could not work at its best as several burners were u/s. The recent number of burns, long periods of stand-by and large amounts of petrol to be offloaded has put a severe strain on an inadequate staff. Experience with wet fog drifting across the runway has again emphasized the need for double rows of burners.'

John Sampson was engaged on the Mülheim attack, as navigator in Flt Lt Derek James's Oboe Mosquito of 105 Pathfinder Squadron operating from Bourn:

> We were detailed to mark the Mülheim target and carried four red TIs. This was a daylight operation and we took off at 12.40. The whole area was fogbound. My pilot pointed the Mossie down the main runway at Bourn, waited for the ASI to register 120 knots and then pulled us up through the fog. In a few seconds we had cleared the fog and it was a brilliantly sunny day. The operation was successful and as far as we were concerned was without incident except for four flak shells fired at us over the target, which caused the rapid disappearance of two Mustangs which were escorting us.
>
> At briefing we had been warned that the fog would not clear and that we were to land at Graveley

which was equipped with FIDO. We arrived overhead just before four o'clock. It was still very foggy but from overhead the runway was clearly visible, even if viewed slightly obliquely. On the approach for landing it wasn't quite so easy, for a cross-wind had cleared the fog to one side of the runway which could not be directly seen. However, the FIDO system was of considerable assistance and Derek made a good landing.

Three of 105 Squadron's Mosquitos landed safely at Graveley, H, K and Q; but John Sampson recalls that the rest of the squadron finished up all over East Anglia and were still being rounded up days later. By the time 35 Squadron's Lancasters returned to base, conditions had become so bad in the descending darkness, with the wet fog limiting visibility to 100 yd, that there was no way in which the clapped-out Mk IV burners could light their way home and the whole squadron was diverted to West Raynham where acceptable conditions prevailed.

The total consumption of petrol by FIDO at Graveley from 19 to 24 December had been 326,000 gallons. In view of the demand being made on the system at this time, consideration was given, first of all to the installation of a double row of burners on each side of the runway, and then to equipping the airfield with the much more powerful Hades burners. In the event neither proposal was adopted and Graveley had to soldier on with the obsolete Mk IVs for another three months.

The abominable weather gave no quarter over the Christmas period, but four Lancasters of 35 Squadron were on daylight ops on 26 December, leading an attack on communications targets at St Vith. The temperature was below freezing for most of the day and the only warm place was near the FIDO burners when they were lit in an attempt to clear the snow from the runway. As the burners were placed 50 yd back from the edge of the airstrip and their heat was directed upwards it had no effect on the snow, but was much appreciated by the gangs of erks who shuttled between the burners and their shovelling on the runway. We do not know if FIDO was needed to facilitate take-off for the Lancasters or whether it was alight anyway, but it was most certainly required later as daylight faded and 200 ft of radiation fog deepened over the fenlands. A clearance over the runway was obtained in calm conditions at about 15.30, in time for Mosquitos J and Y of 105 Squadron to make unscheduled landings after a training exercise. Nearly an hour later, the men who had been engaged on more serious matters began to arrive, following diversions from their own airfields: six Mosquitos of 105 Squadron and six of 109 Squadron. Following hard on their heels from 16.54 onwards came Graveley's four Lancasters, a Halifax of 433 Squadron and seven Lancasters from 635 Squadron at Downham Market, whose FIDO installation had been unable to cope with the severity of the elements.

A total of twenty-six aircraft landed in safety; the twelve Mosquitos averaged two minutes each from clearance to land to touch-down and seven of the Lancasters put down within the space of 16 minutes. The fog dispersal report noted the satisfaction of all pilots at the great help in difficult conditions, but complained that broken heater pipes had outpaced the capacity of the contractors' ability to repair or replace them, as only two men, who worked well, were available to carry out work requiring a couple of dozen.

Graveley's Lancasters were out again the next day. Two hundred aircraft carried out a daylight raid on the marshalling yards at Rheydt, complementing attacks by over 600 USAF bombers escorted by nearly 400 fighters to targets at Fulda and Eusenkirchen. Six of Graveley's Pathfinders were in the lead. By the time the force was homeward bound there was thick mist and haze 1,000 ft deep. This, together with the fact that aircraft were landing into the setting sun, caused pilots to complain that they could see forwards and obliquely for only 100 yd.

The approach funnel only of FIDO and two burners on each side of the runway were lit at 16.00, and five of the home aircraft, four more from stations unknown and an Oxford in transit put down safely within the hour. The station commander was pleased:

. . . for the expenditure of 9,000 gallons of petrol made it possible to land nine Lancasters without difficulty. These aircraft were required for further operations and FIDO saved them from being diverted to airfields where they might subsequently be immobilized. I consider this a substantial return on the modest expenditure involved. The extreme variation in temperature (down to 29° F) caused two preheaters to break. If we had been burning the whole line, doubtless many others would have gone. As it was, the shut-off valves froze and two were completely u/s.

The usual method for freeing such valves was to douse them in anti-freeze, but in extreme cases it was known for them to be soaked in petrol and an airman to 'light the blue touch-paper and retire immediately!'

Raids were intensified on 29 December when fifteen of 35 Squadron's Lancasters led a daylight raid on Gelsenkirchen, part of a force of 346 Lancasters and Mosquitos. FIDO was lit at 19.40 at the request of Group because of general weather deterioration in the area during the return flight. Visibility was down to 1,200 yd and there was particular difficulty with oblique vision. As 8 Group Mosquitos were expected back before the Graveley aircraft were due, it was thought better to light up early in case the under-maintained burners took a long time to burn clearly. In the event, visibility was better than expected and the Mosquitos were able to land at their own stations. As 35 Squadron's aircraft were well on their way home by this time, it was decided to keep the approach box and the first few burners on each side of the runway going, and this was found to be sufficient. When the Lancasters arrived, twelve all told, it was possible for every one of them to land safely inside 15 minutes.

December 1944 eventually came to an end for FIDO. By then many of the burners were in a sorry state, beyond repair and in need of replacement. Their 40-yd lengths looked like miniature switchbacks from distortion. It was only because the weather was so bad in succeeding weeks, and flying severely restricted that FIDO was spared further embarrassment. During December the system had burned operationally for about 15 hours, plus tests and adjustment trials, and consumed about half a million gallons of petrol. Eighty-seven aircraft had landed or taken off safely, forty of them in thick fog. Just how thick it could be can be judged from the remarks of Gp Capt George Grant, the station commander:

> During the Ardennes offensive in 1944 the system was used extensively. . . . We collected aircraft of all sizes and types. One incident which occurred involved our watch tower orderly. He was detailed to guide a visiting maintenance crew to a strange aircraft which had landed shortly before. He told them to follow his instructions for reaching dispersal. When they reported their arrival there, he asked them if they could see their aircraft. When they said 'No', he asked them, 'Well, can you feel it?'

FIDO was required on 16 January 1945, when seven Lancasters of 35 Squadron were detailed for an attack on Zeitz, seven more to Magdeburg and four Mosquitos of 692 Squadron to provide Window cover for the latter. There was cloud, much drizzle and a 15 mph head wind at about 18.00 hours, and Group HQ ordered the approach funnel and a couple of burners some way down the runway to be lit so that the aircraft could get under way and keep well lined up as they approached take-off speed. This meant that although FIDO was alight for nearly two hours, 'only' 21,740 gallons of petrol were used to despatch eighteen aircraft into the murky skies. The necessity for replacing the aged Mk IV burners can be judged from the fact that although it was only a limited burn, 'two pre-heaters broke, making eight broken today'.

Alan J. Card, bomb-aimer of J-Jig (35 Squadron) has vivid recollections of landing with the aid of FIDO following a raid on Bonn on 4/5 February 1945, when their crew acted as visual centrer:

> I had an unrivalled view ahead, and first saw the great glare of the fire as we crossed the English coast at Orfordness, some 60 miles from base.

When we were five or six miles from Graveley, the light from the flames was so brilliant that Kiwi, our pilot, Flt Lt Basil Lawson, began to lose sight of the soft phosphorescent glow of the instruments in front of him. He spoke to Eddie (Flt Sgt Edmondson, our flight engineer) and told him to keep his eyes inside the cockpit and to read off the air speed to him as we approached, because the light would blind him.

The main runway had a sheet of fire ascending on either side of it, and as we joined the circuit and passed along the downwind leg, it was as though a clean block had been cut in the solid fog which lay over all; as clear as day within and blackest night surrounding us. It was a relief to see that we did not actually have to fly through the flames to land. We had to hope that we did not have a punctured tyre to swing us off the runway and into the pipes.

We made our approach and Eddie called out the air speed. 'A hundred and ten knots, a hundred and five, one hundred.' We were over the outer boundary. He cut back the four throttles. 'Ninety-five.' Suddenly the aircraft bucked then fell like a mad thing as we met turbulence created by the great heat.

The pilot had been warned about this, but even so it was a startling experience as Kiwi sweated at the controls. 'Ninety.' The rising hot air was still holding us off as though we were a light-weight glider instead of thirty tons of bomber. He stalled the aircraft to force it down, making one of his less graceful landings. As we ran forward with the curtain of fire rising on either side, we could feel the radiant heat penetrating the aeroplane. With the engines cut back we could hear a menacing roar like controlled anger from the flames. To the end of the runway and turn left and to the perimeter track. It was a relief to taxi away and roll on to the hardstanding at our dispersal point.

Up to this time Graveley had been operating with the Mk IV type of FIDO burner (as shown in Fig. 5), common to the other airfields. It was a comparatively simple burner to construct but prone to distortion and uneven burning under prolonged use. Since about the middle of 1944 the Mk IVs had been progressively replaced by the Mk V (Fig. 6), as materials and labour became available. The Mk V, 20 yd in length, was only half as long as its predecessor and altogether a more substantial piece of apparatus. Curiously enough, though it was at Graveley that it all began, the station was the last to be equipped with Mk Vs, which in the event were little used.

Probably the last men to use FIDO and its Mk V burners in earnest were 608 Squadron's Mosquitos from Downham Market on 20/21 April 1945. Among them was a former classmate of Sir Edward Heath, Charles Owen, flying R-Roger:

It was a Berlin trip and we were all diverted to Graveley on R/T, probably twelve in number. A lot of fog was experienced by the Group, but we were flying well above it in good weather. We could see FIDO for miles and miles. The fog layer was lit up as though by searchlights so that it was easy to do a circuit over the top and find the lead-in lights.

The next morning I flew back to Downham Market to get ready for the next trip, which was to Kiel and my very last operational trip of the war.

Plate 43 Pipe dreams? Remains of FIDO piping at Cotton Farm, Graveley, 1988 (D.H. Foreman)

This, as far as surviving records and recollections can tell us, concluded FIDO's war at Graveley. An Air Historical Branch *Brief History* estimates that 183 machines took off or landed operationally with FIDO's aid, but we are inclined to put the figure nearer the 200 mark.

Much, much later D.H. Foreman organized a 35/635 Squadron Reunion Association return to Graveley in 1988, and found it

> . . . a vast area of farmed land . . . such a lovely green . . . still as bleak and cold as ever; in fact so cold that the ladies in our party turned blue. . . . All that remains now is a board which reads 'R.C. Eayers Ltd, Cotton Farm, Graveley Airfield' . . . As we stood there, was there a tear in our eye as we recalled the events, and could hear the throb of Merlin engines . . . visualize those great aircraft, Halifax, Lancaster, Mosquito? Yes, these and all the memories came flooding back through the wind of that cold day.

He also recalled 'Today, FIDO is but a heap of pipes on the side. Frankly, we never realized the size of those pipes.'

ELEVEN

Ludford Magna

... a solid white mass with one very clear hole in the middle

Den Weygang, navigator, 619 Squadron

Ludford Magna aerodrome, to the south of the villages of Ludfords Magna and Parva, was built on an irregular plateau above the 400 ft contour mid-way along the road from Market Rasen to Louth, about eight miles from each. Before the war the villages had a joint population of about 400. The land on which the airfield was built belonged to Major John St Vigor Fox and was farmed by Stafford Hildred from whom it was requisitioned in 1942. Andrew Brookes records that Ludford was a standard heavy bomber station which had cost around £800,000 to build. Its runways were laid out in a triangular pattern, the main one 5,850 ft long on a bearing almost due north–south (196°) and the intersecting runways, 4,290 ft (286°) and 3,600 ft (329°). The usual perimeter track, 50 ft wide, encircled the runways and branching off were dispersals for thirty-six bombers. Topographical considerations made Ludford something of a lop-sided site. There was ample room for the domestic side in Ludford Parva, but the runways were restricted in their siting in Magna.

Eighteen months after Ludford opened, station commander Gp Capt Patrick King was forced to comment: 'Ludford is not the most delightful of health resorts. In fact, it might be described as a joke in very bad taste by the Air Ministry at our expense.' By all accounts Ludford was not a good site for an airfield, high up on the Lincolnshire Wolds. 'If I'd been puttin' an aerodrome at Ludford, I'd ha' built it somewhere else,' was one piece of Lincolnshire logic contributed to a discussion on the airfield's location. Another was to the effect that with forty-five airfields in the feasible parts of the county (on average one every seven miles, according to Ron Blake's estimate) there was hardly anywhere else they could have put it.

Whatever the reason, from June 1943 Ludford Magna provided a home for 101 Squadron which was earmarked for the code-named Airborne Cigar (ABC) apparatus. This entailed the aircraft carrying an extra crew member, who would transmit on the German fighter control radio frequency with the aid of special equipment, in an effort to confuse the night fighter pilots. As it was deemed necessary for not less than eight ABC Lancasters to accompany all main force raids, spaced not less than 10 miles apart, it was decided to install FIDO so that the aircraft could operate whatever weather conditions might prevail.

The main contractors were A. Monk & Co., and the Strongarc Welding Co. of Lincoln carried out the on-site construction work. As can be seen from Fig. 18, almost 2,000 yd of the main north–south runway and approach box were lined with burners. The last 650 yd were covered by staggered burners. This configuration avoided the installation of special IRBs as at most other stations. Four petrol storage tanks holding over half a million gallons were built in the north-east corner of the aerodrome, next to the road from Ludford Magna to Burgh. Petrol was brought by road tanker from Market Rasen or Louth.

*Plate 44 Ludford Magna aerial. Runway 19. FIDO scorch marks faintly visible on each side of runway.
Very short approach box. Storage tanks to right of touchdown. See Fig. 18 (RAF Museum)*

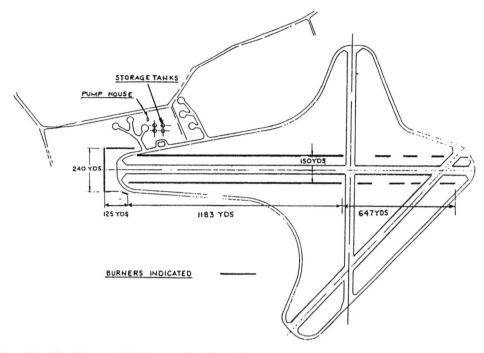

STORAGE TANKS

PUMP HOUSE

ISOYDS

240 YDS.

125 YDS   1183 YDS   647YDS

BURNERS INDICATED

Fig. 18 Ludford Magna, FIDO layout. See Plate 44

Optimistic progress reports in September 1943 expected the fog dispersal system to be completed, if not actually ready for operational use, before 20 November. On the 5th, Denys Fox, the PWD's engineer, visited the site and found it nowhere near ready. On 26 November work was held up due to flooding and so the system was not expected to be ready for testing until the end of the year. To add to the hiatus, work was being delayed because a number of welders had been withdrawn to work at Fiskerton, some 10 miles away.

Ludford was fully operational meantime and work on fabricating the Mark IV burners (see Fig. 6) and piping had to be carried out with one eye open for aircraft. George Gillam was the supervisor of Strongarc's workforce and recalled frequently having to work lying on duckboards to avoid sinking into the ooze. He well remembers an occasion when he: 'had just finished a weld on a 10 in diameter pipe-line abut 50 yd from the runway end, when a Lancaster with full bomb load returned after take-off with no undercarriage working. The pilot calmly put it down as if everything was normal. It didn't catch fire or blow up – but I was lying there in the mud, saying my prayers and wondering how I was ever going to get my trousers dry! Funny now, but not when it happened.'

Even before FIDO was put to the test, doubts were expressed about the likelihood of its successful operation at Ludford. The system was chiefly designed to cope with the normal radiation fog experienced at inland aerodromes, but conditions at Ludford were much more akin to a coastal airfield, despite its distance from the sea. Low stratus and advection fog, one indistinguishable from the other on high ground, were commonly experienced and provided a limitless supply of fresh clag, fret, haar or roke as fast as the burners sought to disperse it. Nevertheless, the station had to make do with the system as it existed at that stage of its development and FIDO was handed over on 15 January 1944. The first trial burn took place at 19.29 on 16 January 1944 when visibility was only 100 yd. The airfield was 'washed with a cold grey mist, the vapoury breath of the east wind', as Longfellow might have put it. Conditions were severe, for the advection fog was rolled along by unusually high

Plate 45 G-George of 101 Squadron by the FIDO lines at Ludford Magna, 21 January 1944. Airmen insist that the 7 in high pipes were designed to prop up RAF issue bicycles (101 Squadron archives)

winds, of the kind which had to be reckoned with at St Eval, and was particularly wet. A number of welded joints gave way during this test burn causing additional smoke and the 'results achieved during the burn (clearance to 400 yd on the runway) would not justify attempted landings'.

The first aircraft to use FIDO at Ludford Magna was a diverted Lancaster of 50 Squadron which arrived very early on the morning of 10 March 1944. With visibility at 900 yd FIDO was lit at 05.18. The burn was carried out at a time when the installation was only partly serviceable. A large part of the left-hand burner line was already in need of repair and awaiting the removal of a crashed aircraft. It was considered that good results were obtained, given that the wind was from the western side, 'but it cannot be claimed that the aircraft was saved from disaster'. Nevertheless, the pilot of the Lancaster reported that though he had never landed with FIDO before, he was very impressed with the facility and had no difficulty in making his landing, apart from the tendency to come in too high.

A further trial was held at 07.30 on 28 March with visibility only 90 yd, due to low stratus scudding across the airfield at ground level at 15–20 mph. The wind direction was SSW, which drove the clouds diagonally up the open end of the runway, covered only by intermittent burners. At this end visibility did not improve much, but further up, where the continuous burners were, the cloud base was raised to a couple of hundred feet. Gp Capt Blucke was not happy with the performance of the system and reported: 'I consider that the weather conditions were such as to preclude successful operations at this airfield. The main runway is sited across the prevailing wind and it will never be practicable to clear fog if there is a wind of more than 5 mph. I do not recommend any extension to the system, because I do not think it would effect any improvement.' The station commander's comments were apposite. FIDO was lit for trials for operations on at least twenty-four occasions in 1944. When the wind direction was recorded, the wind was across the runway on fifteen out of seventeen occasions.

Weeks were to pass before fog conditions occurred again, on 30 May, with the wind from the north-east. A 20 mph wind blew 700 ft of stratus across the airfield at ground level, a condition which FIDO could not deal with. The windward line of burners raised the ceiling to a mere 25 ft, and when the heat from the leeward line was added to it the clearance just about reached 100 ft. This, however, was achieved out to the west of the runway and any aircraft attempting a landing would have been deposited among dispersed and parked aircraft. The station commander reckoned, on the basis of this test, that extra lines of burners would be required to deal with such strong winds. This method had been adopted at St Eval. Not only was far more heat needed to evaporate the fog, but the burners needed to be further from the runway, so that the full effect in a cross-wind would be felt over the airstrip and not in no man's land to one side.

Unfortunately, as can be seen from the airfield plan (Fig. 18), to put in an extra row of pipes 75 yd further out on a restricted site would mean carving up perimeter tracks and hardstandings all over the place. In addition, the easterly side would be right against the FIDO storage tanks, and nearly down the banks of the River Bain. Nothing more was heard of the proposal.

Not until 30 June, six months and umpteen tests after the hand-over of the installation to the RAF, could FIDO at Ludford be said to have earned its keep. Sixteen of 101 Squadron's Lancasters were part of a force of 107 aircraft of 1 and 8 Groups which attacked a flying bomb launch site at Oisemont. No aircraft were lost during the raid, but poor visibility threatened their safe return.

There was no fog, but as 09.00 approached there was low stratus over much of the Wolds, sitting only 200 ft above Ludford's runway and reaching 1,200 ft above that. Moving in from the North Sea the stratus, which was several hundred feet above ground at the coast, found the earth rapidly coming up to meet it as it approached the Lincolnshire Wolds, and pilots hoping to squeeze through the gap below it found their chances lessening with each succeeding mile. The wind was quite gentle, about 6 mph, but when FIDO was lit at 09.15 it strengthened to 10–12 mph directly across the runway, causing a clearance somewhat to the west. Nevertheless, it was possible for pilots to pick out the runway without much difficulty, and in just over an hour twelve aircraft were able to land safely, taking an average of two and a half minutes per machine, using SBA.

The first four pilots to land all said that their landings would have been impossible without FIDO, and though the weather conditions improved towards the end of the burn the rest of the pilots declared that they also had been greatly helped. That same night of 30 June/1 July, 101 Squadron was off again, fulfilling its requirement that ABC machines should accompany every major raid. An attack on the railway yards at Vierzon-ville, south of Orleans, was carried out by 118 Lancasters of 1 Group. Although the raid was considered successful, fourteen Lancasters were lost. Dennis Goodliffe, flight engineer aboard G-George saw the raid as 'a 5 hour 10 minute trip which had been fairly quiet'. As they approached home, however, in conditions of deteriorating visibility, G-George returned to find Lincolnshire in 'quite a soup'. Dennis brought to mind that:

We had a fair reserve of fuel and were asked to circle Ludford airfield above the mist until FIDO was lit. This took a fair time, but at last we saw the glow lighting up the fog from below and slowly making quite a hole through which we could see the ground. Of six aircraft landing (nine had taken off) we were fourth, and by this time a cross-wind had got up and was causing the hole in the fog to drift off the runway, which made things somewhat difficult. We made an approach into the funnel through the fog, but could not see the runway until we actually entered the cleared area, when we found that we were too far to the left – and had to go round again.

On the next approach my pilot said to me, 'Look out for a runway and as soon as you see it, yell.' This I did and we got down, only to hear, halfway down the runway, a voice from Flying Control saying, 'You've landed downwind.' Nevertheless, it was agreed by all who turned out to see, it was the best landing of the six.

Returning from a similar flight in Lancaster ME616, flight engineer Fred Cole of 101 Squadron brought to mind that:

About three-quarters of the way home the weather progressively worsened and talk was of diversions because although Ludford was one of the airfields to have FIDO it has seldom been used by squadrons for actual night landings. We were informed that FIDO had been lit and was ready for use. We made our normal bad weather approach to the airfield and could just see an orange glow in the sky. We were told that this was FIDO burning and not a crashed aircraft. We carried out our usual circuit-joining checks and proceeded to do a bad weather circuit, taking care to watch out for other returning aircraft. All was as normal as could be expected on the circuit until we got to the final approach position. When we were down to about 500 ft, ahead was a huge wall of flame and it looked a formidable problem. As we got even lower and nearer we could see two lines of flame with gaps in between. We were now at a point of no return – we had to land on touchdown, and we literally entered a tunnel of heat and flame; but visibility was A1, very good.

Fred went on to say that the crew's main hope was for their pilot to keep the plane on the runway and that nothing would prevent them from getting safely to the end; but also that he would not overdo it and cause them to overshoot into the fields beyond the perimeter. On reaching the end of the runway they ran back into fog again and had to be guided to dispersal by marshals. He concluded: 'Many aircraft landed that night by the aid of FIDO and ironically, more damage (minor) was caused after landing by such things as wingtips touching, getting bogged down, taking wrong turnings, etc. The general consensus of opinion was, good effort, well done, will use again if required.'

A heavy raid on flying bomb sites in northern France was carried out on the night of 31 July 1944. Only 79 were able to bomb of the 777 aircraft that took part. 'Bomber Command records do not state why the remaining sorties were aborted, but poor weather conditions were the probable cause. No aircraft were lost.'

Ludford's fog dispersal report supports this, for it records advection fog no less than 4,000 ft deep at about 22.00. Horizontal visibility at ground level was 250 yd, but there was no way in which aircraft could descend through the clag to experience it. FIDO was lit in the hope that some aircraft might benefit from it. The burners had little effect and the runway was cleared to a mere 20 ft. The station commander, Gp Capt Blucke, considered that:

The runway clearance was totally inadequate. An experienced pilot who made a trial run, intended to be at 500 ft, lost height rapidly and drifted to starboard after entering the heated air zone. He did not see anything until he was right on the ground, and before he could open up to climb, his port outer propeller struck the mound covering an air-raid shelter about 300 yd west of the main runway. Fortunately his undercarriage was not down and he was able to open up his engines and climb; equally fortunately he missed a hangar and some large trees by inches.

After informing us by R/T that he had had enough of FIDO for the time being, he went off and landed safely at his allotted diversion airfield, where he discovered two bent propeller blades and thistles in his radiator as his total score.

This episode strengthens my belief that FIDO will never be satisfactory at Ludford in QBI conditions, because the runway is in the wrong direction. Furthermore, it is impossible to fit double burners owing to the peculiar topography of the airfield.

Over 800 sorties were flown on the night of 26/27 August, principally to Kiel and Konigsberg. Eight of 101 Squadron's ABC Lancasters accompanied the force attacking Kiel; the raid on Konigsberg was carried out by 5 Group. This attack involved a round trip of nearly 2,000 miles.

The aircraft engaged on the Kiel raid were able to return to their base without difficulty, but those returning from the far distant Baltic port were less fortunate. A number of Lincolnshire bases were fogbound and orders were given for FIDO to be lit to aid any that were in dire need. Conditions at Ludford were not as bad as on some previous occasions, but a thick valley fog 50 ft deep lay over everything. There was a cross-wind blowing, but not sufficient to distort the clearance effected by the burners, and from about 05.00 visibility up to 3,000 yd was obtained.

619 Squadron from Dunholme Lodge were sent to Ludford en masse and within an hour fourteen of them had made safe landings – A, C, W, U, H, Q, M, L, S, E, O, Y, X and D. At last the station commander was able to report favourably: 'The fact that fourteen tired pilots, inexperienced in FIDO techniques, made successful landings on this occasion indicates without doubt the usefulness of the installation. Pilots had been briefed before take-off, but expected the same layout as at Fiskerton. They found that increasing their landing speed by 10 mph was better than a steeper approach as briefed. They had been airborne for 10½ hours.'

Second plane home was C-Charlie, navigator Den Weygang:

The unusual events which occurred that night and the following morning began with us being routed over Sweden, a neutral country. As we crossed the coastline, all blackouts were removed and the skipper switched on all interior and exterior lights. In front of us we could see masses of flak – or was it a gigantic firework display? Tracers were coming up from the deck and seemed to be bursting in what looked like a variety of star shells. It had us completely beaten, for none of us had seen anything like it before. Then it stopped, leaving us with a clear path and very puzzled minds.

Returning to the coast of Sweden homeward bound, we were once again greeted by the firework display, which conveniently ceased as we approached it. Puzzled? You can say that again; but I suppose the main concern was to stay in one piece. On reaching England we were greeted with fog, visibility being nil, and so were diverted to Ludford Magna which had FIDO. This was after 9 hours 40 minutes in the air. I can be that precise as I still have my logbook and charts.

That night was to be the first time we had ever used FIDO and I would not recommend the experience. Below us was a solid white mass with one very clear hole in the middle; so clear that we could even see the lights of the flight path as we descended. Landing was a dream, although unusually turbulent, but who were we to complain with our wheels once again safely on the deck? Taxiing to the end of the runway the skipper turned off and within yards we could not see a thing. We finally made our way by following ground staff on foot with torches and not the usual van to a dispersal point. Once we had safely cleared the runway we were instructed to shut off engines and leave the aircraft there instead of taxiing to dispersal; for which the ground crew, not being Olympic athletes, were probably very grateful.

You can tell that we were flying at extreme range, for, prior to take-off, once all the preliminaries such as warming up, ground testing and taxiing to the head of the runway had been completed, we shut off to be topped up with fuel. On return we were so pushed for fuel that one of our aircraft made the landing, turned off the runway and then stopped through lack of petrol. The next plane in promptly rammed him in the rear – not that it was a major accident, but it most definitely happened.

Back at base came the explanation for the Swedish fireworks. Apparently their ack-ack spent night after night doing precisely nothing and were bored to death. Our unusual presence allowed them the opportunity to let rip, drawing tracer patterns in the sky. The better the pattern the better the gunner – never was so much fun had by so few!

Each four-engined bomber consumed about 2,000 gallons of petrol on its flight. In its 2-hour burn to welcome them home, FIDO got through 164,192 gallons – 'and worth every cupful!'

Three weeks later FIDO was called into action again when 646 Bomber Command aircraft raided targets in the Calais area on 20 September 1944. Thirteen aircraft from Ludford's 101 Squadron accompanied an attack on troop concentrations west of Calais. Losses were light and none of 101's aircraft suffered too much damage, but on approaching base towards 18.00 they found the airfield obliterated by a thick smoke haze. Visibility was down to 350 yd, but on light-up at 18.27 it gradually increased to 2,000 yd, though the poor condition of some of the burners created a quantity of smoke which initially added to the problem. The fog dispersal report says that fourteen of 101 Squadron's Lancasters made successful landings, although their pilots had no previous experience of FIDO. As the station ops record book only gives thirteen as taking off, a cuckoo must have appeared in the flock en route.

Thirteen of Ludford's ABC Lancasters accompanied a major raid on the town of Saarbrucken on the night of 5/6 October. During their absence it was decided to carry out a test burn. There was fog about, some 50 ft of it, with horizontal visibility down to 200 yd. The system was not performing well and a number of welded joints fractured, adding smoke to the existing fog. Consequently, when the station's aircraft neared home at around midnight, they were advised to land elsewhere by 1 Group HQ. Four machines, M2, V, P and E-Easy, managed not to receive the instruction, however, and appeared overhead – or would have done if it had not been foggy. In deference to them, FIDO was kept alight.

Special operator aboard M2 was Gerhard Heilig. When not operating his radio counter-measures equipment his main view of life aloft usually consisted of the big feet of the mid-upper gunner. Not being required for the last stages of the flight home he 'surfaced' to take a look round:

> Soon after we crossed the English coast on our return from the raid we saw the glow of a fire up ahead. As we got closer we realised that its source must be at, or very close to, our own base, and we feared the worst, thinking that Ludford or one of its neighbours must have been the victim of a massive enemy strike. When we joined the circuit our relief was great that this had not been the case, and we marvelled at the sight which presented itself to our eyes.
>
> Above the blanket of fog which covered the countryside for miles around was a gaping hole cut straight as with a knife on the upwind side of the gently moving air and billowing in a great curve on the other; the parallel lines of flaming petrol below and a billowing cloud of cumulus above, like some monstrous bonnet. It was an eerie feeling as we made our approach, like a headlong plunge into a flaming furnace; but all went perfectly smoothly and along with the others we made a safe landing, albeit with no little relief.

All four aircraft did indeed land in safety, although what Gerhard omitted to mention was that they did so downwind!

To the best of his recollection, Ronald Homes, 101 Squadron pilot of L-Love, also made use of FIDO on his return the same day/night: 'The memory begins to play tricks, but I can still remember seeing the long orange glow amid the fog below, the rough turbulence on late finals and the arrival into Dante's Inferno. All very exciting but greatly appreciated when there was nowhere else to go. Hence my *Homage to FIDO*.' Ronald's painting of that title, now most appropriately in the possession of Mrs Octavia Alexander, the daughter of A.V. Roe, illustrates the dust-jacket of this book.

A day of intense activity throughout Bomber Command was 16 November, with over 1,100 aircraft attacking the towns of Düren, Jülich and Heinsberg, in support of the American 9th Army advance. For 101 Squadron it was a maximum effort occasion. Twenty-four ABC Lancasters were detailed to raid Düren. The machines were bombed up, but then the operation was called off owing to the density of the fog which covered most of eastern England. No sooner had the air and ground crews dispersed than they were recalled.

Eventually take-off was achieved and the raid was carried out with the loss of only three Lancasters out of the 485 which took part. None of 101's was lost. Homeward bound, however, the weather worsened and widespread diversions were ordered. At Ludford, runway visibility was about 1,000 yd with some rain and it was deemed advisable to light FIDO at 16.40. The system was working well below par, with fractures in a number of burners, but quite a rapid clearance was achieved. Such smoke and haze as had been created by the burners themselves was driven upwards and formed a large cumulus cloud high over the airfield, marking its presence from afar.

Within a short time, all twenty-four machines and two more caught out on training flights homed in on the fiery cloudy pillar and were pancaked in rapid succession, a number having only a narrow margin of fuel left. Outside the airstrip itself the fog had thickened if anything, and when all aircraft were safely down, three of the burners were kept going so that tractor drivers could find their way around the perimeter tracks and tow aircraft to their dispersal points.

After twenty-three of 101 Squadron's Lancasters had taken off for a 1 Group raid on Wanne-Eickel during the afternoon of 18 November, darkness descended and shortly afterwards deteriorating visibility set in. By half past seven the decision had been taken to divert all the station's aircraft to Tuddenham in west Suffolk, but at the same time to light Ludford's FIDO system for experimental purposes.

A wind of over 20 mph was blowing, most unusually almost straight up the north–south runway, it was raining, and low cloud was barely 200 ft above the surface. On previous occasions such conditions had been beyond FIDO's capabilities, but the wind being parallel to the runway made all the difference, and within a short time the whole runway was cleared up to a height of 300 ft. 'Furthermore,' says the station ops record book, 'the high wind carried the clearance zone out as far as the funnels on the approach.' Two pilots, Flt Lt Massheder in J-Johnnie and Flt Sgt Roberts in P-Peter, had not received the diversion call in the first place and they came sailing home oblivious. Much was their delight to see the home fires burning, although their welcome may not have been quite what they expected. 'The two pilots who made their FIDO landings undoubtedly helped the cause of science, but they were nevertheless unpopular with the station commander [Gp Capt P.R. King] for failing to act on their diversion orders.'

After days of briefings and cancellations twenty-four aircraft of 101 Squadron were detailed to attack Bonn, with an H-hour of 18.20 on 21 December. This was to have been a major 1 Group operation, but owing to foggy conditions at many bases the number of participating aircraft was reduced and 101 Squadron was required to supply only six ABC Lancasters. Eastern England was covered with fog as far as Reading. The raiders experienced 10/10 cloud up to 7,000 ft over the continent and bombing results were indeterminate. Moreover, as mile succeeded mile on the homeward run visibility decreased and widespread diversions were ordered. At Ludford horizontal vision at ground level was about 600 yd in a WSW wind, bringing advection fog 200 ft deep and 100 per cent wet. Instructions were given for FIDO to be lit at 19.30. On this occasion the wind direction and strength were just right, enabling FIDO to clear enough of the normal approach so that landings could be made from visual orbits. All six of 101's Lancasters put down safely, Flg Off Andrews in L-Love reporting that the glow of FIDO was visible from 60 miles out. In addition, four of 625 Squadron's machines from Kelstern and two of 12 Squadron's from Wickenby landed with no difficulty, although it was their first experience. Total petrol consumption for the burn was 112,000 gallons.

While 101 Squadron's aircraft were homeward bound late on the 21st, a large force of 5 Group Lancasters was also winging its way back from the far distant target of Politz, on the Baltic. Alas, conditions had changed in the space of a few hours. At Ludford, continuous rain was reported from 22.00 until 04.00 next morning. The conditions were described by Air Cdr S.O. Bufton in a report to Sir Archibald Sinclair:

> On the night in question, weather conditions deteriorated during the period of the operation. The bombers which operated in the earlier part of the night on shorter range targets were able to land at their bases or diversions under reasonable conditions. The Lancasters of 5 Group on the other hand, which took part in the Politz raid, did not return until after 1 a.m.
>
> At the midnight met conference it was apparent that bases in 5 Group would be unsuitable except Coningsby and East Kirkby. At the 1 a.m. met conference all except Coningsby and East Kirkby aircraft were diverted to airfields in Scotland, and the FIDO airfields in Scotland, and the FIDO airfields at Metheringham, Fiskerton, Ludford, Carnaby and Woodbridge were asked to stand by.

By the time of the 1 a.m. conference, the wind had freshened at Ludford and low stratus with pouring rain had drifted over at ground level. Visibility was only 100 yd. Tom Bennett, 617 Squadron's historian, takes up the story:

Gp Capt King received a request from 5 Group HQ through his own 14 Base HQ at 01.15 on 22 December to bring the FIDO installation into operation. He consulted his specialist officers and was told that with Ludford being over 400 ft above sea level and the clamp-down almost to the foot of the Wolds, previous experience of lighting FIDO in these conditions had proved the facility to be grossly inefficient. He reported this back to his base. However, 5 Group repeated the request to the point of insistence and the installation was lit at 02.30. Conditions remained hopeless for landing aircraft, but the glow of FIDO attracted aircraft to the area.

One of them was Lancaster T-Tare of 617 Squadron, piloted by Flg Off Arthur Joplin. Originally diverted to Scotland, instructions were then received to return to their home base at Woodhall Spa. This was followed by a W/T order that: 'aircraft should now set down at the first available airfield.' Sadly, while seeking to do this at Ludford, T-Tare crashed north-west of the runway.

The weather was still poor by the afternoon of the 22nd, when 101 Squadron was detailed to take part in an attack on the marshalling yards at Koblenz. A hundred and sixty-six Lancasters from 1 Group raided the Mosel yards, while another force attacked Bingen in an attempt to cut supply routes to the Ardennes battle front. Seventeen crews were briefed and with FIDO going full blast fifteen eventually lined up for take-off just after 14.00. By this time low stratus was masking the whole neighbourhood, reducing visibility to 500 yd, decreasing steadily with a gentle cross-wind blowing. Anxious that 101 Squadron's ABC aircraft should play their part, Gp Capt King tried an unusual ploy:

I decided to send them off from south to north so that they began to take off in poor visibility and had the maximum clearance at the point of becoming airborne. In this way, they avoided the feeling of flying into a brick wall and were well and truly airborne before transferring to the instrument panel to climb through the overcast. I watched the proceedings from high ground north of the runway and all pilots took off perfectly steady and straight. Taking off without FIDO with full bomb and fuel loads would have been very risky indeed.

Following an H-hour raid at 18.50, conditions became so bad on the return flight, with visibility down to 100 yd at Ludford, which FIDO was unable to shift, that widespread diversions were ordered throughout 1 Group. 101 Squadron's Lancasters landed with FIDO at Woodbridge along with thirty more while numerous others put down at Manston.

In the cross-winds and low stratus to which Ludford was frequently subject, clearance often took place not over the runway but to one side of it. To the east this could be a menace, for the main runway lay along the eastern extreme of the aerodrome. A short distance beyond, the land dropped down into the valley of the River Bain, and an unwary pilot could find himself descending on a runway which was not there – although a sewage farm was! Dick Ogden, meteorologist at Ludford, recalled one such occasion which nearly ended in disaster:

The pilot approached on a roughly correct heading, but well to the side of the runway. His bomb-aimer, peering through the murk, suddenly realized that they were about to crash into the fuel storage tanks containing hundreds of thousands of gallons of petrol. Fortunately, the pilot's reaction to the bomb-aimer's urgent warning was immediate. The aircraft just cleared the tanks, and although it nearly stalled in the process, it was saved by the fact that the ground fell away sharply at the scarp edge of the Wolds not far away. The pilot was thus able to bring the aircraft under control at an altitude below airfield level, and after climbing and making another circuit, he landed safely at the second attempt.

Christmas Eve was not yet out when 101 Squadron was called upon again. Eight aircraft were detailed to take part in a 1 Group attack on the marshalling yards at Nippes, a north-west suburb of Cologne. Due to engine and turret trouble two dropped out, but the six which took off carried out their attack and returned to England safely. Because of deteriorating weather two of them landed away but the other four, plus two cuckoos, homed in to make landings at Ludford with the aid of FIDO. By this time the condition of the system was causing grave concern to the station commander, and the ops record book comments more upon that than any other aspect of station life. With reference to the night of the 24th, it records:

> Conditions for the operational landing were distinctly tricky. This was the eighth burn since 19 December and the burners are in a bad state. Moreover, the petrol level in the tanks was lower than it had been, and we found that the pumps could hardly draw enough to keep the burners going. Apparently the pumps were really designed for pumping water, and unless there is a certain head of petrol, gassing takes place in the suction side of the pipelines, which sets up a back pressure and causes a gas-lock. To remedy this, we put on No. 1 tank which we do not normally use because it leaks slightly.

To prevent the poisoning of local cattle beyond the perimeter, or setting fire to any airman having a quiet smoke in the vicinity, the bottom of this tank was always covered with a layer of water; deep enough to cover the leak, but not sufficient to reach the outlet. Alas, Murphy's law had to be fulfilled, and when No. 1 tank's waterbed was topped up, some enthusiastic soul overdid it and poured in an excessive amount. The result was that when it was brought into use during the burn on 24 December, cold water sped through the pipes instead of petrol. Clouds of steam, soot, scale, rust and smoke practically obliterated any good work that FIDO was doing. 'By the grace of God,' continued the report, 'Six aircraft were landed safely in these conditions, but some of the approaches were quite alarming. One pilot came in at an angle to the burner line and turned off at a very low height before touching down halfway along the runway!'

This aircraft was one of the cuckoos, flown by Flg Off Davidson of 550 Squadron from Killingholme. His WOp/AG was Bill Evans who reminisced that:

> We were indebted to FIDO for saving our lives on Christmas Eve 1944, when limping home from a night raid on Cologne in Lancaster F-Fox. We had been badly hit; my radio was u/s due to flak coming up through the bottom of the aircraft. I therefore didn't receive the message diverting the squadron to an American base in Norfolk due to dense fog over our airfield.
>
> When our skipper, Flg Off Davidson, called up on the R/T for landing instructions, we were ordered to follow the squadron to Norfolk, but we were nearly out of petrol so were told to make for Ludford Magna which had FIDO facilities. There we descended in fear through the fog and were finally relieved to see the first glimmer of the flare-path from zero feet.
>
> We made some sort of a landing, ending up by slewing off the edge of the runway on to the grass before coming to an abrupt stop. We extolled our praises to God and FIDO for a remarkable escape, as there was barely enough petrol left to fill a cigarette lighter.
>
> The only regret I have is that the rest of the squadron had a marvellous time at the American base, being entertained lavishly (after all, it was by then Christmas Day) while we waited impatiently at Ludford Magna for transport to return us to camp in the early hours of Christmas morn, where we eventually arrived, tired, bedraggled and unshaven – but nevertheless seven very grateful and humble airmen.

The first FIDO burners to be installed at Ludford were Mk IVs (Fig. 5), which were adequate, but only just, and under prolonged operational use developed the faults which the station commander described. As materials and artisans became available the Mk IVs were replaced by a better burner, the Mk V (Fig. 6), which was shorter and less liable to distortion. Unfortunately, they had not reached Ludford by the end of 1944 when they were most needed. Gp Capt King concluded:

> FIDO is completely unserviceable and beyond local repair. It is useless to botch up the existing burners; the only remedy is to fit a completely new set of burners of the latest pattern throughout the installation. If FIDO is to be of value in the worst weather conditions met with at Ludford, it will be necessary to extend the installation considerably. The first job should be to make the burner lines continuous for the full length of the main runway and to provide an additional box at the southern end so that the full installation will be an enclosed rectangle of burners. Later, it would be desirable to deal similarly with the east–west runway.

Thus December ended with a recorded number of nineteen landings and sixteen take-offs, which cost the taxpayer a total of 227,000 gallons of petrol. Small wonder that Ron

Nightingale was impressed: ' . . . because I had then acquired a small car and I was always on the scrounge for coupons, even half-gallons if I remember correctly. I remember watching over two miles of pipes with a jet every few inches belching flames and thinking how far the petrol would have taken me in my car.'

From this point there are no further references to the use of FIDO at Ludford, either by way of fog dispersal reports or entries in the station's logbook. Gp Capt King left the station in mid-January, so his contributions are lacking. References to bad weather occur in abundance. On 4 January 1945 for example, 'Topographically Ludford is just made for snow and she is living up to her reputation.' On the 5th, the temperature did not rise above 27° F and no thaw set in until the 12th. On the 19th a severe blizzard was reported; and so on through the month. It took all day to clear the runway on 28 January before 101 Squadron's aircraft could take off for a raid on Stuttgart, and on the 30th RAF crews helped to clear 10 miles of road to Louth.

Although operations continued under these atrocious conditions, when the weather did eventually improve the Mk IV burners were dismantled and replaced by Mk Vs, but there is no record of their operational use, or even, for that matter, of their being tested. The problems at Ludford Magna are well discussed by meteorologist Dick Ogden, who was based there from its opening in July 1943 until after VE-day:

> From a forecaster's point of view it was a fascinating but often exasperating location, with its own extremely local pattern of weather, quite different, for example, from nearby Binbrook. The airfield was sited on the top of the Lincolnshire Wolds very near the scarp edge, some 400–450 ft above sea level. As Bomber Command's requirements called for a system to deal with radiation fog, to a meterorologist Ludford seemed a very odd choice as a FIDO station.
>
> We certainly had plenty of fog, and during 1944 clocked up the remarkable average of about two hours per day; but as the mean wind speed during the fog periods was about 10 mph it was clear that this fog resulted for the most part from up-slope effects. Pure radiation fog was a comparative rarity and occurred only during prolonged anticyclonic spells in winter when there was time for fog over the low ground inland from the Wolds to build up to a depth exceeding 400 ft and so overlap the airfield.

Dick commented that the decision as to when and whether FIDO should be lit was taken by the station commander, who might or might not follow meteorological advice as to whether the system was likely to clear fog from the runway. There were several predicted failures because he seemed reluctant to accept that FIDO would not clear fog from the north–south runway in the stiff cross-wind which often accompanied up-slope fog. There was often a clearance, but frequently it took place several hundred yards to leeward of the airstrip:

> The limitations of the Ludford FIDO were appreciated by Air Cdre R.V. Blucke, the commander of No. 14 base at Ludford. At a meeting held in London in March 1944 to discuss developments to the FIDO system, he proposed that 'no more installations should be located at high level stations which were prone to high cross-winds and low stratus rather than radiation fog'. This was agreed, but it was decided to leave FIDO at Ludford, although there seemed little point in trying to develop the basic system. It was felt that No. 1 Group's requirements for a FIDO in the area would be met by the planned installation at Sturgate.
>
> It is interesting to note that in a postwar evaluation of the effectiveness of FIDO during the period 1943 to 1945, it was estimated that taking all fifteen stations together, only some 10 per cent of fogs could not be dispersed, but a substantial contribution to this figure came from Ludford, where it appeared that no less than 36 per cent of fogs fell into this category.

It is not possible to put an exact figure on the number of aircraft which successfully used FIDO at Ludford Magna, since not all the fog dispersal reports have survived and not all its station commanders recorded as assiduously as did Gp Capt King during his tenure of office. The writer has a record of sixteen take-offs and ninety-six landings, 112 in all, but there is every likelihood that the actual figure exceeds this.

TWELVE

Manston

. . . a great confidence uplift and morale builder

Wg Cdr R.W. Oxspring, Wing Leader – Detling Wing

Manston, on the Isle of Thanet in east Kent, was the last of three emergency aerodromes to be constructed in England during the Second World War. Work on the first, at Woodbridge in Suffolk, began in October 1942. Construction at Carnaby, near Bridlington on the Yorkshire coast, commenced in February 1943 and at Manston in June 1943. The first two were virgin territory, but Manston had been in use as an airfield since 1916, though it had no concrete runway, only Summerfeld tracking. It did, however, have some permanent buildings. Oddly enough, in early Bomber Command documents Manston is referred to as the Canterbury site.

The essential requirement of an emergency airfield was a 3,000 yd long runway with additional 500 yd under-and-overshoots. The runway was to be 250 yd wide, five times the normal width, marked by day and by night into three lanes. The south lane (all emergency runways ran approximately east–west) was to be marked by green lights at night and to be that on which any aircraft in distress could land if necessary without contacting Flying Control. Emergency runways also had to have unimpeded approaches from either end. On a course of 290° or its reciprocal, this presented no problem at Manston. If any stacking up was necessary, it could be carried out over the sea, with circuiting over the almost deserted Minster Marsh area to the south. Occupying almost the highest part of the Isle of Thanet at approximately 150 ft above sea level, when seen from afar, aircraft on the runway appeared to be running along the skyline.

The grass runways at Manston continued in use while the new one was being built. They were at about 45° to it and in theory stopped some way short, but if a pilot using one of the minor airstrips took an unusually long time to get airborne, workmen on the main runway cast very anxious looks over their shoulders. In dire circumstances they uttered the workers' equivalent of 'Stuff this for a game of soldiers!' and beat a hasty retreat.

If emergency runways were to fulfil their purpose, they had to be equipped with fog dispersal apparatus. Each was considered by the Petroleum Warfare Department in turn and designated Station X, Woodbridge; XI, Carnaby; and XII, Manston. Because of their vast size there was some hesitation over the installation of FIDO. The early system at Graveley, the 'guinea-pig' station, was still under development and changes had to be made in the light of experience, which had a knock-on effect at subsequent stations, including the first of the emergency airfields at Woodbridge. There, the runway was being flanked by a double row of Haigill Mark IV burners (Fig. 5), but had not been used in earnest at the time construction of the Manston runway began. FIDO at Manston was delayed in the hope that something might be learned from experience gained at Woodbridge. The decision was also put back on the grounds that Manston was only obscured by fog for about thirteen days a year, and that its bulky storage tanks would be a target for hit-and-run attacks. In addition it was noted that the airfield was within range of long-distance enemy cross-channel gunfire.

Once it was agreed to go ahead, work began late in 1943 by contractors J.L. Eve, who had recently completed a FIDO installation at Hartfordbridge in Hampshire, and were later to tackle a far more difficult task at St Eval in Cornwall. As at Woodbridge, a double row of Mark IV burners was built, 20 and 40 ft back from the 250 yd wide runway. An approach box of 280 yd preceded the touchdown point, which was marked with a double row of cross-burners, broken in the middle in case an aircraft touched down too soon. The main lines of burners continued for 2,000 yd on each side of the runway, but on the south side they had to be interrupted to allow exit from the runway on to the crash bays and perimeter track. These concrete pads, twelve of them, each 100 ft wide, were installed so that any aircraft which failed to make it to the final turn-off point could be unceremoniously hauled, shoved or bulldozed clear of succeeding machines. Accordingly, intersecting runway burners (IRBs) had to be trenched across the recently concreted bays, which pleased the foreman not at all (see Fig. 12; Plate 33).

Nearly 200 Mark IV burners at 40 yd each were required in double rows to line the runway, needing over 32,000 yd of piping of various diameters to feed them. The burners were to be fuelled from four huge storage tanks adjacent to the Ramsgate Road. The steel tanks were each 60 ft in diameter and 27 ft high, encased in 14 in brickwork, the whole being protected by an earth embankment about 12 ft high. The tanks had a total capacity in excess of a million gallons. Their construction caused a hiccough quite early in the proceedings, 'due to site difficulties which were not apparent from the plans'. It may be that relative ground levels posed a problem, but these were subsequently overcome.

Supplying the vast quantities of petrol required some ingenuity. Long convoys of road tankers were undesirable, so a single-track siding was built on the north side of the railway line some way east of Minster junction. Approximately 150 yd long, it had room for up to

Plate 46 C-Charlie of 101 Squadron tangles with FIDO at Ludford Magna, January 1944. Aircraft crash landed following damage by enemy action during raid on Augsburg (101 Squadron archives)

Plate 47 Manston aerial. Approach on course 290°. Emergency lane on south side. FIDO scorch marks extend beyond tenth crash bay. Storage tanks to south of approach box. See Fig.20 (Crown/MoD)

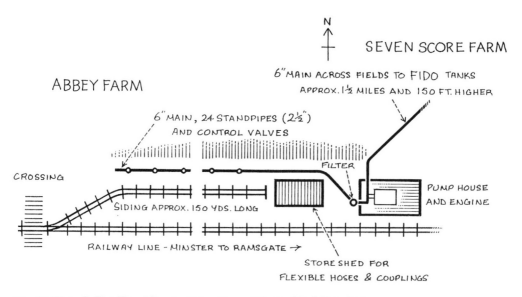

Fig. 19 Plan of offloading siding by Abbey Farm, Minster (Jack Peppiatt)

twenty-five rail tank wagons (Fig. 19). These were emptied via flexible hoses and couplings through a 6 in main with twenty-five standpipes and control gear. From the main, the petrol was drawn into a nearby pumphouse serviced by a four-cylinder Morris Commercial stationary engine and a Bradford pump. Another 6 in main, buried 3ft 6in below the surface, led from the pumphouse across fields for a distance of a mile and a half to the FIDO storage tanks on the airfield (Plates 49–52). As this pipe climbed 150 ft in its travel, the engines of the FIDO complex provided the power to fill the tanks. Two pumphouses, 45 ft x 25 ft, each containing six Sulzer pumps driven by Ford V8 engines, stood near the storage tanks, being brought into operation as required (see Plate 27). Usually up to eight were in use during a burn, delivering 500 gallons per minute each at a pressure of 90–100 lb per sq. in.

The runway itself was declared open on 5 April 1944 and it was expected that FIDO would be operational by the end of May. At this point further prevarication occurred, for a new and more powerful type of burner was under test at the PWD experimental station at Staines – the Hades, described on pp. 32–4. Its size meant that it would probably be more suitable for use at Manston than the Haigill. The PWD was undecided whether it should complement or replace the existing system. In either case, being a sub-surface burner considerable trenching alonside the runway would be involved as well as conversion of feed piping to a larger diameter. A complaint from the contractor on 21 April grumbled: 'We still await details of the new type of burner to be installed on the north side of the runway. This runway has now been made operational and Flying Control consider that considerable use could be made of the FIDO installation before the below-ground burners are installed.'

The Haigill system of burners was eventually completed, although in the early days of summer, as one would expect, there is no record of FIDO being in operation. Manston's emergency runway accepted fifty-six aircraft in the first three weeks of its operation, apart from its own planes, mainly due to battle damage or technical failure. In May the figure soared to 535 as intense pre-invasion activity increased; 79 because of enemy action, 74 with technical problems, 377 (mainly fighters) from fuel shortage, and 5 diversions.

One of these was a Stirling from 190 Squadron operating from Fairford, aboard which was flight engineer M. (Taffy) Hughes. As the Stirling neared Manston, they were brought down by 'QGH, a primitive descent-through-cloud method controlled by wireless'. On the approach, having descended through murk and darkness on their blind flying instructions to

Plate 48 Mk IV burners idling. Said to be Manston. If so, likely to be approach box, pre-August 1944 (D.B. Robertson)

Plate 49 First of 25 standpipes fitted to 6 in main alongside offloading siding near Minster (Author)

Plate 50 Storage shed for flexible hoses and pumphouse (right) (Author)

Plate 51 'Petroleum Spirit. Highly Inflammable. No Smoking or Naked Lights', warns the sign on the pumphouse wall (Author)

Plate 52 Four-cylinder Morris Commercial engine, driving pump (Author)

an altitude which would not have been considered prudent under normal conditions, they were relieved to see the thin glow of FIDO ahead of them:

> This became clearer and more distinct as we drew nearer and lower; and the final approach felt more like a descent into Vulcan's domain as we dropped our thirty tons of metal between the fiery lines.
> I can vividly recall the flames and billowing smoke each side of us as the wheels touched; and our Australian skipper made a passable landing in the circumstances. . . . The idea was that FIDO would disperse fog, but in my experience it did not really do so – the smoke given off rather added to the problem. Where its merit lay was in the heat and light given off, which was strong enough to penetrate the gloom for a long distance.

The Hades burners installed at Manston to the design of W.T. (Bill) Moore, described and depicted on pp. 32–5, comprised fifteen 80-therms per yard per hour burners (twice that of the Haigill burners), eight on the north side and seven on the south of the 250 yd wide runway, 20 ft back from its edge. Beyond them at the western, upwind end, was a smaller 40–therm burner on each side, the whole system covering nearly a mile and a half of runway.

The approach box was enclosed by a double row of 40–therm burners at its beginning and one 40–therm burner on each side. The touchdown point was marked by two short burners. Since the Hades burners sat in trenches they presented no problems when they crossed the entrance to crash bays, but to be on the safe side the burner pipe was not drilled with holes for the middle 30 ft of each crossing.

The lengths of individual burners varied. Along the north side of the runway they ranged from 563 ft up to 900 ft, and on the south side they varied from 715 ft up to a giant 1,024 ft. In each case the vaporizer occupied the first 130 ft and contributed its flames to the conflagration throughout. The elevation of the runway varied somewhat along its length, and it was necessary for the Hades trenches to minimize this. Those on the north had to compensate 16 ft in a 6,720 ft length and on the south by 12 ft.

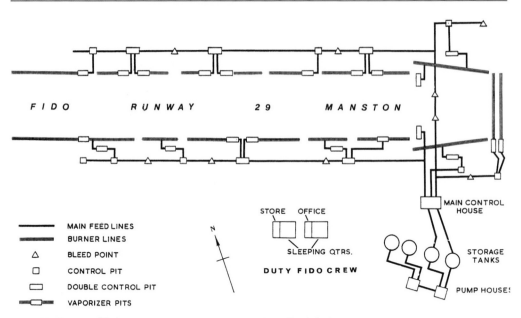

FIDO   RUNWAY   29   MANSTON

────────	MAIN FEED LINES
▬▬▬▬	BURNER LINES
△	BLEED POINT
☐	CONTROL PIT
▭	DOUBLE CONTROL PIT
▬▭▬	VAPORIZER PITS

STORE   OFFICE

N

SLEEPING QTRS.

DUTY FIDO CREW

MAIN CONTROL
HOUSE

STORAGE
TANKS

PUMP HOUSE!

Fig. 20 Manston, Hades system, simplified layout (Peter Cooksley)

The changeover from Haigill to Hades burners began somewhere around August 1944, and was not completed until the week the war ended in May 1945. When the new piping was laid section by section, it was decided to retain the original 12 in and 10 in main feed-lines, but to cut out the 2 in feed-pipe to each Haigill burner and weld in a 6 in pipe to the Hades trenched vaporizers. Reg Hughes had the job of doing this.

> The pumps were used to draw the petrol out of the mains which had been full of fuel for months and return it to the storage tanks. I was then asked to go down the holes where the mains had been exposed and cut out with my oxyacetylene torch the old branch and weld in a 6 in one. I was assured by Mr Laing, the Shell-Mex engineer, that there was no danger, and that to prove it he would come down with me – which he did.
> Terrified, I cut into the mains which were full of explosive petrol vapour. Everything went all right, however, and there was only an occasional waffle or burp. The job at one time became very slow because we were not allowed to excavate much of the 10 in piping at a time due to the large number of Horsa gliders which were standing at the edge of the runway in preparation for Arnhem.

This same period of intense activity brought about the occasion for which FIDO at Manston is best remembered. On 21 September 1944 hazy conditions prevailed during the afternoon with visibility down to 500 yd, and mist 500 ft deep being blown across the runway by a 10 mph wind. Two local aircraft were experiencing difficulty with their approaches and it was decided to light part of the system, more as a visual aid than to disperse the fog. Accordingly, a double length of the north line of Mark IV burners 200 yd long and a single length on the north side 500 yd long, were lit at 12.30. It took about 10 minutes for the smoke to clear. Because of the absence of a proper Tannoy system, communication was a bit hit and miss at the control points, especially as at one stage some of the burners had to be turned out for a while and their jet holes cleared of 'a white deposit'. The welding on an IRB pipe gave out at one point, adding smoke to the fog for a time. Eventually, however, a clear approach to the runway was possible, the fog being lifted to 150 ft and the burners distinguishable from 8,000 ft.

By their light the home-based machines made safe landings, and the station met flight Spitfire took off and later landed with FIDO's glow as a homing beacon. Rather like moths attracted to a candle, numerous other aircraft which were lost or in serious trouble hove into view over a 6-hour period. Between 12.40 and 18.45, nine Spitfires, an Auster, an Albemarle, the local Tempests, two Mustangs, three Norsemen and a Stirling took refuge on Manston's enormous runway.

The Stirling was piloted by Paul Deacon of 620 Squadron based at Fairford. Being stormed at with shot and shell was bad enough, but trying to land on an airfield which threatened to perform a disappearing act was less than sporting, as he recalled:

> We had been taking part in the re-supplying of the airborne troops at Arnhem that afternoon. My rear-gunner, Gordon Smith, had been wounded in the chest by an armour-piercing bullet as we crossed the first of three branches of the Rhine on our way into the dropping zone near Oesterbeek outside Arnhem.
>
> As soon as we were able to complete the drop, I headed back as fast as I could to England via Bruges to get prompt help for our badly wounded gunner. The greater part of south-eastern England was covered in fog, so we headed for the big emergency 'drome at Manston. I called the tower and alerted them to the fact that we had wounded aboard. Then we came down through the murk on to that enormous runway. All I could see at first was a slight glow from the FIDO fires. It was a great relief to suddenly break clear a couple of hundred feet above the ground, shortly before we touched down.

Paul Deacon's air-bomber on that occasion was Arthur Kempster, who assisted with the controls of the battle-damaged machine on the last leg:

> I cannot recall that we made a correct circuit, but came straight in on the approach to the runway with undercarriage down and one-third flap. Neither can I recall that full flap was put out as we landed, so we ran a long way down the runway. The approach, low and flat, was rather like entering a tunnel of red oily smoke, flames and swirling fog, but did not seem to last very long. Visibility on the whole was quite reasonable, but there was a bit of turbulence. I seem to recall a distinct roar as we landed, at the time when the engines were throttled back and intercom off.
>
> I know that I saw iron pipes with oily red flames coming up from something like old gas burners, and it passed through my mind that if the undercarriage was damaged and we swung off the runway, it would have been pretty grim, particularly as we had seen quite a number of burning aircraft in the past few days. Somehow or other the effect was similar to a mighty gathering of the old goose-neck flares standing in rows along the runway.

Rear-gunner Gordon Smith's recollections of the events are somewhat different:

> The reason for the emergency landing was that I had suffered a through and through flak wound to the chest while over Arnhem and required immediate medical attention. The wireless operator, John Everitt, was able to extricate me from the rear turret and administer a shot of morphine. Needless to say, I drifted in and out of consciousness throughout the flight. The only thing I actually remember was exploding anti-aircraft shells and being tossed about on the floor of the aircraft as the pilot took evasive action. The crew took a lot of chances to get me to the nearest possible landing ground in the shortest possible time, and FIDO enabled them to do this.

An ambulance raced along the runway in pursuit of the Stirling and as soon as it turned off Gordon was picked up and rushed to station sick quarters and then to hospital. He subsequently made a good recovery, bloody, battered but unbowed!

Surveyor Geoffrey Adams, engaged on the conversion of the Haigill burners to Hades, remembered well the aircraft coming in above his head, for he was stranded on the north-east corner of the runway when his survey van refused to start; and he recalled it as a terrible day, hardly light with a cloud base down to 200 ft. In fact, the weather closed right down, and Bomber Command was not able to carry out any major operations for the next forty-eight hours. The total landings at Manston during September were estimated to be nearly 6,000, and 600 of these were reckoned to be emergencies, with, so far as records confirm, about a score with the use of FIDO.

During the last quarter of 1944 trials of single Hades burners took place from October, although the system was not sufficiently advanced to replace all of the existing surface burners. The weather in December 1944 was as poor at Manston as anywhere in Britain. Emergency landings galore took place, and several times more than 100 aircraft landed in a twenty-four hour period.

On 8 December over 200 5 Group Lancasters attacked the Urft Dam in the Eifel region of West Germany and 163 more of 3 Group raided Duisburg. Part of the escort for these forces was provided by the Detling Wing (1 and 41 Squadrons) Spitfires led by Wg Cdr R.W. Oxspring and the Manston Wing under Wg Cdr Balmforth. On their return nineteen of the Lancasters were diverted to Manston, 'the majority having had to abandon their task of bombing a dam owing to the target being obscured by cloud'. We do not know if FIDO was required to assist their landings, but the Detling Wing certainly required it. Flying his personalized Spitfire RW-O, Wg Cdr Oxspring recalled:

We in the Detling Wing had taken part in a Ramrod to Heimbach, and after leaving the bombers we landed in Belgium to top up with fuel and then set course for the UK. It was pretty late in the afternoon and getting dusk when we crossed the Belgian coast. I hadn't got much of a weather forecast, but I knew that whatever the conditions at Detling, Manston would be okay [at 600 ft a.s.l. Detling is 450 ft higher than Manston]. Over the North Sea it was nearly dark and the haze was getting thick. I called Manston for a confirmatory course to steer and ordered all aircraft in the wing to switch on navigation lights to keep station.

At Manston the station commander, knowing that his FIDO was operational, was just dying for an opportunity to fire it up and accordingly called me from Air Traffic asking if I would like FIDO assistance. I answered 'Yes please!' and a few minutes later, in the haze and fog ahead of us we saw a ruddy great glow. The weather conditions had been worse than I anticipated, and when we arrived over Manston the scene was quite spectacular. The heat from the fuel jets along each side of the runway had, as intended, lifted the precipitation to about 700 ft and the twenty-four aircraft in the wing were able to perform a normal run-in and break by flights for landing. I should add that on this particular occasion we could not have followed such procedures without FIDO and some of us could have been in a not too pleasant position.

Crossing over the flares at the downwind end of the runway at about 100 ft on the approach for landing, we all experienced a noticeable kick in the pants as we flew through the upcurrent of hot generated air, but this was in no way dangerous because we were past it in a moment. Every pilot could see what he was doing as per normal daylight flying, which was a boon and blessing with two dozen aircraft potentially at risk. All in all it was a great confidence uplift and morale builder, considering the sometimes fraught weather conditions which could build up at base before we returned from a sortie, especially on short winter days.

Wg Cdr Oxspring has commented in detail here, but his logbook entry is confined to 'Extremely fraught – fog – FIDO!' Flt Lt (later Gp Capt) James Dalley put even less in his logbook, but remembers the occasion equally well. Flying Spitfire IX NH246 of 1 Squadron:

By the time we reached Manston it was very black indeed above and below and we were formating on navigating lights. The first view of FIDO was rather like looking at very faint neon lighting on our left as we were directed towards the downwind end of the runway. We were flying in two boxes of twelve aircraft, each squadron in close 'vics' of three, line astern, which was standard for cloud penetration or bad weather flying and also ideal for landing in threes.

The wing leader [Wg Cdr Oxspring] told us to break off and follow in 'vics' at about 400 yd intervals, which proved accurate for the conditions, and every aircraft landed first approach with all twenty-four on the runway at the same time. The only casualty was a minor mishap to Bobby Bridgeman of No. 1 Squadron whose undercarriage leg was damaged well down the landing run. His aircraft stopped at an angle on the edge of the runway but did not obstruct following aircraft.

So far as FIDO was concerned, it looked faint from 1,000 ft, but as we turned into the final curved landing approach at about 400 ft it became clear that it was burning fires several feet high with black smoke intermingling. It was simple to follow the lead-in fires on a curved approach, and as one reached 100 ft or so the runway lights could be seen and one's appropriate runway could be selected. The flames on either side of the runway were impressive as the landing was completed and speed reduced to taxiing rate. It was even more impressive flying over the flames as the runway was approached, though there was no turbulence as far as I can remember.

We were marshalled into a squadron group of aircraft at the end of the runway on a side dispersal. Collecting our flying kits we walked across the end of the runway near the flickering fires under the control of a corporal RAF policeman with strict instructions not to lose sight of the person in front. It was not until we left the runway that we actually appreciated the wisdom of his advice. Visibility was no more than 5 yd and one could only see two people ahead clearly. After a long walk in a crocodile, with visibility between 5 and 10 yd, the corporal brought us to the officers' mess where we booked in and eventually had a meal (after a visit to the bar).

As we entered the mess we ran into a group of bomber aircrew who had arrived earlier, had a meal and were leaving to find their beds. We were wearing Mae Wests and carrying our helmets and they asked 'Have you all landed in this weather?' This was too good an opportunity to lose and a squadron member quickly replied with something like 'Of course. We are fighter pilots. Members of the original squadron, No. 1, nothing will beat us!' We did not tell them about FIDO which they had apparently not seen from the mess.

We returned to Detling next day, but curiously enough, a week later the squadron moved to Manston. It was subsequently rumoured that £25,000 worth of fuel had been burned to get us down on 8 December.

The weather did not improve as the month progressed and by the 13th 'fog conditions persisted throughout the day and there were no operations by Manston-based squadrons'. The appalling conditions suited Gen Runstedt at this time, and he launched his Ardennes offensive to halt the Allied advance to the German border on 16 December. For several days it was not possible for Bomber Command or the US 8th Air Force to intervene, but on 19 December concerted air attacks were made on communications targets in and near the battle zone. 'Bad weather limited the effort and caused diversions of the returning bombers.' We know that seventeen Lancasters, eight Thunderbolts, six Liberators and a Marauder landed at Manston but have no evidence that FIDO was brought into use.

Fog persisted in Thanet for the next three days and nights, and a test of that part of Hades so far completed was carried out in the intervening period. According to the station ops record book it was successful, 'blue sky being observed in places'. Heavy raids continued on the 21st, on the night of 21/22 December and on 22 December. Following these FIDO was lit at nine airfields on the 21st, three on 21/22nd and seven on 22 December. During that time nearly 200 aircraft landed safely with its aid countrywide. In addition to these figures we know that two Halifaxes of 100 Group and 4 Group and thirty-two Lancasters of 1 Group landed at Manston between 19.40 and 22.30 on 22 December after taking part in a heavy raid on Koblenz, but cannot confirm that FIDO was used.

Similarly, on 24 December, 338 British aircraft carried out heavy raids on the airfields at Lohausen and Mulheim, while the US 8th Air Force mounted its biggest operation of the war so far with nearly 3,000 bombers and fighters attacking airfields and communications centres in Western Germany. Freezing fog caused many accidents and diversions as the squadrons returned and FIDO was called for at six airfields. As only three bombers landed at Manston during the day we are tempted to think that perhaps FIDO was not in a fit state to receive any more, though since there is no record of FIDO being called for at either of the other emergency aerodromes at Carnaby and Woodbridge it may be that sufficient airfields in East Anglia were fogfree to accommodate the machines from the Midlands and northern county bases.

The foggy weather continued throughout the Christmas period and so did the attacks on communications targets behind the enemy lines. On Christmas Day the USAF was only able to 'field' 422 bombers, most of its 1st Air Division still being stranded away from home, and on Boxing Day this was further reduced to 151. Bomber Command was able to play a major part in the Ardennes offensive for the first time, sending nearly 300 Halifaxes and Lancasters to attack German troop positions near St Vith. Weather conditions were poor over the eastern side of England, widespread diversions were called for and FIDO was in use at five airfields, including Manston. No fog dispersal report has survived and the station ops record book suggests that somehow the bombers and their escorts found sanctuary nearer to home than the Isle of Thanet: 'A very quiet day owing to fog. Seven operational landings only – all by visiting aircraft – one Mustang, six Thunderbolts. The remainder of today's thirty landings are made by non-operational aircraft, three of which are assisted by FIDO.'

The air offensive intensified on the 27th. Two hundred Lancasters raided the railway yards at Rheydt, while over 1,000 American bombers and fighters attacked similar targets at Fulda and Eusenkirchen to oppose the German advance. Freezing weather conditions hampered operations and many diversions were called for as the aircraft returned home. FIDO was again ordered at five airfields, including Manston. The station ops record book notes the day thus: 'Fogbound again and there are no operations by Manston-based squadrons. One landing only, which is by a Fortress. This aircraft, after making an unsuccessful attempt to land, crashes at No. 406 dispersal. All members of the crew are killed.'

This gives an incomplete picture, however, for a fog dispersal report for 27 December has survived, and contact has been made with the flying control officer of the day. From these sources it emerges that the Fortress was from the 384th Bomb Group at Grafton Underwood in Northamptonshire. Suffering battle damage her pilot had sought permission to make an emergency landing at Manston. Visibility that afternoon was appalling, down to only 20 yd, with fog 200 ft deep and the temperature 4° below freezing point. FIDO was lit at 14.40 and the apparatus was burning clearly within 10 minutes. It was soon possible to see for 1,000 yd along the runway and through to the sky above. Unfortunately, only the 280 yd approach box and 500 yd of the Hades system was complete on the south side and 800 yd on the north, and one of the burners there was malfunctioning. This meant that within a few seconds of touching down an aircraft would be back in fog again. The pilot made one unsuccessful approach before landing. Almost immediately the B–17 which was suffering from 'directional damage' swerved off the runway and careered across the airfield into a number of 406 Squadron Mosquitos at their dispersal. In the thick fog it was impossible for crash crews to reach the scene quickly and there were no survivors of the collision. Geoffrey Field, Duty Flying Control Officer, was of the opinion that the crash occurred at a time when the apparatus was turned down: 'an accident that shouldn't have happened'. The system was only turned down for 20 minutes in a two-hour burn, as not sufficient of the burners were complete to hold the fog back at low pressure. Despite the sad result of this particular burn, the station commander commented: 'The length of FIDO that could be operated worked successfully, and gave every indication that the completed installation will be eminently successful under similar conditions.'

By the end of 1944 it was reckoned that 42,000 aircraft had used the airfield since it became an emergency runway. Nearly 3,000 landed in December, but no precise figure exists for the use of FIDO. A possible clue is offered in the serial numbers on the few fog dispersal reports which have survived, suggesting that in 1944 it might well have been only six. If this is so, the most likely reason is that construction of the Hades burners was so slow that the diversions to other airfields equipped with fog dispersal apparatus were considered wiser alternatives.

Fog dispersal reports may have been scarce in December 1944, as were references in the station ops record book. In January 1945 they were non-existent. That month, 2,137 landings took place, 246 of them by night, a substantial number of which were classified as emergencies, but nowhere is there any reference in station records to the use of FIDO.

There was an apparent need for FIDO on New Year's Day. Three Manston squadrons were briefed to escort a force of 152 Lancasters of 5 Group to attack the Dortmund-Emms canal. 'Half an hour before take-off time, however, the airfield was covered with thick mist and the squadrons were unable to take off.' We can only assume that the installation was inoperable due to delay in its completion.

As we proceed through the month, the same kind of report occurs day after day; operations planned and then cancelled or curtailed due to inclement weather; any number of operational visitors and frequent emergency landings, but no reference to FIDO. A major diversion occurred on 16 January following raids by the US 8th Air Force on oil and industrial targets in Germany. Over 600 bombers took part, escorted by nearly 700 fighters. Roger Freeman records in his *Mighty 8th War Diary* that because of heavy ground fog over English bases there were many diversions. One of the airfields designated was Manston. None of its own Spitfire squadrons was operating, which left the runway free for sixty-five Mustangs to land in safety from the American missions and a total of 116 aircraft during the day. Alas, there is again no reference to FIDO.

Ten days of awful weather then set in, with winds gusting up to 80 mph on the 18th, and not more than a handful of operational landings per day for a week. During the foggy period, however, John Peaty, flying a 287 Squadron Spitfire was glad to take advantage of the system early in 1945, although his landing is not detailed in any surviving Manston record:

> When returning across the channel just before nightfall, I approached the south coast, only to find that Kent was completely covered in dense fog. It was rather like flying through a mountain of black cotton wool. I contacted Manston by radio and after telling them of my plight, the radar boys managed to track me. I was given a course to steer for Manston, was told to reduce height at the appropriate moment, drop my wheels in due course and – according to them – would be on my approach to the runway. Everything went well and I landed without difficulty. Although I was told that it was a very expensive business to light FIDO, on that occasion and subsequently, I felt that it had been worth every penny of the expenditure, even if the Air Ministry might not have thought so!

Manston's ops record book shows a total of 2,574 landings during February, of which 459 are listed as emergencies, nearly half of all those made at the three major emergency airfields of Carnaby, Woodbridge and Manston. Of Manston's emergency landings 63 were due to technical failure, 11 from damage by enemy action, 131 from shortage of petrol and 254 were diversions. We can identify almost all of the diversions from the station ops record book, but it makes absolutely no reference whatever to the use of FIDO, from the beginning of the month to the end. There is, however, a pointer to the use of FIDO at this time in a local newspaper report, published at the end of hostilities, to the effect that 'although only partly operational during the war, it has landed 122 aircraft'. We can only note the most likely occasions when FIDO at Manston might have been called into service.

Five bombers landed on the night of 2/3 February, three of them suffering battle damage. The station ops record book includes: 'A Halifax of 426 Squadron crashed while making a wide circuit with controls shot away. All attempts by police, NFS and our own ambulance parties to find the aircraft failed. One survivor who baled out, thought that the aircraft crashed in Minster Marshes. 11 Group laid on land and sea searches for the aircraft.' We know that FIDO was called for at both of the other emergency airfields that night and wonder if, although FIDO may have been used, fog hindered the discovery of the wreckage, which was found next day with, unfortunately, no further survivors.

The poor conditions heralded a sustained period of foggy weather over east Kent which continued for nearly a week, noted in local newspapers if not in station records. Although only a crude guide, Lympne airfield about 25 air miles to the south-west experienced fog on fourteen days during the month. Following deep penetration raids to Dresden and Leipzig, further raids almost to the Czech border were carried out the following night. On 14/15 February Bomber Command laid on one of its most elaborate night operations: a two-phase main force attack on Chemnitz, with a 5 Group raid on Rozitz involving nearly 1,000 bombers, with over 300 more ranging abroad in sweeps, mine-laying and RCM patrols and Spoof raids. From the night's activities twenty-three aircraft failed to return.

As the bomber streams made their way home a number made diversions, some to Manston – a 1 Group Lancaster with engine trouble, two from 5 Group, damaged by flak and enemy fighter gunfire, an 8 Group Mosquito, a 100 Group Fortress and five Halifaxes returning from Chemnitz. One of them was T-Tommy of 578 Squadron from Burn in Yorkshire, flown by Flg Off Doug Millard. His rear-gunner was Ken Kemp, very anxious to complete his second tour of operations safely:

> The country was pretty well fogbound and we were short of fuel when we were instructed to land at Manston as the necessary facilities were available for an emergency landing. I can recall that it was very cold and we were all tired and hungry after an eight-and-a-half-hour grind; and there was the thought of having to make a landing using FIDO, knowing that Doug had problems bringing an aircraft in even when visibility was perfect!
>
> You can imagine the turmoil going through my mind, four to go to complete my fifty, as I sat in the tail turret, listening to the patter over the intercom. With the fuel shortage it was a case of the pilot making it first time. As we made our approach far out to sea, ground control were giving instructions on heights, line etc, bringing us down slowly in stages, until we were a matter of a hundred feet above the runway. The first thing I saw was the glow through the fog and the next we were down, with the sensation of travelling down a mist-shrouded tunnel and a strong smell of burning fuel. Strange to relate, it was one of Doug's better landings!

It was four days before the weather was clear enough for them to return to Burn, and during the wait Ken and his mates scrounged a lift into Ramsgate in search of a pub; but with only half-a-crown between them, their joy was very limited.

Aerial activity increased with gradual improvement in the weather. American Air Divisions mounted Operation Clarion on communication centres in Western Germany on 22 February, and on the following day almost 3,000 of the 8th Air Force's bombers and fighters were aloft. Bomber Command also had 475 heavy bombers out, raiding oil refineries and benzol plants with Fighter Command escorts. As the aircraft returned to English shores in deteriorating weather conditions, FIDO was called for at Woodbridge, Tuddenham, Foulsham and Bradwell Bay and, on the same night, Carnaby. Over 100 machines landed with its aid, and so widespread was the low cloud and haze that we think it likely that FIDO at Manston was pressed into service too. Twenty Mustangs from Bentwaters and twenty-eight from Honington would have been the most likely users, although sixteen machines from various other bases landed at Manston during the day; and by night a Halifax and two Lancasters made emergency landings following a raid on Neuss. For lack of confirmatory evidence these instances can be but an approximation of the possible occasions when FIDO was used at Manston during February 1945.

Although emergency landings continued to take place, bad weather diversions decreased during March, the last for which PWD figures survive, and only fifty-four landings are recorded between all fifteen FIDO-equipped airfields. Such a figure would have been regarded as amazing eighteen months earlier. What may have been the last wartime use of FIDO at Manston is recalled by American crewman Harvey Mace:

> I was assigned to the 3rd Air Division HQ as Fighter Controller after finishing my tour. In a weak moment I volunteered to go along on a B–17 combat mission to see how the other half lived. True, it was only a one-plane milk-run reconnaissance, barely over enemy territory; but I figure that if it was far enough over enemy territory to overfly a V2 launch, where the rocket came close enough to read numbers on it, then it was a combat mission!
>
> Anyway, we were up ten hours, and on our return to England there was low thick fog over everything. The PIC called for FIDO at Manston. As we approached, the solid white fog below us was smooth everywhere except for a beautiful, raised rectangular shape the length and width of the huge Manston runway. All we had to do was to aim our approach at the end of the block of white, and after riding through the bumps of rising air from the heat of the burning gasoline, make a nice landing. It had worked as advertised, much to my relief.

Not until 3 May 1945 does the station ops record book make further reference to FIDO, noting that:

> Today marks the great event of a full FIDO burn, witnessed by the following very eminent gentlemen; Sir Donald Banks, Lord Suirdale, Sir William Wiseman, AM Johnson, Mr A.C. Hartley, Gp Capt Thunder, Wg Cdr Thompson, Gp Capt Robinson, Wg Cdr Ingall and Mr W.T. Moore [to

whom the system owed its being]. The burn was carried out according to plan, and following is the test report of Flt Lt G. Field, i/c FIDO. . . .

The report referred to a number of constructional defects causing distortion of components and break-up of reinforced concrete slabs. Such was the intensity of heat generated by Hades that the feed-pipes to the igniters, several yards away from the burner lines, had buckled, despite being underground, and had to be moved another 5 yd back. The report also recommended increased numbers of personnel in the pumphouse; but otherwise concluded that 'the full-scale test burn has proved the FIDO installation at Manston generally satisfactory', which, from Geoffrey Field, was quite a compliment. The burn which had taken place in clear weather, consumed petrol at a maximum rate of 4,000 gallons per minute. Karel Zouhar of 313 Spitfire Squadron carried out the test flying on the day of the burn, but found the experience not at all sensational: 'I was asked to take off and land while the FIDO system was being operated. My logbook shows that I did 40 minutes flying time and six or eight take-offs, landings and low flying over the runway. I recall that there was some turbulence which had to be allowed for during the operation.'

A week later the war in Europe finished and FIDO was not used again under operational conditions. It was estimated that a total of 5,796 emergency landings had been made at Manston in its time as an emergency runway. For lack of documentary evidence the number which were assisted by FIDO can only be guessed at, but we hazard that they might have approached 140. Unlike most of the other installations, FIDO at Manston was not immediately dismantled, but continued in position and occasional use during the postwar

Plate 53 Postwar test burn of FIDO vaporizer at Manston (D.B. Robertson)

Plate 54 Airman prepares to light burner line when control valves open. Burner pipes varied from 500 ft to 1,000 ft in length (D.B. Robertson)

Plate 55 FIDO operators in a double control pit at Manston. Airman on right controlling inlet from supply line to vaporizer (D.B. Robertson)

Plate 56 Approach to Manston, 1991. Although foreshortened in appearance, runway is 3,000 yd long. Only middle 200 ft strip now in use. Originally 750 ft. Storage tanks to left of touchdown (Terence McKenna)

years, when most of the Hades photographs were taken. In November 1949 it is recorded that FIDO fuel stocks at Manston were to be reduced to half a million gallons and the system was being tested approximately once a fortnight.

Units of the USAF joined Manston in 1950, gradually taking over most of the station's activities. During the American occupation, the runway was restructured. The landing strip was narrowed to 200 ft, left of centre, and a wide sterile area created to the north of it. The FIDO layout was not changed, though it meant that on completion in August 1955, the centre line of the runway was 285 ft from the burners on the south side, but 485 ft from those on the north (Plate 56). The American units departed from Manston in May 1958, and the FIDO installation was reduced to a Care and Maintenance basis.

In the early 1960s the FIDO storage tank site was acquired by Norman Steed who farmed in the area. He hoped to be able to utilize the large quantities of rainwater which drained from the runway and were channelled down to Pegwell Bay via a huge 33 in storm-water sewer running beneath the site. Unfortunately, this scheme did not materialize, due as much to contamination of the water as anything, and eventually the site was sold to local contractors Brown & Mason.

In 1971 the late Mr Norman Jenkins and his son Anthony acquired the site, where they established what has since become the Jentex Group of Companies, fuel oil distributors. The twelve Ford pumping engines were removed from their sheds, which are now vehicle workshops. The four storage tanks were retained and restored and are in use at the time of writing. Additional tanks were installed in 1987, as can be seen in Plate 57. The current capacity of the tanks is in excess of two million gallons.

Before the acquisition an inventory of the system had been taken prior to dismantling, and this revealed that an astonishing 76,000 ft (nearly 15 miles) of piping had been installed in the Hades system of burners and supply pipes. This takes no account of nearly as many miles which had been used in the Haigill burners which preceded it. On the airfield itself, little of Hades can be seen without close examination. The control pits on the south side are still

Plate 57 Manston, FIDO storage tanks, 1992 (Tony Jenkins)

there, minus controls, but fortunately with their concrete covers intact, and there are traces of the filled-in burner trenches where they cross the crash bays. Down by the railway line near Minster, the 6 in main storage shed and pumphouse still survive. Inside the latter the Morris Commercial engine and Bradford pump are still in situ, firmly rusted in place (Plate 52). Probably only their inaccessibility has preserved them so long.

A good few years after the war, Fred Searle remembered that part of the pipe-line leading from the railway siding to the Manston FIDO tanks was unearthed. There was some disagreement as to ownership, but when an attempt was made to pump water through it in the hope that it would be used for irrigation of the farmland under which it passed, the problem was solved, for every kind of debris imaginable emerged and it then collapsed into heaps of rust – so Fred says!

THIRTEEN

Melbourne

'Milkpail' keep that FIDO burning
For the boys on their returning,
Driving through the mist to Home,
Help them find the mother 'drome.

'To Our Skipper' *by Leslie 'Mac' Cunningham, navigator*

Melbourne airfield in the Vale of York, 12 miles south-east of the cathedral city, takes its name from the village north west of the aerodrome. First brought into operation as a satellite to Leeming in 1940 when there was only a grass surface, Melbourne was the home of 10 Squadron throughout the remainder of hostilities, save for the period when it was closed for the construction of three concrete runways. In the spring of 1943, while the Halifaxes of 10 Squadron were heavily engaged in the Battle of the Ruhr, it was proposed to extend the recently commissioned system of airfields to be equipped with the fog dispersal apparatus, FIDO. Among the bases named was Melbourne, confirmed in July 1943 as the FIDO airfield for 4 Group, north of the Humber. It was designated Station VII.

After survey, work began on 23 August, with George Wimpey as contractors. As can be seen from the plan (Fig. 21), the layout was ostensibly straightforward, an approach box of 210 yd being followed by a continuous series of burners on each side of the runway for

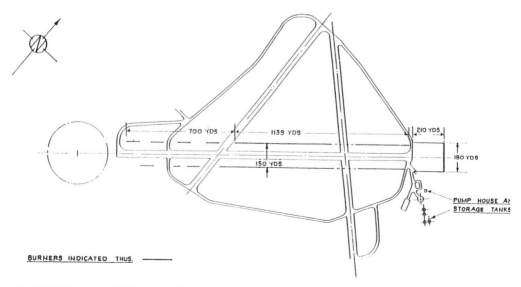

Fig. 21 Melbourne, FIDO layout. See Plate 58

Plate 58 Melbourne aerial. Runway 24. Approach box visible and scorch marks on either side of the runway. Storage tanks to south of touchdown. Also see Fig. 21 (Brian Rapier)

another 1,340 yd and then 700 yd of Mk IV burners placed on alternate sides. The main runway was approached on a heading of 242° (approximately SW), but only about 400 yd after touchdown it was crossed almost at right angles by runway 33. This created a complication in the FIDO design, for if the chain of burners alongside runway 24 continued unbroken it would put runway 33 out of use; and if the line of burners was interrupted, fog could intrude from north or south almost as soon as an aircraft had landed. Such a difficulty had been foreseen, and a burner set in a narrow trench had been designed to obviate it. This was known as an IRB (Plate 22), but little experience of installing and operating it had been gained by the time FIDO at Melbourne began. As ill-luck would have it, cross runway 33 was under repair at the time, and as fast as one gang laid the surface another dug it up for the IRB – or so the story says.

The greatest challenge to the construction crews, however, was the weather. Aircrews may have been engaged in battles over Berlin, Hamburg or the Ruhr, but for the fitters, welders and labourers it was a battle of the elements. The PWD's resident engineer and troubleshooter, Denys Fox, sallied north on his classic Vincent HRD 1,000 cc twin motor cycle to give advice in the foulest of November weather, and spent ten days at Melbourne with the technicians, seeking cures for all kinds of snags. Murphy's Law seemed to apply there; for if valves were not blocked, they were stuck open or shut. The ground sloped slightly down towards the south, so that mud and water found their way across the airfield into the burner pipes on that side of the runway. At times, the control pits, which were not much more than depressions in the ground, a foot or so deep, acted as miniature reservoirs for the rain which fell persistently. Perhaps it was as well that tadpoles were out of season! The burners frequently sprang leaks, allowing petrol also to collect in the control pits, but when crews tried to drain them, no petrol bowser was to be found. On 14 November the station experienced a day-long storm, after which a temporary pumping unit and tanker arrived to remove the contaminated fuel from pipes and pits. These proceeded to get bogged down in the mud and required a whole morning to disinter them.

Denys Fox's diary comment reads: 'All this work on the fouled-up lines was taking place while the station was on normal operations, and therefore one had to keep a wary look-out for the odd Halifax coming in; and I well remember being caught out in one of the valve pits, lying flush and praying that a rather erratic landing would diverge from this valve pit or at least leap over the protective rampart. Honorary membership of 4 Group "Halibar" was much appreciated.' Bad weather was still causing trouble at Melbourne a month later, the station ops record book complaining: 'Installation pretty well flooded. Water seeping into pits. Burner lines lying in water. Spilt petrol spreads on water-logged ground.' On New Year's Day 1944, however, is noted: 'The fog dispersal apparatus is now practically complete. Runway 33 and one IRB are also completed and the one on the other side is being installed.'

On 11 January 1944 the inspector general, AM Ludlow-Hewitt, came to inspect the station and the FIDO system. Later he reported his experience to Geoffrey Lloyd, the Minister for Petroleum:

> I was in the CO's office, which must have been quite 800 yd downwind from the nearest point on the runway when I noticed through the window that the fog had suddenly disappeared. I was then told that a test of the clearance apparatus was in progress. The wind was directly across the runway and I should say that the fog was cleared to leeward of the flares for a distance of at least half a mile. On the windward side of the runway the fog was just as thick as ever . . . There is no question at all that the apparatus does clear fog and is of practical value for getting aircraft down in a fog if they cannot be diverted elsewhere. A pilot properly trained in the use of Standard Beam Approach . . . should experience no difficulty in making a safe landing with the use of this apparatus at night, especially if the wind was down the runway. This is the ideal condition. A cross-wind is unfavourable, particularly if the mist extended upwards for more than, say, 200 ft, as the aircraft would be in thick mist until it actually reached the end of the runway. Under these conditions the use of the apparatus at night might be dangerous.

The experiments which AM Ludlow-Hewitt witnessed, incidentally, had set the taxpayer back the cost of 102,000 gallons of petrol.

FIDO was officially handed over as complete on 15 January 1944 and by the end of February, the completion of repairs and the installation of sodium and funnel flares on all runways had at last 'given Melbourne a fully serviceable set of runways; a turning point for Melbourne-mounted operations'. It also gave most of the populace a heart attack during a night burn on 29 February, when some thirty NFS engines headed there in panic from all points in Yorkshire. Mr D.V. Wenford was a flying control officer at Melbourne then:

> Soon after my arrival, there took place a demonstration of FIDO for the benefit of visiting top brass. I do not know if it was the first occasion on which it had been used. However, it was a suitably foggy night when the 'show' was put on. On lighting up, the noise was similar to that of about 10,000 primus stoves blowing full blast on each side of the runway. This produced an orange glow in the sky. Apparently no one had thought to inform the fire services in that part of Yorkshire, and they thought there had been a major disaster, and turned out in force.

Ron Day, rear-gunner with 10 Squadron, made his first operational flight with the squadron to Tergnier on 18/19 April 1944 in W-Willie, piloted by Sgt Alan Bruce:

> On the return flight, the flight engineer, Sgt Archie Tolmie, reported fuel low after much evasive action and RAF Stradishall was called for permission to land at 01.16. As we touched down a burst of tracer fire shattered the darkened sky and later I learned that intruders were active in the region and that four aircraft were shot down between 02.09 and 03.48 on their approach to land.

At 12.04 on 19 April we took off for Melbourne. The airfield there was shrouded by very low cloud and drizzle. FIDO was ignited and after several passes over the airfield with just a glimpse of the flares for seconds, it was gone. We eventually approached to land at 13.30. The heat from FIDO seemed to lift the aircraft and we landed well up the runway, but safe.

Not until 27/28 May, when the risk of fog might be thought minimal, was FIDO next put to the test operationally. On that date 1,117 Bomber Command aircraft were airborne on seventeen separate operations. Of these, 331 attacked Bourg Leopold in Belgium, including nine Halifaxes of 10 Squadron. Three other Melbourne aircraft were engaged in mine-laying off L'Orient. General visibility decreased during their absence because of radiation fog; not very deep, but obliterating the ground from view. By 01.00 it was impossible to see for more than 1,000 yd and by the time the first Halifaxes crossed the coast it was as low as 300 yd in patches. FIDO was lit at 03.00, clearing horizontal visibility to 1,400 yd within the burners.

'Considering that about 50 per cent of the burners require replacing,' wrote the station commander Gp Capt D.L. Thomson, 'it proved very successful.' A total of fourteen Halifaxes landed on the cleared runway during a 47-minute period. All twelve of 10 Squadron's aircraft put down safely, though with no previous experience of the system, plus two machines diverted from Snaith and Breighton respectively.

'A' flight commander, Flg Off Menderson reported that he had seen the glow of FIDO from 80 miles out; that the waves of heat tended to keep the aircraft aloft; and that it took most of the runway to get down. Sgt Bond found that the glare from the burners when circuiting the aerodrome made it necessary to turn the instrument panel lights full on in order to read the dials. Sgt Bourner, who returned short of fuel, picked up FIDO at a range of 200 miles, found the glare so bright on approach that other aircraft and airfield lights were not visible and that the thermal effect caused 'a floating effect'. Colin Birds recalled that after leaving the runway and the effect of FIDO: ' . . . the fog was so dense that I got out with two torches to guide the pilot on to the perimeter track. We were very soon on the grass and hit a part of the airfield lighting with our port outer propeller.'

Ron Sutton was the pilot of Halifax R-Roger, one of those detailed for mine-laying off St Nazaire:

> When still a considerable distance from Melbourne, I drew the attention of my navigator and bomb-aimer to a bright light ahead, which, we agreed, appeared to be an intense and large fire. We wondered if the Germans had managed to mount a concentrated fire bomb attack on some town or other. The mystery was not solved until I called base to advise my ETA in minutes and to ask for landing instructions. The reply was that due to very low visibility I could either divert to an airfield which was clear – or use FIDO. The thought of the bacon and eggs and my own bed waiting below soon decided me to give FIDO a go.
>
> My memories of the landing are:
>
> (a) the clarity of the runway as we approached. (b) the tremendous bump as we crossed the threshold of the runway, although I crossed rather higher than usual as we had been advised, and (c) the strange feeling on the landing run between the leaping lines of flames on each side. As one of my crew remarked, 'Hell must be like this.' FIDO made the landing comparatively easy – we would not have been able to land at Melbourne without it that night.

On 1 July 1944 a force of Halifaxes took part in a raid on the V1 flying bomb launching sites at St Martin-l'Hortier, seventeen 10 Squadron aircraft among them. Sqn Ldr John Hullah on the last operation of his tour led in B-Baker. The squadron suffered no damage during the raid, but experienced low cloud at 1,000 ft and intermittent rain throughout. In his book *Melbourne 10* Brian Rapier records the Sqn Ldr's comments:

> The return flight was uneventful . . . except that upon reaching Melbourne there was low cloud at 500 ft from a front and it was absolutely teeming with rain which reduced forward visibility to virtually nil. I was only able to approach with my head to one side looking through the small frontal window opened up, and with my flight engineer Obbie Byrne calling out speeds and heights. By

flying this way I was able to lead in a very new pilot (I believe he was on his first op), who had overshot for the umpteenth time. Eventually, things were made a little easier when some bright 'Erbert remembered to light up FIDO. After shutting down engines we went to inspect the aircraft for damage, but 'Lady Luck' had obviously been with us that day, for we found only one small hole!

Among sorties of Stirlings and Halifaxes on the night of 4/5 August were seven machines from Melbourne. Six of the Halifaxes laid their mines without difficulty, but L-Lion flown by Flg Off Cembroski was unable to do so because of a failure in his H2S equipment and he elected to return with his cargo still aboard. Flt Sgt Alan Bruce and crew in X-X-ray were on their 34th operation since 18 April. Their rear-gunner, Ron Day, recalled being third plane home just after 03.00: 'The trip was flown at 15,000 ft in bright clear moonlight, but on return to base, ground mist had risen and blotted out the ground by 02.50 on the 5th. FIDO was put on, but not before an aircraft attempting to land at a nearby airfield without FIDO had crashed. We again had that feeling of the heat as we came in, and we landed well up the runway, but safely.' All seven of 10 Squadron's Halifaxes, Y, N, X, M, A, L and F, put down without mishap, including Flg Off Cembroski's L-Lion, between 02.45 and 03.31.

On 17 September, only twenty-four hours after a heavy raid on Kiel, eighteen of 10 Squadron's Halifaxes were detailed for a daylight raid on Boulogne by a force of over 760 planes preparatory to an attack by Allied troops. Brian Rapier reports that visibility was down to 200 yd and that FIDO was lit for the first time to cover an operational take-off. Within a short time the level of visibility increased to 1,800 yd and all aircraft took off without mishap. *The Bomber Command War Diaries* record that shortly after the raid the German garrison surrendered. Following this, there is no record of FIDO in use at Melbourne for another two months.

Ten of 10 Squadron's Halifaxes were among 500 bombers which raided Munster on 18 November 1944. Predicted fog descended during the evening and visibility decreased rapidly from 3,000 to 1,000 yd. As the main force split into Groups and the groups into squadrons homeward bound, airfield after airfield 'went red'. For pilots it was almost as if the aircraft was suspended in mid-air with only an occasional patch of thinner fog sweeping past to suggest forward motion; and as for wings – in dense fog, only rarely did they seem to have any beyond the outer exhaust stubs. When FIDO was lit at 17.10 to receive the first of the returning aircraft it was possible to see 1,500 yd horizontally once the machines had descended through the fog. All ten landed safely, except one Halifax which overshot, fortunately without injury to any member of the crew.

This was F-Freddie, the aircraft which overshot. Its crew had already completed one tour with 77 Squadron. Tom Treadwell was air-bomber:

On Saturday 18 November (my birthday) we took off from Melbourne on a daylight operation against the town of Munster. Our pilot was Flg Off R.J. Daffey and our aircraft, the current F-Freddie.

We got off the ground at 12.45 and attempted the unfamiliar task of flying in formation with other aircraft of the squadron, with moderate success. It was 10/10 cloud at the target and we had to bomb on sky markers dropped by the Pathfinder Force.

As it was November, it was getting dark by the time we arrived back at our base at about 17.30. Unfortunately, dusk was accompanied by a very thick pea-soup fog, down to ground level over the whole of Yorkshire. This meant that not only were our own squadron's planes attempting to land at Melbourne, but as it was the only 4 Group station equipped with FIDO at the time, so were many aircraft from other squadrons.

All aircraft were being stacked at 500 ft intervals in the fog and cloud above the station awaiting landing instructions, and there were some near-misses by other machines crossing the area. When it eventually became the turn of F-Freddie to land, they could see that not only were the parallel lines of FIDO jets all alight, but the approach and cross-burners at the near end of the runway:

We had little knowledge of FIDO and no experience of these approach burners. As Daffey trimmed the aircraft ready to land at the near end of the runway, it seemed that the heat kept us airborne and we actually touched down over halfway along the runway.

As a Halifax air-bomber, it was part of my duties to sit alongside the pilot for take-off or landing, to assist him in these operations. My own practice on landing was to slide back the starboard cockpit window and keep watch outside. On this occasion I did just that, and noticed what I thought was a deep crack in the runway.

Just after that there was a sudden bang, considerable jolting, and the whole aircraft seemed to drop towards the ground. The crack turned out to be the end of the runway and the jolts were the aircraft leaving several tons of undercarriage in a ditch as we careered onwards. We carried on with the Halifax on its belly, propellers beating up the ground, until we came to a stop many yards further on.

As soon as it dawned on him what had happened the pilot switched off the engines. Luckily there was no fire. He then checked via the intercom system with the crew each of whom was sitting in a dazed condition:

All except our flight engineer answered immediately. Then someone spotted that Chuck was already out of the aircraft, standing on the starboard wing with a small fire extinguisher at the ready, having got there via the astrodome. While Chuck was a good flight engineer, he had never been noted as a fast mover – till then. We rapidly revised our opinion of him!

As we did our long walk back around the aerodrome, still in our flying kit, the scene was like something from Dante's *Inferno*; the swirling fog, the rows of blazing jets and the accompanying smoke from the petrol, burning thousands of gallons per hour.

Next morning's visit to the airfield confirmed that F-Freddie was a complete write-off, and left us wondering how it was that not one of us had been so much as scratched.

During the first three weeks of December, 10 Squadron experienced a series of cancellations and postponements; half of its sorties were called off. The railway yards at Bingen were the targets for the night's attacks on 22/23 December, in order to hinder the German Ardennes offensive, and 106 planes took part in the raid. Melbourne's station ops record book says that twenty crews were briefed for Bingen. Fifteen actually took off, of which four had to abandon the mission and one bombed an alternative target. The weather had been very poor for days on end and 1 Group, which was also operating, reported that all but two of their entire Group had to land away. At Melbourne, 'Conditions at base on return were very poor, due to fog, but all aircraft landed safely on FIDO.' O-Orange of 78 Squadron was also talked down, short of fuel, and circling hopefully, waiting for FIDO to warm up.

Brian Davies was captain of J-Juliet that night. He brought to mind:

The landing frequency of returning aircraft was vital. Delays by landing and taxiing aircraft created a backlog for those still in the air. Flying Control worked hard to maintain the rhythm of the normal landing pattern; so much so that as an aircraft crossed the threshold, the CFCO would instruct 'Cut' by radio. Once the habit had been accepted, this was very helpful, as momentary lack of sight occurred until night vision had been adjusted to the surrounding glare; similar to coming off unlit roads into sodium lighting.

On the morning of 24 December 1944 143 bombers set off to raid the airfields at Lohausen and Mulheim. Fifteen of 10 Squadron's Halifaxes were detailed to take part. The weather was so bad that no aircraft from neighbouring bases could take off. Midway through 10 Squadron's departure, drifting fog reduced visibility to only 300 yd, and instructions were given to light FIDO. In the space of only 11 minutes from full burn, horizontal vision was increased to 2,000 yd and the remainder of the aircraft took off just after 11.30. Nine of the Halifaxes were hit during the raid and Brian Rapier records that although FIDO was required again by the time they returned, there was insufficient petrol left to operate the system and all the Halifaxes had to be diverted.

Finding room for many visiting aircraft and their crews at a FIDO airfield was no small problem for a station already operating a full squadron of bombers. Bryan Purser of 107 Squadron remembered:

> . . . the heat, the uplift on crossing the threshold, the vulnerability to attack by German intruders on approach and the intense darkness when we taxied clear of the runway. Where ground control parked so many aircraft returning to a strange field I have no idea – they were everywhere when we went to collect them next day.

The attack was continued on 29 December when 192 aircraft bombed the railyards at Koblenz. The ground was frozen hard, with a heavy white frost and a shallow fog which kept visibility down to 500 yd. FIDO was lit at 10.25 and twenty Halifaxes took off into the gloom. They had a rough reception over the target area and six of them were damaged by anti-aircraft gunfire. Two, T and X, made emergency landings with the aid of FIDO at Carnaby. Having expended 57,000 gallons of their newly delivered fuel getting 10 Squadron off, Gp Capt Ling could but repeat the process as they began to home in just after 16.30 in fog which had persisted all day. When all eighteen were safely down, FIDO was kept running for a further 20 minutes, just in case.

The anxieties of a pilot approaching the end of a tour are well illustrated in a page from the diary of Canadian pilot, Don Brown. Operations planned, postponed and cancelled did nothing to ease the strain, and bad weather requiring the use of FIDO did not help either. With 28 ops and a recall behind him, the page reads:

1944 December

19 Tues   Still not on. Another call scrubbed. Foggy tonight.

20 Wed   Call scrubbed. York, saw Graysham.

21 Thur   Finally on crew list. Briefed twice for Cologne, didn't go. Took tests for rehab. in evening.

22 Fri   Call on. Finally went, Bingen. No trouble. Made ropy landing on FIDO. Another call fairly early. Harrison finished. 19½ + 10.

23 Sat   Nothing on. Party tonight but didn't go because I hear there is an early call.

24 Sun   Call not so early. Got airborne just before fog closed in. Mulheim airfield. Good trip, landed back at Driffield. Back to base in truck. 20½ + 10.

25 Mon   Christmas Day. Slept in. Served in airmen's mess. Some fun. Formal dinner at night.

26 Tues   Slept in. Three kites on ops, St Vith. Still foggy. Barny Yates missing. Stood by to pick up 'Willie' [ZA-W] at Driffield but weather duff.

27 Wed   Weather closed, so collected kite at Driffield. Bus broke down halfway there. Small op early in morning, but not me.

28 Thur   Kerr screened. Trip near Cologne. Supposed to be a call early tomorrow. Janes [his flight commander] back from leave.

29 Fri   Morning op to Koblenz. Rough as far as concentration goes. Grim landing on FIDO. No trouble otherwise. 'Willie' going in for inspection. One more. 21½ + 10.

30 Sat   Boys went to Cologne. I'm waiting for 'Willie'. ENSA show.

31 Sun   No trips. New Year's Eve. Station Dance.

1945 January

1 Mon   Back on crew list again. Hope we don't get many scrubs. Briefed and actually went first go to Dortmund. Awful route, but we had no trouble. Beat PFF to the punch, but they were late. First home. Ground crew happy as hell. So am I. They had a beer waiting. All over. 22½ + 10.

Though Don and crew celebrated in the mess after the flight others were not so fortunate for his diary page concludes, 'Flying Officer Winters pranged last night and two were killed. Tough luck. Boys out again tonight.'

Altogether, during the month of December, PWD records note that thirty-five aircraft landed and forty-four took off at Melbourne with the aid of FIDO. A total of 330,000 gallons of petrol was consumed – this in a month when it was only possible for 10 Squadron to fly 167 sorties. There is then a gap of six weeks before further use of FIDO appears in the station's records. Then Melbourne's ops record book for 17 February 1945 reads: 'Twenty-two Halifaxes of 10 Squadron to Wesel. Due to fog at base all aircraft diverted. Aircraft S and T did not receive the diversion signal and landed at base by FIDO.' A total of 298 machines were despatched on this daylight raid: 'The target area was covered in cloud and the Master Bomber ordered the raid to be stopped after only eight Halifaxes had bombed. No aircraft was lost, but three Halifaxes crashed in England.'

Why Melbourne thought it necessary to divert its own aircraft is not known. Neither is it clear where all of 10 Squadron's aircraft were at the time of the diversion order, but when acknowledgement did not come from two aircraft it was decided to light FIDO at their approximate time of arrival, 16.15, in conditions of rain and low cloud. Flight Commander Chick Janes, flying T-Tommy, recalled: 'Arriving back at base after a five-hour flight, the cloud was down to 150 ft. My crew had failed to give me diversion instructions so as FIDO was working I decided to have a go and landed on Beam Approach much to everyone's surprise. As you may expect, it was very bumpy but I managed to land. Two other bombers who were following me were not allowed to land and were sent south to a cleared field.'

Halifax S-Sugar, the other aircraft which did not receive the diversion call, was flown by Ted Cook:

> Thinking that other aircraft were in the same position as myself, I proposed to do an instrument circuit at 700 ft to minimize the chance of mid-air collision (standard circuit height was 1,000 ft). This decision was fortuitous as another aircraft passed very close overhead on an opposite heading, though heaven knows why he was on that course.
>
> Seven hundred feet was held until turning finals. Although the weather was thick fog, the glare of the FIDO installation enabled me to pinpoint the runway and carry out a timed approach on the downwind leg. We were slightly closer to the airfield than standard, which necessitated a steeper turn on the final approach. Ground reference was not made until about 150 ft when some approach burners loomed into view. At this stage, appreciable turbulence was experienced due to heat from the installation. However, visibility for landing proved to be quite adequate and on touchdown more than half of the runway was visible. On de-briefing I remember complaining bitterly about the fool who nearly flew into me.

Operations cancelled and postponed and aircraft recalled because of impossible weather as tension mounted imposed a considerable strain on aircrew, even when a successful end to the bombing offensive was in sight. The chances of completing a tour were now stronger, to which FIDO must have contributed, but there were still times when the magic number 30 approached very slowly. Geoff Parnell words it thus:

> When even the owls refused to fly
> And they exhausted drop
> These poor, misguided youths press on
> – For only half an op!

What was probably the last operational use of FIDO at Melbourne took place on 25 March 1945. Twenty-one Halifaxes were part of a force of 156 bombers attacking the Osnabruck railway yards. This was a morning raid with take-off in poor weather. Visibility did not improve as the day progressed and as the time for 10 Squadron's return approached it was deemed difficult for pilots to see obliquely. A smoke haze gathered over the area and as the first of the force arrived they landed with considerable difficulty. Ten of them put down safely but then a further deterioration set in and the first seven burners on each side of the runway were lit. This restored visibility within the funnel and the remaining nine machines landed within 16 minutes, plus a French-crewed Halifax, P-Peter, from 346 Squadron.

Although like most FIDO stations Melbourne's records are likely to be incomplete, something in excess of 120 aircraft made use of the system during the sixteen months of its existence, over half of them during December 1944. Apart from Carnaby it was the northernmost of the FIDO airfields, and it could be that fog-threatened aircrews of 4 and 6 Groups returning from the major targets in the Ruhr and to the south of it opted for a nearer haven.

FOURTEEN

Metheringham

... solid earth in the unearthly glow of FIDO

Sid Jones, pilot, 106 Squadron

The parish of Metheringham lies some 10 miles north of Sleaford and about the same distance south-east of Lincoln. It is positioned on a plateau almost surrounded by the 50–ft contour, edging on to Linwood and Martin Moors, the ground dropping away northwards into Blankney Wood and Car Dyke, an old Roman canal.

The land for RAF Metheringham was requisitioned early in 1943, and the station opened as a heavy bomber base within 5 Group on 20 October 1943. Syerston-based 106 Squadron moved in during November. The airfield had three runways in a fairly regular pattern, the main one, approached from almost due south (015°), is nearly 2,000 yd long. There were no hills for miles around, which made for gentle approaches, although an overshoot would take an aircraft into the remains of Blankney Wood.

Metheringham was earmarked for fog dispersal equipment in the second group of airfields drawn up in December 1943 and designated Station XX. Messrs A. Monk & Co. were the FIDO contractors and their work began immediately, while 106 Squadron was heavily engaged in the Battle of Berlin. The welding sub-contractors were Messrs Strongarc of Lincoln, and their on-site supervisor George Gillham recalls that most of the work on this and the other Lincolnshire airfields was carried out in a sea of mud.

The FIDO layout was reasonably straightforward, although as can be seen from the plan (Fig. 22), four sets of IRBs, as shown in Plate 22, had to be installed. Initially, it seems as if

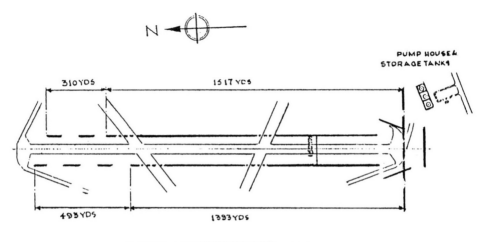

Fig. 22 Metheringham, FIDO layout. See Plate 59

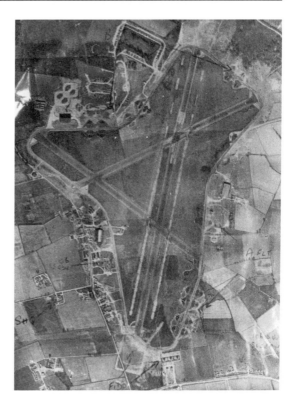

Plate 59 Melbourne aerial. Runway 01. The only FIDO airfield with south–north runway. Approach box visible and scorch marks on either side of the runway. Storage tanks to right of approach box. See also Fig. 22 (Peter Green)

Metheringham was going to dispense with an approach box, but as the aerial photograph (Plate 59) shows, a 250 yd long enclosure was constructed though it meant interfering with traffic on the B1189 to the south. Over seventy 40 yd Mk IV burners (Fig. 5) were required to cover the runway and approach box, and more than 14,000 yd of piping to fuel them. Three petrol storage tanks encased in brickwork, with a capacity of half a million gallons, were built adjacent to the approach box, near Martin Moor Lane, opposite Site 8 Mess. They were supplied by a two-and-a-quarter-mile underground pipeline from a siding on the old Great Northern and Great Eastern Joint Railway line near Blankney and Metheringham station. The location of the siding is not known, but its layout and equipment would have been similar to that shown in Fig. 19 and Plates 49–52.

Construction began in January 1944, and for the first few weeks work was up to schedule. The April report was not so favourable:

Work on this site has been badly held up by weather and the Easter holiday. Trial offloading of gasoline by road was carried out on 18 April, but the Petroleum Board's other commitments [six other FIDO stations were under construction at the same time] prevented them making further deliveries by this means; and as the railway siding will not be completed before 30 April, we have put the operational date back to 13 May, by which time we hope to have all the burner units tested, and sufficient gasoline in stock for operational purposes.

In fact, the installation was not yet fully operational and only half the burners were serviceable when FIDO was first burned in earnest on 19/20 May 1944. The difficult task of attacking the railyards in the centre of Tours was attempted by 113 Lancasters and four Mosquitos of 5 Group. Sixteen of the Lancasters were from 106 Squadron based at Metheringham. The raid was accurately carried out and little damage occurred outside the target area.

T-Tare was forced to return early with both W/T and R/T failure, and by the time Plt Off C.E. Thomson and crew neared home, a radiation fog 70 ft deep covered the area of their base, and visibility was down to 400 yd. Crewman Arnold White had seen the fog dispersal system under construction at Metheringham, but until then had no idea what it was for. T-Tare, devoid of communication, struggled back to the airfield and made three attempts to land. Recollected Arnold:

> We were on our final approach to the runway when our pilot was ordered to make another circuit of the field. Then flames and smoke began to arise from each side of the runway and we were given permission to land. It was like running the gauntlet between two banks of flame and disconcerted our pilot, Flg Off Thomson, who made a very bumpy landing. We later found that the CO had wanted to try out the new system to show it to someone. We were the first crew to land with the system on the airfield.

FIDO had worked well on its first operational burn and, despite a 7 mph cross-wind, 'penetration of the fog was so complete that the pilot was able clearly to discern the runway from 300–400 ft on his final approach'. Visibility dropped to only 500 yd when FIDO was extinguished. 'The FIDO personnel worked exceedingly well in this, their first emergency,' commented the station commander.

Following this incident there is no further reference to the use of FIDO for another three months while the Mk IV burners originally installed were being replaced by Mk Vs (see Fig. 6). These were only 20 yd long, prefabricated, better anchored and transportable on trailers. It is likely that Metheringham's turn for updating came during the summer of 1944. The new system was lit on 4 August in conditions of low stratus cloud as a demonstration to pilots and other members of aircrew on the station. The results were considered satisfactory.

Similar conditions pertained when FIDO was next lit on the night of 6 August. The station ops record book says that sixteen of 106 Squadron's Lancasters took part in a daylight raid on the submarine pens at L'Orient. FIDO was lit at 21.30. Nine of the Lancasters landed during the burn itself and another six landed in the clear air which still remained as the burners were being turned off. The new equipment must have been working vigorously for a number of the pilots complained of glare and asked if it could be reduced.

On 11/12 August 1944 179 Lancasters and ten Mosquitos carried out an exceptionally accurate attack on the railyards at Givors. No aircraft were lost. Twelve of the Lancasters were from 106 Squadron. By the time Metheringham's aircraft were coming over Lincolnshire on their return flight, low stratus cloud 10/10 thick covered the area at 1,500 ft, although it was somewhat better lower down. A 10 mph northerly wind was blowing. The order to light FIDO was given at 04.45. . . . only about the first 600 yd were lit. By their light seven of Metheringham's aircraft landed safely. Five were diverted to other airfields.

A raid on Konigsberg was reckoned to be a long haul indeed for aircraft of Bomber Command, and that on 26/27 August was no exception. The important supply port for the German Eastern Front was some 950 miles from the 5 Group bases, which contributed 174 Lancasters to the force. Fourteen were from 106 Squadron.

After a flight which had already lasted over 10 hours, the tiredness of the crews was not relieved by the knowledge that visibility was deteriorating as fast as their remaining petrol. Widespread diversions were ordered when horizontal vision fell below a mile and it is known that Graveley, Ludford Magna, Woodbridge, Tuddenham and Metheringham put their fog dispersal systems on standby. At Metheringham FIDO was lit at 05.35; it was only a partial burn to enable weary crews to line up with the runway as much as to improve visibility.

Seventeen Lancasters landed safely in the space of 43 minutes; all of 106 Squadron's and three diverted from elsewhere. The burners were kept going for a total of two hours in case more machines came in, but none did and FIDO was extinguished at 07.35. None of the pilots experienced difficulty with their landings, although a 10 mph tail-wind caused them to float over the cross-bar rather faster than expected. The whole two-hour burn of part-runway only had consumed 26,662 gallons of petrol.

John Keats described autumn as the 'season of mists and yellow fruitfulness' but it is doubtful whether his lyrical words would have been appreciated by the crews of twelve of 106 Squadron's Lancasters who took part in a raid on Deelan on 3 September 1944. They were among a force of 675 aircraft which carried out a series of attacks on airfields in southern Holland. By the time Metheringham was neared on the homeward flight, the weather had become appalling with low cloud and driving rain. Visibility was down to 200 yd by 19.00 with a 20 mph wind from the south-east. FIDO was lit at 19.10 and successfully raised visibility to full runway length at ground level, though the pilots coming in reported that the moment they ventured into circuit, out of FIDO's influence, it dropped back to 200 yd again. The machines were well bunched up and sixteen of them, all of 106's and four cuckoos, put down safely in 26 minutes. It speaks well for the efficiency of the ground operatives and the discipline of the aircrews, for six of the pilots had never seen FIDO before. The whole operation was over in half an hour at a cost of 'only' 8,339 gallons of taxpayer's petrol. Sid Jones recalled:

> . . . weather 10/10 cloud and me as pilot with not a clue as to where we were, but my navigator with the aid of GEE giving me headings to steer and saying in a very calm voice, 'In two minutes we should see FIDO on the port side.' Sure enough, in two minutes a red glow developed in the blankness and there we were over base.
>
> Circuiting the red glow and heading down through the funnel to the runway was like entering the gates of hell – airspeed increased to counteract the heat and turbulence – and the great joy of touching down on solid earth in the unearthly glow of FIDO, with flames leaping up on both sides, is something I'll never forget. It was a great comfort to know that if we were lucky enough to return, FIDO would give us a safe and warm welcome.

Munich was the target of a 5 Group raid on 26/27 November 1944, when 270 Lancasters and eight Mosquitos took part. Twenty-three of the Lancasters were from 106 Squadron. The operation took place in good visibility, but the last part of the return flight was hampered by mist with horizontal vision below a mile, and decreasing. With so many of the Squadron's machines aloft, a sign of Bomber Command's increasing strength, it was decided to light FIDO at 08.45, as it was anticipated that pilots would find the final approach to the airfield difficult. It was only deemed necessary to light the first seven burners on each side to aid lining up with the runway in a 7 mph cross-wind.

The whole 106 Squadron contingent landed at the rate of less than two minutes each, earning unanimous praise from the air crews for the 'additional facilities that FIDO had given them'. They were followed almost immediately by five C-47 ambulance aircraft. These machines were 'regular visitors, being chiefly employed in evacuating US airmen from the American hospital at Nocton Hall to Prestwick for repatriation'. All pilots found the effects of FIDO most satisfactory.

The Polish port of Gdynia had not been attacked since August 1942. On 18/19 December 1944 fourteen of 106 Squadron's Lancasters returned, as part of a force of 236 5 Group aircraft attacking the naval ships sheltering there. The pocket battleship *Lutzow* and several heavy cruisers were among the targets. Four Lancasters, including D-Dog flown by Flt Lt Pritchard of 106 Squadron, failed to return. No fog dispersal report for this date has survived, but the station ops record book notes that FIDO was alight between 02.17 and 04.20, during which time thirteen of Metheringham's aircraft landed safely.

An RAF film unit visited Metheringham on 20 December 1944 to record the use of FIDO for an instructional film. Visibility at 10.00 was down to 80 yd and although the fog dispersal system burned full blast for nearly two hours, it never succeeded in raising visibility beyond 200 yd. The fog was thick enough to prevent the safe landing of an aircraft even if it could have taken off, so the film crews confined their activities to ground shots. Even so, a staggering 116,250 gallons of petrol were consumed.

The next day was slightly better and FIDO increased initial visibility of 300 yd to 2,000 yd along the runway. A Lancaster of 106 Squadron made several take-offs and landings and filmed FIDO from the air between 09.00 and 11.30 at a cost of nearly 200,000 gallons of petrol. At about 300 gallons per ton, the contents of about 100 railway tankers were consumed over the two days! But had the unit stayed on for another 12 hours it would have seen FIDO working in earnest.

On the night of 21/22 December 1944 the synthetic-oil refinery at Politz was the target for 207 Lancasters of 5 Group. At the same time ten of 106 Squadron's aircraft went mine-laying in the Kattegat and two more raided Schneidmüll as a diversion for the Politz attack. Further south, 136 aircraft raided the Nippes railyards at Cologne and ninety-seven more attacked the railway area in Bonn. No aircraft were lost on the last two operations, but for the Politz crews it was a different story. Weather conditions deteriorated during the period of the operation and widespread fog required wholesale diversions to be ordered. Most of Metheringham's mine-laying and Spoof aircraft were home before the emergency arose, but any number of the main force Lancasters were still en route. Many obeyed the diversion instructions and Bomber Command records show that 145 aircraft landed in Scotland. Tom Bennett, 617 Squadron's historian notes, however, that on the homeward flight: '. . . the weather at base was not as bad as expected, so orders were transmitted to aircraft to cancel diversion instructions and return to Coningsby. However, at the last minute, conditions deteriorated, and although several aircraft managed to land, a large proportion had to report to Metheringham and their FIDO aid.'

The order to light FIDO at Metheringham was given at 01.45 in conditions of drizzle, mist and low cloud 1,000 ft deep, which had reduced visibility to well below 1,000 yd. Part only of the system was ignited and clearly marked the runway for landing, rather than fog dispersal, purposes. With its aid, ten aircraft landed, from 617, 97, 83 and 189 Squadrons and a few from 106 (Metheringham's own). In the process disaster struck one aircraft and threatened others during the landings. John Pryor, pilot with 617 Squadron, recalled his experience:

> On returning to base we could see in the distance, but only intermittently, the Drem lights at Woodhall. Aircraft were landing, but conditions were rapidly getting worse. As we approached, having been given permission to try and land, two aircraft on the circuit were forced to go round again by the weather conditions. We were then told to try FIDO at Metheringham.
>
> As we neared Metheringham we could see aircraft already on the circuit and landing. We joined the circuit, being careful to come in low, because the heat given off by FIDO caused uplift. We could see other aircraft coming in too high and going higher due to the heat. FIDO was such a wonderful sight in a sea of fog that words failed us.
>
> As our turn came to land we were following another aircraft round, and as it landed it ran through the flare path to the right of the runway. I believe that petrol was thrown up by the wheels and set fire to the aircraft. This forced us to go round again. The burning aircraft was only just off the flare path and might have exploded, so it had to be dealt with quickly. Other aircraft were now landing and eventually we did too.

One of the other machines was S-Sugar, also of 83 Squadron, with flight engineer Frank Harper in its crew:

> We had a difficult flight home and after being airborne for some ten hours, received a radio message that fog was closing in rapidly over Lincolnshire and that we were to divert to a Scottish airfield. Due to serious damage to our aircraft, fuel shortage and other problems, we could not do this and attempted to land back at Coningsby. This was not possible and we were instructed to climb to 2,000 ft and bale out, but damage and fuel shortage prevented us doing so. I would mention that another 83 Squadron aircraft flown by our Flight Commander Sqn Ldr Hatcher was also in the Coningsby circuit, in similar difficulty and with fuel gauges reading zero.

An immediate decision was made to divert both of us to Metheringham which was equipped with FIDO. Within seconds we could see this glow through the fog as it was lit. Sqn Ldr Hatcher reported that his engines were cutting due to fuel starvation, and our pilot Flt Lt Cassidy told him to go in first. As Sqn Ldr Hatcher was approaching the runway, his engines cut out and he crashed, killing all on board except the rear-gunner.

We flew in through swirling fog to the tremendous roar and glare from FIDO on either side of the runway and it was just a question of pulling hard back on the throttles while the pilot did the same with the control column, and the aircraft just dropped on to the runway. My recollection of those moments is most vivid as FIDO was so bright that we were blinded as we approached touchdown; and once down, the heat and light were frightening as we fought to keep the aircraft straight. Had we swerved off the runway we would have run into the FIDO jets.

Once the Control Tower knew that we were down and no other aircraft were about, they cut off FIDO. That was an equally frightening experience, as the fog and silence came down and we could see Sqn Ldr Hatcher's machine burning behind us. We logged 10 hours 25 minutes on that flight. As a crew we completed 35 ops together, but I guess that experience with FIDO was the most frightening.

This brought the recorded use of FIDO at Metheringham during December to twenty-four landings and 113 for the period of its operational existence so far, though it is quite possible that others have gone unnoticed.

The weather during January 1945 was as bad at Metheringham as anywhere else and snow-clearing was an all too familiar fatigue. The station ops record book summarized it as: 'Noteworthy only by reason of the atrocious weather which has been responsible for the lowering of our operational effort. Snow persisted, culminating in a blizzard on the 30th which deposited ten inches of snow on the airfield.'

No use of FIDO is recorded during the month, and it does not appear to have been used in February either. On 15/16 February, when four of 106 Squadron's Lancasters had been engaged on mine-laying sorties, the station record book says 'Owing to low cloud and fog in the base area all four aircraft were diverted to Kinloss.' This suggests that the winter months of 1945 were so severe that, the limitations of FIDO being understood, it was not considered feasible to expect clearance from the system.

The burners were lit in low visibility conditions on 14 March. The difficulty was caused by thick haze 1,000 ft deep and bright morning sunlight. Horizontal visibility at ground level was 600 yd, but pilots were dazzled when they tried to descend through the overcast. Four American C–47 air ambulances, making a routine drop-off en route for Prestwick from base A42 in France, asked for assistance in outlining the runway, and FIDO was lit at 09.50. Visibility was improved to 2,000 yd for them. 'The American pilots had not seen FIDO before and were unanimous in their approval,' notes the fog dispersal report. No other wartime uses of FIDO are recorded.

Metheringham was by no means the busiest FIDO station during the war, although the total number of landings may well have exceeded 120. Nevertheless, with the nearby airfields of Fiskerton and Ludford also equipped for fog dispersal, it shared in making Lincolnshire a safer place to come home to. With the postwar disbanding of squadrons 106 Squadron came to the end of its time in February 1946. On the 20th the station ops record book sadly notes: '106 Squadron's aircraft were flown to Waddington, and so a squadron with a grand record fades into the past. A funeral service was held, complete with coffin containing squadron photographs of interest, which was buried with full military honours.' It would be fitting to wonder if a few yards of FIDO piping might also have been interred.

FIFTEEN

St Eval

. . . at intervals the piping doubled back on itself like giant trombones

Arthur C. Clarke, Glide Path

The site of RAF St Eval occupies a crude plateau just inland from the 300 ft high cliffs which are the main scenic feature of this part of Cornwall. Work began in 1938, and the station officially opened on 2 October 1939. In 1940 three concrete runways were constructed, being progressively extended as the war continued and larger aircraft operated therefrom.

The main, 2,000 ft long runway lies on a heading of 261°, with aircraft approaching over the village of Little Trevisker and departing above Trenance. Approaching from the east the land rises from a valley. The runway follows this slope, and the first 300 yd are on an upward gradient before falling gently away. This rise and fall caused frequent palpitations to crews of landing aircraft, as unexpected occupants of the airstrip came into view when they breasted the rise, and Chris Ashworth recalled the alarm of an airman he saw taking a short cut across the runway when an aircraft being scrambled suddenly swept over the crest. The airman almost became airborne himself in his haste to vacate the concourse.

The proposal to install FIDO at St Eval was made at least as early as April 1943, and was confirmed on 27 July. Initially, Coastal Command had requested it at Ballykelly in Northern Ireland as well, but settled for the Cornish airfield alone. St Eval appears in Petroleum Warfare Department records as Station XVI. Although the necessity for a FIDO-equipped airfield in the south-west was agreed so that round the clock patrols of the Western Approaches and the Bay of Biscay could be maintained, the weather peculiarities of the area taxed the ingenuity of its designers at a time when the apparatus was still in a somewhat primitive state. It has occasionally been said that one cannot have fog and wind together, but Cornish conditions belie that statement; in fact Chris asserts that: 'It is the only coast where gale force fog is a feature. In reality this is of course cloud formed when very moist air is forced upwards by the cliffs; but it results in virtual fog conditions, accompanied by a strong and often turbulent wind.'

St Eval's was the eighth installation to be commenced, by Messrs J.L. Eve, in August 1943. Almost immediately a warning note was sounded. St Eval

. . . presents a special problem. These south-west coastal airfields rarely suffer from radiation fog, i.e. due to cooling of the ground by radiation on clear nights. . . . They are however, subject to sea fog which drifts in with a wind of 10–15 mph. A special layout is needed to clear a lane in these conditions. No particular difficulty is anticipated in designing a suitable layout and this is being pressed on urgently. The installation proposed should enable aircraft to take off in fog although it may not be possible to use it for landing. Diversion to airfields clear of fog would then be necessary.

When told, the prime minister obviously did not regard the difficulties as insurmountable, for he cheerfully replied, 'Good. Press on!' Press on they did, although each progress report stressed the difficulties which were being encountered. That for 20 September records: 'Sea fog and other unusual conditions have to be dealt with. Practically double the normal amount of equipment will be required and it is not yet possible to give a date for completion.'

The much greater wetness normal to sea fog made it necessary for St Eval to be provided with sources of heat considerably exceeding that provided on a normal land station. The three runways intersected rather less than halfway along the runway. Therefore at these points the Haigill Mk IV surface burners (see Fig. 5) had to be replaced by IRBs (Plate 22), sunk in trenches covered with iron gratings.

FIDO was required for use in taking off as well as landing. The land surface rose sharply a short distance before the beginning of the runway, with irregular contours; the differences of level over the area being of the order of 40–80 ft within 250–500 yd of the end of the runway. Owing to this, a standard approach length of 250 yd between touchdown and approach cross-line was only just attained. To meet the requirements for taking off, the principal side-lines extended the whole length of the runway. Normally the last 500 yd were covered by burners placed on alternate sides; and a double cross line was constructed beyond its south-west end. All these were 30-therm lines.

While this would suffice for an inland station, the greatly increased water content of the heaviest sea fogs rendered the provision of one 30-therm line on either side of the runway insufficient for dealing with the fogs that commonly occurred there. To overcome this difficulty it was found better to install two more lines of 30-therm burners 75 yd outside the inner lines rather than increase the output of the inner burners. By meeting cross-winds at a greater distance from the runway, the outer lines provided more effectively for the higher layer of fog over the runway. Four lines of burners were installed over the first 1,300 yd of runway and two rows for 690 yd beyond that. The layout is perhaps best understood by reference to Fig. 23 and Plate 60.

Substantial construction work was necessary to ensure adequate fuel supplies for the system. A report of 24 November 1943 says that: 'Road diversions to be carried out will take two months. New railway sidings and lorry-filling facilities have to be installed at Newquay to handle railway tank wagons.' Over a period of time two spur sidings were built at Shell-Mex's Newquay Quintrell Down depot, large enough to contain a trainload of 10-ton petrol wagons and equipped with a 50-ton pump to load up to four road tankers at a time. A shuttle service of tankers plied between the depot and the airfield. Chief of Air Staff Sir Charles Portal confided in November 1943:

> We have as yet no experience of fog clearance in low stratus conditions, but a special equipment is nearing completion at St Eval, which is particularly liable to low stratus and sea fog conditions. Operational trials will take place in March [about a month later than originally hoped for]. PWD is confident that the equipment will clear the runway sufficiently for take-off. This will be a great advantage to the anti-U-boat patrols. The problem of landing in these conditions is more difficult, but it is anticipated that experienced pilots will be able to land by use of fog dispersal and the GCA unit which is to be placed at this airfield.

Some of the best descriptions of FIDO at St Eval come from the pen of Arthur C. Clarke, a natural communicator, in his novel *Glide Path*. As an RAF officer he was in charge of the first Ground Control Approach (GCA) equipment during its experimental period there and has embodied his experiences in its pages. Although the characters are fictional, 'the incidents are based upon real events and are indeed unadorned reminiscences'. Returning to the aerodrome after a period of absence he commented:

> It was indeed an impressive shambles, and it was quite hard to believe that despite it all the airfield was still in full working order. Stretching the entire length of the runway, on each side of the broad concrete strip, were rows of pipes, supported a foot above the ground. It looked as if all the plumbing of an oil refinery had been laid alongside the runway. At regular intervals the piping

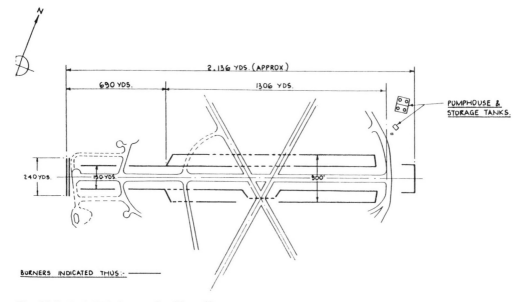

Fig. 23 St Eval, Fido layout. See Plate 60

doubled back on itself to form sections like giant trombones, and at other strategic spots were huge valves and control wheels. All that was needed to complete the picture were the derricks.

Arthur C. Clarke describes an operational burn:

> A mile away, over by the fuel storage tanks a great gout of black smoke billowed up into the sky. Beneath it was a lurid yellow flame which raced along the lines of pipes faster than a man could run. Within seconds a wall of fire had extended the whole length of the runway, while above it rolling thunderheads of oily smoke drifted across the airfield. The nearest of the burners was more than 100 ft away, but even at that distance the roar of the yard-high flames was impressive and Alan could feel the heat against his face. The smoke seemed to be getting worse, and it was coming closer. Presently he began to cough in the oily clouds which were rapidly reducing visibility to zero. Slowly and none too soon, conditions improved . . . The roar of the flames became still more deep throated as the pumps increased their pressure. Now that the system had warmed up, the fuel was burning clearly as vapour, not smokily as liquid. . . .
>
> And now, apart from a stubborn section over there on the far side of the airfield, the parallel walls of fire were almost smokeless – roaring jets like those from a gas burner, but thousands of feet in length. The entire landscape quivered with heat. Was it imagination, or were the very clouds themselves being driven upwards by the columns of rising air?

Determined to establish just how FIDO could counter difficult conditions which were not experienced by any other station so equipped, station commander Gp Capt R.C. Meade took off at 21.00 on 21 April in deteriorating conditions. Low cloud had reduced visibility to only 1,000 yd and the wind had moved round so that it blew straight up the runway. When the burners were lit, they seemed to create air conditions of their own and the wind moved to an angle off the airstrip. It was only possible to lift the cloud to about 50 ft. The Oxford managed a safe take-off and landing but it was not thought likely that a cumbersome four-engined machine could have done so except in extreme emergency. As a result of the observations made it was proposed to extend the outer lines of burners over the whole length of the runway, making a double row throughout.

Further observations were made on 11 June, when 1,500 ft of advection fog swept in from WSW at 10–12 mph, reducing visibility to below 200 yd. When FIDO was lit an enhanced wind was created along the runway, rising to 30 mph at the approach end. Visibility

Plate 60 St Eval aerial. Runway 26. The complicated burner layout is best explained by reference to Fig. 23 (Crown/MoD)

improved to 2,000 yd and the cloud base lifted to 500 ft at the touchdown and 100 ft at the other. The tunnel of clear air extended eastwards so that visibility in that direction increased to nearly two miles. Unfortunately, during the course of a burn the wind direction often changed, and so did the position of the tunnel; so that although a beam approach would position a pilot where the runway began, the clear air might well be a quarter of a mile to one side.

The pilot, Flt Lt Tilley, was accompanied by the station commander and GCA officer in an Oxford which took off to probe the problem. In *Glide Path*, Arthur C. Clarke has reconstructed the exercise in graphic detail:

It was easy to understand how in the days before blind flying instruments were invented, pilots in fog had become hopelessly confused. There was no sensation of motion; they were sitting in a dimly lit resonating void that had no contact with any other world. The perspex windows might not have been there for all the help they gave; all that could be seen through them was the fitful glare of the exhausts and the more distant twinkle of the navigation lights on the wing-tips. Sometimes even they were lost as the aircraft plunged into a thicker stratum of fog. . . .

And now, unmistakably, there was a lifting of the darkness ahead. An ill-defined glow like the first hint of dawn appeared where until a moment before had been nothing but the blackest night. It warmed Alan's heart to see it; they were nearly home. . . .

The first line of fire appeared so suddenly that it took them by surprise, even though they had been expecting it. Marching into the mist, both behind and ahead of them, it lay at an acute angle to their course – and that was absurd, for they should have been flying straight along it. Something had gone badly wrong; the aircraft heading was wildly in error and the runway was certainly not 'a little to your left', as the controller had said.

Dennis was struggling to get C-Charlie back over the runway, but it was too late. The error had been so unexpected, so completely unreasonable, that he had no time to correct it. One by one the four lines of fire slid beneath them; then they had crabbed across the runway and were once more out into the darkness.

After an abortive circuit, they let down for another attempt:

They hit the updraught from the burners and caught their first glimpse of the runway at the same instant. The fog parted before their eyes, so that suddenly they were looking along a glowing canyon walled with flame. . . . But they were still separated from the runway by an infinite 30 ft and an appalling 120 miles an hour. The concrete slabs flickering backward beneath their wheels might have been a universe away.

Now that rising gale was upon them again, tearing at wings and fuselage, trying to fling them back into the sky. But this time Dennis was ready for it; he opened the throttle, pouring on the power in an attempt to drag C-Charlie through that wall of wind by brute force.

The runway accelerated beneath them, gaining speed instead of losing it. Then, as Dennis had hoped, the turbulent buffeting died away and they passed into smoother air. But he was using up runway at a terrifying rate – the end of the luminous canyon was only 1,000 ft away. Better hit the deck now, before it was too late.

He cut the engines a second before impact. All things considered, it was not too bad a landing. Aircraft tyres, however, can stand only so much. C-Charlie was still doing a good 90 miles an hour, when there was a loud report on the starboard side, followed instantly by a violent lurch and a horrible squeal of metal on concrete. A stream of sparks trailed from the naked wheel hub as it ground against the runway, and like a lop-sided drunkard C-Charlie veered even more steeply towards the right.

It was moving almost sideways when, with great reluctance, it left the firm safety of the concrete and slithered on to the soggy, yielding earth. The starboard prop turned itself into a plough. There was a fantastic symphony of groaning metal and twanging control cables and a final lurch as the aircraft tried to stand on its nose, failed, and flopped heavily back on a level keel. For a moment there was silence in the cabin. It was, they suddenly realized, utterly dark. Someone had promptly extinguished FIDO as a safety precaution within seconds of touchdown. 'Not one of my better efforts!' said Dennis.

Dr A.O. Rankine, who had conducted the wind tunnel experiments in London, was present when this test was carried out; which incidentally had cost the taxpayer 155,000 gallons of petrol. After consultation it was sought to make the approach end of FIDO at St Eval into a fan-shape, half a mile long and a quarter mile wide, tapering to the width of the approach box itself to allow for veering or backing of the winds during a burn, and capable of clearing the air to a height of 200 ft. With the existing terrain to the north-east of the airfield there was no likelihood of this being done. The only possibility seemed to be to add yet another line of burners each side of the runway at the approach end, covering the first 600 yd of the airstrip. Nothing eventually became of the proposals. It was never found possible to construct an approach system capable of clearing the enormous apron required, and when conditions were too severe, aircraft just had to be diverted, even if St Eval was their home base.

Some home-based Liberators were aloft as well, and it was decided to light FIDO in order to bring down one of 53 Squadron's machines just after midnight; more of an experiment than an emergency.

Visibility was down to 600 yd with 300 ft deep fog being blown in from the NNE, over the pilot's right shoulder. The inner lines and two cross-burners at the approach end of the runway were lit, and the wind speed immediately increased to 15 mph. The fog soon began to disperse and the sky could be seen above. Horizontal visibility improved for the whole length of the runway and for some 600 yd downwind of it. The liberator, Z-Zebra flown by flt Lt Burton, landed safely and its pilot said that he had no difficulty in landing and that a cross-wind did not worry him. 'In my opinion a simple and safe landing could easily be made in conditions twice as bad as experienced on this occasion.'

Early on 6 August, the opportunity was taken to use FIDO for the take-off of a fully laden Liberator. Sea and radiation fog had reduced visibility to 300 yd, with only 100 yd in patches, extending from 40 to 100 ft deep. Light-up took place at 03.40, the inner burners only being fired. It was decided not to ignite the western end cross-burners lest they be a danger to a heavily laden aircraft barely clear of the ground. In the event the clearance was perfectly satisfactory for the take-off and the pilot reported no problems. The fog dispersal report, however, adds the following anecdote:

> When the burners were turned off, but still running on residual fuel, a Lysander made an emergency landing at the western end of the runway. The landing was unobserved, and with visibility deteriorating to 30 yd again, the aircraft was totally enveloped in fog. This Lysander, without R/T, was not in touch with Flying Control. The pilot, who was lost, had seen the glow from the burners 50 miles away, and seeing the Liberator after it took off, decided to make a landing. Having landed his aircraft with no apparent difficulty, the pilot himself was two hours wandering about the airfield in the fog trying to get his bearings!

There was, however, rather more to it than that. The Lysander in question was from 161 Squadron based at RAF Winkleigh near Exeter, engaged on SOE operations. Flown by Flg Off G.J.E. (Alex) Alexander, it had delivered two agents to a field near Chartre sur le Loir and picked up a man and a girl with a damaged hip:

> At approximately 02.00 on 6 August 1944 I landed on ground L22. From the air the ground seemed excellent and the landing signal was well sent. My first approach was bad and I overshot. On my second attempt I touched down on stubble, but on coming level with lamps B and C ran into a narrow belt of standing crop. Coming out of this I ran into stubble again, but this seemed to have obstacles in the form of stooked corn or bundles of hay. On hitting one of these I damaged my tail oleo. The field, in my estimation, was not fit at the time although it would be excellent if the crop was cut and the other obstacles removed. To make sure of a safe take-off, I taxied to a point about 30 yd before lamp A and with emergency boost managed to clear the obstacles.

Alex reported that the ground level photographs of the field were useless; to which his flight commander added that the landing information had been provided 'by a rather clueless escorting officer', and doubted whether the flare path was even in the right field.

Gp Capt Hugh Verity, who includes this incident in his book *We Landed by Moonlight*, goes on to say that in his encounter with the obstacles, Alex's Lysander was so badly damaged that he could not steer it normally on the ground and that it would only go round in circles. Besides that, damage to his elevator meant that he had to fly home on the trimmer. His stick only controlled the ailerons. It could not move fore and aft. Additionally, due to damaged aerials, he had to fly home without radio to south-western England which was covered with fog by the time he arrived. In these circumstances a very lucky chance led him to St Eval just as the Liberator had taken off. Alex landed from the 'wrong' end of the runway and had no sooner come to a standstill than FIDO was turned off by ground crew unaware of his presence. As he could not steer the Lysander round the perimeter track, he left his passengers in the back cockpit and set off on foot to find help. By this time of the war the Lysander pilots no longer bothered to cover their civilian clothes with RAF uniform. Alex took off through the fog in a dark grey suit, rather wondering how he would explain himself when he met someone on duty. He walked round the perimeter track for an hour before he found the Control Tower. Eventually he found himself explaining his arrival to the station commander, who made his own quarters available for the agents until they could be collected by road. Alex went back to the Lysander in the CO's car and found his two passengers deeply entwined on the floor of their cockpit. Obviously they had grown tired of waiting!

Conditions were just as bad early on 8 August, with sea fog 200 ft deep and visibility right down to 50 yd. FIDO was lit at 03.00 to bring in five Liberators from patrols over the Bay of Biscay; H, O and X of 224 Squadron, Z of 53 Squadron and N of 547 Squadron. The whole apparatus was ablaze in a short time and the sky became visible overhead, though there was considerable intrusion of fog where the perimeter track crossed the runway. Twenty-five faults were subsequently found in the system, but even so the pilots agreed that the clearing of the runway was adequate. In between the landings of the last two aircraft, Liberator L of 547 Squadron made a satisfactory take-off for the Bay.

Liberator N-Nan, the last to land, was flown by Flt Lt E.M. Allies, who submitted a model report on his arrival:

> I approached the airfield from the north and saw the glow of FIDO at a distance of 36 miles. I homed towards the glow, flying above cloud at 1,000 ft, and when directly over the aerodrome I looked down to see the runway and all the area enclosed by FIDO clearly visible, as if all the fog above the runway had been dispersed. I lined up on the runway, setting my directional gyro and made a circuit at about 700 ft, flying in and out of cloud tops . . . I made a rather fast approach (115 mph), expecting bumpy conditions near the ground, but experienced no bumps at all. I found it difficult to judge my height off the runway owing to the brilliance of FIDO, but experienced no difficulty with smoke from the burners. I saw the contact strip half a mile from the beginning of the runway, but at no time saw the flare path lights from the contact strip to the end of the runway. Neither did I see the gooseneck flares which I believe were burning at the far end of the runway. Consequently I braked fairly hard to ensure that I stopped by the end of the contact strip. I suggest that a row of goosenecks or Money flares, stretching from the end of the contact strip to the end of the runway and spaced at the same distance as the lights of the contact strip, would reassure pilots who may imagine that they are overshooting.

Some two hours later, with no improvement in the weather, three Liberators were urgently required for operations, and FIDO was lit again. C, T and M of 574 Squadron took off without difficulty, though the station ops record book notes that M-Mother was subsequently hit by gunfire in the rear perspex turret over the Ile de Groix for its trouble. Liberator H of 53 Squadron, returning late from ops, then made a safe landing after experiencing some difficulty in approach. It was considered that none of the landings or take-offs that day could have been accomplished without FIDO.

Further bad weather trials continued during the autumn of 1944, with a severe test on 22 November. A WSW wind of 20 mph blew surface-based stratus clouds almost straight up the runway. The cross-burners at the western end never got going because of the strong wind; some burners along the lower parts of the field became waterlogged and belched continuous smoke; the wind became so noisy that orders given through the loudspeakers could not be heard and the airfield remained firmly clamped in fog. Even so, 107,100 gallons of petrol were used.

Inconclusive results were also achieved during a burn on 5 February 1945 when 'an interesting trial' took place in 'severe conditions'. A 20 mph wind had brought sea fog in, reducing visibility to 50 yd. When FIDO was lit, two valves stuck shut and four burners broke down, and although a clearance of 800 yd was achieved within the lines of burners which did function, it was considered doubtful whether a large aircraft would have been able to land in safety. The cost was 59,200 gallons.

Plate 61 St Eval. Runway 26. Viewed from the north. Approach from left. Storage tanks bottom left. 224 Squadron Liberators dispersed nearby. Inner lines burning cleanly. Outer line smoking on initial light-up. (R.A. Bell)

Another burn which impressed itself on Bill Howarth, formerly of 206 Squadron, occurred: '. . . one night as I was returning from Newquay. The sky was lit up and there was a sound like a million blowlamps in operation . . . Legend had it that two lads cycled the length of it towing torches of burning rag to set it alight . . . There was a major shortage of fuel the following morning; visitors' tanks were checked and topped up with only enough fuel to get them back to base.'

The last recorded occasion when FIDO was used at St Eval (always remembering that not all fog dispersal reports have survived) was on 5 April 1945 when several Wellingtons were in the area about dusk. Visibility was about 2,000 yd but deteriorating, so two burners at the approach end were lit as markers. Then, however, the clouds thickened and lowered until they were on the surface and a full burn was ordered. A complete clearance was obtained 'over the whole of the runway and to leeward of it, the low stratus being banked up on that side'. When that was achieved, three Wellingtons landed without difficulty, but a fourth, which arrived after darkness had set in, found it impossible to line up with the runway, and after several attempts to land was diverted elsewhere. Again, prodigious efforts were made to achieve clearance and 120,000 gallons of petrol were expended in holding back the clouds for three hours.

The sum total of FIDO usage at St Eval seems to have been five operational take-offs and twelve landings, and four test take-offs and landings. The amount of petrol consumed was enormous. The severest weather was too much for the Mark IV and V burners to deal with. Whether the giant Hades system as installed at Manston would have done any better we cannot know. There are numerous occasions recorded when aircraft were diverted to such places as Chivenor and Davidstow without FIDO even being lit. The good news is, however, that there is no record of any such diversions resulting in disaster.

SIXTEEN

Sturgate

. . . throwing lighted matches at three pipes along the runway!

George Gleeson, flying controller

Sturgate is about four miles south-east of Gainsborough in Lincolnshire. In pre-war *Kelly's Directories* it is listed merely as a hamlet south of Springthorpe, consisting of two farmhouses and a few labourers' cottages.

Bruce Halpenny records that RAF Sturgate was built as a Bomber Command station within 1 Group, but was never operational as such, only being used as a circuit training field and a relief landing ground for RAF Blyton. Sturgate had the usual three concrete runways, the longest being 2,000 yd on a west to east heading of 078°. The airfield was among the last batch of stations to be earmarked for equipment with FIDO in December 1943, and was designated Station XXI.

Work on the installation began early in January 1944, A. Monk & Co. being the FIDO contractors and Strongarc of Lincoln the welders. No FIDO plan of the airfield has survived, but from aerial photographs it is likely that the runway had an approach box of about 250 yd, followed by about 1,300 yd of Mark IV burners (see Fig. 5) on each side of the runway. These were 50 yd back from the runway and ended just before the junction of the main runway with runway 20. Runway 14 crossed the FIDO runway only about 100 yd after touchdown, so IRBs (Plate 22) set in trenches were installed at that point. To fuel the burners, three cylindrical steel storage tanks encased in brickwork with a capacity approaching half a million gallons were built to the south of the approach box, a few hundred yards from Mr Labley's Lodge Farm. A siding alongside the railway line running south from Gainsborough was built near Lea (its exact position is unknown). There, up to two dozen tank wagons could be accommodated and their petrol pumped 2¾ miles through a 6in underground pipeline to the storage tanks on the airfield. The layout of the siding and its equipment would have approximated to that shown in Fig. 19 and Plates 49–52.

Not much more than 10 per cent of work had been completed on any part of the system by 20 January 1944, but a fortnight later it was pronounced ahead of schedule, with an anticipated completion date of 6 May. This forecast had to be revised a month later when it was reported that: 'This airfield has no less than sixteen old ponds on site which have had to be filled in and difficulty has been met in excavating the trenches using mechanical diggers.' It is likely that the machines were constantly getting bogged down and that the good old British workman had to finish the job.

Donald Sinclair was posted to Sturgate as a member of a crash and fire tender crew at about this time:

When I arrived, the FIDO installation was at a stage of near completion, but had not been given any test burns. Flying activities in those days consisted mainly of Hemswell Lancasters doing circuits and bumps, Sturgate not yet being operational. Sitting on the crash tender one could look towards the Hemswell ridge and see operational aircraft taking off and landing.

My first experience of FIDO was when we were called out on a practice exercise to the large storage tanks for the fuel system and had to set up a curtain of water in between the tanks. On full burn FIDO could consume thousands of gallons per minute of raw petrol, so you can imagine the intense heat given off.

After the system had been given several test burns it was decided that crash tenders would stand by not only at the Control Tower but also at the end of the runway when the FIDO system was used operationally to bring aircraft in.

Sturgate's ops record book begins on 21 December 1944. Curiously enough the opening entry records the first FIDO landing, on that date. Over 1,300 bombers had been active in opposing General von Rundstedt's Ardennes advance and had encountered fog over most of eastern England as they made their way home. FIDO was called for at eight airfields in the early evening, including Sturgate.

There, radiation and smoke-polluted fog up to 1,500 ft deep had gathered during the day and visibility was down to 300–500 yd. Twenty Lancasters of 625 Squadron based at Kelstern, some 20 miles to the east of Sturgate, had been part of a 1 Group force attacking Ascheffenburg railyards. Diversion signals were sent to them as they crossed the North Sea and the squadron divided into two, half going to Fiskerton and the remaining ten heading for Sturgate.

Plate 62 Sturgate aerial. Approach end of runway 07. Little used operationally, the approach box is barely visible, but scorch marks can be seen where FIDO crosses the first intersecting runway, almost as soon as an aircraft has touched down (Crown/MoD)

The FIDO and crash crews were summoned when the order to light FIDO was given at 19.47. Donald Sinclair was on duty:

> The whole of the airfield was bound in fog when we took up station. All we could hear was the engine of the fire tender ticking over, the distant words of NCOs in charge of FIDO crews, and bird calls from disturbed inhabitants of neighbouring hedges. Gradually, a flicker of flame began at the near end of the runway on both sides and spread along its whole length until disappearing into the thick murk of the fog. These flames were the initial heat-up of FIDO. After ten minutes or so the whole system was turned on and with a massive roar, flames shot up on either side of the runway to a height of several feet, lifting the fog as if by magic. One could see the full length of the runway as if looking down a massive tunnel.

The first of 625 Squadron's Lancasters approached at 20.29. Hoping that their instruments were telling the truth, one aircraft after another began to circle at its allotted height, and during the next hour a total of ten landed safely. Ramsey Turner remembered that before take-off at 15.07 the squadron had been: ' . . . told that on our return we were going to divert to a FIDO station. This turned out to be Sturgate, landing time 20.50, obviously due to fog forecast on our return. From memory we made quite a successful landing and we may also have used FIDO for our take-off back to base on 24 December, Christmas Eve.'

The fog dispersal report on this, the first operational burn at Sturgate, rated it: 'A definite success. All ten aircraft landed without difficulty in conditions impossible for landing otherwise.' One pilot expressed surprise that the installation 'lined' the runway; exactly where he expected the burners to be is not clear. As an aside, Air Traffic Controller George Gleeson commented: 'The thing which stuck in my mind was the primitive way in which it was set alight; throwing lighted matches at three pipes alongside the runway!'

FIDO consumed a total of 138,127 gallons of petrol from initial light-up at 19.47 to close-down two hours later. After dispersing the aircraft into the care of Sturgate ground crews 625's personnel made their tortuous way back along the foggy lanes to Kelstern for de-briefing and a good night's sleep.

Plate 63 George Gleeson comments on the crude way in which FIDO was lit. This photograph illustrates his point (IWM)

The fog persisted for three or four days over most of eastern England, and it was not possible for the crews to feel their way back to Sturgate for their machines until Christmas Eve, as Ramsey Turner recalled. Although conditions at Kelstern were suitable for landing, taking off at Sturgate was impossible unless FIDO had been lit. Visibility was down to only 50 yd at times, with 100 per cent wet radiation fog, and it took 25 minutes for FIDO to clear the runway to a visibility of 800 yd. Sqn Ldr Russell, pilot of the first machine to trundle down the airstrip, reported that conditions were excellent for take-off and that he considered that aircraft could also have landed without difficulty.

FIDO was lit at 13.50, but Sqn Ldr Russell did not take off until all of his charges had groped their way round the perimeter track on to his tail nearly an hour later. They then took off post haste at 14.37; nine of them becoming airborne in only seven minutes. Unfortunately, number ten blotted his copybook by getting bogged down off the perimeter track en route. Whether its crew got back to Kelstern in time for their Christmas dinner is not recorded. All told FIDO was alight for two hours, burning 126,157 gallons of petrol.

Not until 14 March 1945 is there another reference to FIDO being in use again, when two glider-tug Stirlings from Rivenhall in Essex were diverted owing to extremely bad weather conditions. Horizontal visibility at 15.00 was 1,200 yd, but vertically the ground was invisible. FIDO was lit at 15.47, and in the course of an hour's burning, consuming 42,000 gallons of petrol, visibility cleared to nearly two miles. Two Stirlings landed in safety. One of the aircraft was flown by Dick Draper of 295 Squadron, normally engaged on Resistance support work:

Following a Group exercise code-named Vulture [preparation for operation Varsity – crossing the Rhine] on 14 March 1945, fog became widespread over a large area of England, causing the diversion of many Group aircraft. I was sent to Sturgate and held there at about 2–3,000 ft in beautiful weather above the fog, awaiting FIDO's operation. The first indication was a darkening of the fog covering an area slightly larger than the expected size of the runway. This dark area grew blacker and began to break into rising smoke and cloud.

The rectangular line of flame surrounding the runway gradually came into view, and eventually it became clear enough to allow a visual circuit and landing. I can't remember how long we had to hold, waiting for the fog clearance, or that there were any great problems with turbulence as we crossed the threshold on the final approach. Normally we never chatted on the intercom, but only spoke about the aircraft's operation. However, when we were circuiting Sturgate waiting for the burners to complete the fog dispersal, a small voice was heard over the intercom, saying quietly, 'Here FIDO, here FIDO!' The rear-gunner had left his switch on.

There are no more records of FIDO's use before the end of the war; but just as FIDO occupied the first entry in Sturgate's ops record book, so it also filled the last. The final lines for March 1946 read: 'During the month, work has been in progress replacing the Mark IV burners on FIDO with Mark V burners' (Fig. 7). On 31 March 1946 Sturgate was reduced to a Care and Maintenance basis.

From 1952 to 1958 the airfield was under US Air Force control, continuing in use by them until returned to the RAF in 1964. Light aircraft activity has been carried on at Sturgate until the present date.

SEVENTEEN

Tuddenham

. . . an awe-inspiring sight when in full flow – a noise like continuous thunder

Jimmy Barclay

The parish of Tuddenham lies seven and a half miles north-west of Bury St Edmunds and about three miles south-east of Mildenhall in Suffolk. It had a population between the wars of fewer than 300. The site for the airfield on Cavenham Heath was requisitioned early in 1943. Civil engineers Taylor Woodrow were constructors for the aerodrome, which was opened as a bomber station within 3 Group, home to 90 Squadron and its Stirlings. Tuddenham's ops record book commenced on 1 October 1943, Gp Capt O.A. Morris taking command on the 6th. The main party and all the aircraft arrived on 13 October, operations beginning four days later.

Aboard the first Stirling to land was aircrewman Ron James, who noted in his diary the following day: 'Had a good look at the heathland and woods at the back of dispersal and it seems a good place for game and some rough shooting!' A friend of his was less complimentary: 'We had to land there once when returning from ops and it was the worst dump we ever went to.' In his book *Chocks Away*, Eric Wannop describes Tuddenham as: 'extremely flat and spacious; so much so that it was impossible to see activities on the far perimeter without binoculars. There were three runways, any trees growing at either end of them having been removed for a distance of 100–200 yd. Two runways were 1,400 yd long and one was 2,000. All were fitted with standard beam approach to aid pilots' bad weather descent.'

Tuddenham was among the final group of airfields to be earmarked as a FIDO station in December 1943, when it was still some way from completion, being designated Station XIX. As a site for such a purpose it was quite well chosen, for eight other aerodromes lay within a distance of ten miles. Tuddenham was not well served by road for the transport of building materials, however, and the nearest railway station was at Higham, 4 miles to the south.

Although no FIDO airfield plan survives, the main runway, which was on an approach of 300°, approximately south-east to north-west, was lined with a series of Haigill Mark IV burners (see Fig. 5) for about a mile of its length. These were set back 50 yd from the runway's edge. Approximately one-third and two-thirds of the way along, the main runway was crossed diagonally by subsidiary runways 06 and 18. To avoid obstruction to aircraft when these were in operation, trenched IRBs (Plate 22) were installed at their junctions. A 200 yd approach box preceded the touchdown point, so that aircraft coming in to land would cross low over the road to Icklingham. To supply the FIDO system with its fuel, a single track siding was built along the railway line near Higham (its exact location is unknown). This was capable of receiving up to about twenty rail tankers at a time. Petrol was pumped from them through a 6 in main by a stationary pumping engine housed nearby, and from there via a 6 in underground pipeline across 4 miles of fields to three huge storage tanks in the south-east corner of the aerodrome. Between them they held about half a million gallons

Plate 64 Tuddenham aerial. Runway 30. Most of approach box visible and burner marks to second runway intersection, after which burners were on alternate sides. Storage tanks SW of touchdown. Twenty-seven aircraft at various dispersals (Crown/MoD)

of petrol. For a likely layout of the siding see Fig. 19 and Plates 49–52. Construction of the FIDO system as well as the airfield itself was undertaken by Taylor Woodrow, beginning in the new year of 1944. Work kept pretty well up to schedule, a progress report of April stating that:

> . . . The first trainload of gasoline is due for delivery on 26 April and the initial testing of the burner units will commence immediately these stocks are received. By the operational date given in our last report (29 April), there should be sufficient gasoline in stock to operate the installation for one hour.
> The railway siding is now practically finished and all work on the airfield is completed with the exception of the IRB crossings; but all arrangements are in hand for this work to proceed, and men are being transferred from siding construction immediately.

When FIDO was put to the test for the first time, the results took everybody by surprise. Early on the morning of 8 August a burn was ordered by the station commander to ascertain the effect of FIDO on low stratus cloud and also as a night exercise for FIDO and flying control personnel. A.D. Stobbs remembers when the system was lit: 'it was a typical East Anglian night; not thick fog but misty enough to prevent flying'. In fact there was a cloud base of only 150 ft, and stratus 350 ft deep:

> I cannot recall why I was on the airfield at the time, but clearly remember being at the end of the runway when FIDO was lit by the ground crew, using a sort of goosenecked flare. The heat generated was very welcome on a cold night from a position some 10 to 15 yd away. Gradually the mist between the two lines of fire dispersed, and in a relatively short time it was possible to look skywards to a clear black night between two walls of mist.

Philip Reilly, a flight mechanic with 90 Squadron, takes up the story:

> It was then, in the middle of all the excitement, as we all asked one another, 'Is the fog lifting?' that the most remarkable happening of a remarkable day took place. Suddenly, and silently, because the roar of its engines could not be heard above the roar of the FIDO flames, an American medium bomber appeared out of the fog above the end of the runway. It narrowly missed cars parked by senior staff watching the test, flew uncertainly between the twin rows of pipes and touched down with something more than a bump!

The machine was in fact a USAF Marauder, lost on a night exercise. The pilot had apparently tried to land four times at each of two other airfields before espying FIDO alight at Tuddenham. *TEE EMM* records what it said were his actual comments:

> I saw the glare of the fire in the sky and flew over to you. I saw the fire through the patch in the clouds and flew round to have another look. I received your QDM and QFE. I made a second run to weigh things up. I'd never seen FIDO before or even heard of it, but the thing made sense to me. I realized that it was a pattern and that it was a runway indication. I decided to make an approach with undercarriage up, to make quite sure. It's the best thing I ever saw.

When asked by the station commander if he thought that FIDO had been any help to him, he replied, 'No sir; it was more than a help. I couldn't have landed without it. I'd tried eight times already and I know!' The station ops record book concludes with the comment, 'Now that FIDO is completed and working, Tuddenham is really on the map and our troubles will be cut to the minimum.'

On the night of 26/27 August 1944 Tuddenham's own aircraft were not operating but 844 other machines were. The Baltic port of Konigsberg was attacked by 174 Lancasters of 5 Group. The weather deteriorated as the time for their return approached, visibility at ground level dwindling from about 1,600 yd to less than 600. The radiation fog was only 50 ft deep and might well have cleared given time; but with nearly 10 hours already spent aloft that was a commodity the pilots just didn't have. Accordingly, all of 97 Squadron from Coningsby were directed to divert to Tuddenham. The installation was lit at 05.50 and as soon as the smoke had cleared, horizontal visibility improved vastly.

> Thirteen aircraft were landed during the burn (and one just prior to lighting up) . . . I estimate that ten of the fourteen aircraft would not have been safely landed without the aid of FIDO. Some of the aircraft were short of fuel and could not have been diverted to any other airfield. The pilots, who all had experience of FIDO, had no difficulty in landing, and there were no overshoots. Considerable turbulence was apparent as machines landed. Pilots all remarked on the considerable glare from the installation,

recorded the station commander.

A day of heavy engagement for the Allied air forces and for FIDO was 16 November 1944. Over 1,200 USAF machines and nearly as many from Bomber Command attacked towns in the path of the American 1st and 9th Armies between Aachen and the Rhine, including 182 Lancasters of 3 Group. Of these, sixteen were of 90 Squadron and eighteen from 186 Squadron which had been formed from 90's 'C' flight in October. They were briefed to raid Sterkrade but the target was subsequently changed to Heinsburg.

Reg Hobden, who was the squadron commander's navigator in O-Orange, remembers that they had to take off with the aid of FIDO in the early afternoon. Although the weather conditions were classified only as mist, with horizontal visibility at ground level of nearly a mile, the mist was 1,500 ft deep, and the FIDO burners were lit to get the machines under way. Reg recalled:

> We viewed FIDO with some misgivings because we had once been a Stirling squadron, and that aircraft had an alarming tendency to swerve on take-off. We often joked about the horrors of having it turned on for this purpose. That actually happened to me for the first time on 16 November 1944, when our target was Heinsburg. It was clear that in the prevailing fog FIDO had to be used. Fortunately we had converted to Lancasters a few months earlier. Nevertheless, Wg Cdr Ogilvie decided that he ought to be in the first aircraft for morale's sake, and as his navigator I went with him. No one experienced any problems.

After landing, Wg Cdr Ogilvie submitted his report on the proceedings:

> When I returned to base area at about 16.55, I was flying at 2,500–3,000 ft, slightly above a layer of strato-cumulus cloud which was 9/10 to 10/10 in amount. Above this cloud, the air was very clear with good visibility, and, although I expected FIDO to be in operation, I found no break in the cloud over the airfield when I homed to it on GEE, and the daylight above the cloud was, in my opinion, still too strong to allow the glow from FIDO to be seen above it.
>
> Since I was not given immediate permission to land, I waited above cloud and commenced to fly a rectangular course around base. However, about 17.00 I was given permission to break cloud. This was carried out in a clearer area about 10 miles north of Tuddenham. The aircraft was below cloud at about 400–600 ft, and I estimated visibility below cloud to be 1,500–2,000 yd horizontally, perhaps slightly worse in patches. In spite of this poor visibility, however, I was able to discern the outline of the FIDO burners at 7–8 miles and it was then easy to home visually to base.
>
> While carrying out a circuit preparatory to landing, the outline of the FIDO was clearly visible from all parts of the circuit, and a normal circuit could be carried out, although it was possible to see only two outer circle lights of the Mk II Drem, at any one time, from the height of 400–500 ft at which I was flying. The approach was commenced, using FIDO as the sole means of regulating my first turn and alignment with the runway. When I approached the sodium funnel, these lights were clearly visible, but only from an angle near the vertical.
>
> On the approach, it was found that the glow from FIDO illuminated the runway to such an extent that it was possible to carry out a normal daylight visual approach, although light conditions below cloud by this time (17.10) would normally have warranted the use of angle of approach indicators. In fact, the light from the FIDO was so effective that the actual flare path was invisible until the aircraft was 300–400 yd from the airfield boundary, at which stage the goosenecks on the runway became dimly visible.

Plate 65 A.C. Plonk takes a chance lighting the Mk IV burner on the leeward side. He only just beat the flames in a 40-yd dash. He might have done better to have given the job to the chap on the bicycle (IWM)

It was possible to carry out a normal hold-off on the goosenecks, or visually on the runway, but it was necessary to prevent oneself attempting to hold off on the FIDO burners. I feel that an inexperienced pilot who did so would misjudge his landing slightly since the glow is fairly dazzling at ground level, if the burners are looked at directly.

Although other pilots mentioned that they had experienced considerable turbulence on the approach, I did not notice any very excessive turbulence in a Lancaster aircraft. This may have been due to the fact that there was a slight cross-wind on the approach which prevented much turbulence directly above the burners and approach path.

I feel that the FIDO on this occasion was an invaluable aid in landing a large number of aircraft speedily under very poor cloud and visibility conditions. Quite a number of the pilots who made use of it were comparatively inexperienced, and had never actually seen it in operation previously.

Throughout the whole operation, spread over 6 hours, the approach burners had been alight for 3 hours 40 minutes and the whole system for 2 hours, mostly simmering gently, which consumed just under 160,000 gallons of petrol. No defects in the system were reported after shutdown.

Commenting on FIDO's usefulness at Tuddenham, Reg Hobden added: 'We could see our FIDO from Ostend at 7,000 ft. Not only could we speed up our landing rate, but, invariably, damaged and unannounced Liberators and Fortresses with no R/T could struggle in between our aircraft. Near misses but I recall no accidents.' But there's more! Attached to the original fog dispersal report is a note in the handwriting of Sir Donald Banks, Director General of the PWD, whose responsibility FIDO was, to Geoffrey Lloyd, Minister for Petroleum and answerable to Winston Churchill: 'For some unexplained reason, this burn was not reported by telephone and we have only just heard of it. It brings the total score for 16 November up to 190 (or 196 if one includes the test flights). FIDO was two years old on 4 November, the day we saw the clearance for the first time at Moody's Down and Staines, so this was in the nature of a birthday party.'

FIDO was required again a few days later in conditions of poor visibility. On 26 November 1944 the area was covered in an industrial haze, borne on a SSE wind; and although visibility at ground level was 1,600 yd, aloft, with no points of reference, it was a disconcerting situation for a number of crews out on training exercises. Four home-based Lancasters of 186 Squadron and one of 90 Squadron, a Stirling of 1657 Conversion Unit and a Lancaster of 195 Squadron were caught out and directed to Tuddenham where FIDO was lit for them at 16.50, 'in time for tea'. All put down safely in the space of half an hour. The pilots stated that the light-up definitely helped them to identify the airfield and to line up the runway. It began to rain hard towards the end of the burn – which may have been FIDO's way of cooling off! The station commander commented: 'The result was very successful and the installation is very popular with my pilots, who, as a result of recent successful burns, had every confidence of being able to land in the worst possible conditions with the aid of FIDO and the beam.'

Aboard the 195 Squadron Lancaster from Wratting Common was mid-upper-gunner K.T. Redshaw. He recalled:

> On approaching Tuddenham, everything was as black as the 'hobs of hell', when suddenly, below us, what appeared to be a blazing inferno opened up, and believe me, it was like manna from heaven (if you'll forgive the mixed metaphors). We had something to aim for, but as we approached, wheels and flaps down, it seemed like landing in a volcano.
>
> Nevertheless, as we touched down and gently came to rest, it was with a feeling of great relief. As I looked out of my turret and saw the outlines and buildings, through the shimmering flames, I thought of what could have happened to us if there had been no FIDO. Certainly I am here today due to it, for I am sure that we would have 'bought it' otherwise.

The following night, 27 November, FIDO was required again. A total of 290 aircraft, including many from 6 Group, had been briefed for a raid on Neuss. Sixteen of 90 Squadron's and sixteen of 186 Squadron's Lancasters were also briefed to attack Cologne railyards but they had returned early in the evening. Fog was widespread by 21.00 and diversions were ordered for many 6 Group and 8 Group machines. Visibility on the ground was 1,400 yd and it was limitless at normal operating altitude, but a solid carpet of radiation fog lay in between. It was only 30 ft deep, but it blotted out the final approach.

FIDO was lit at 21.45 and after clearance of the initial smoke a clear-cut trench was opened up. Into it sixteen Lancasters of 431 Squadron, two of 419 and two of 428 eased their way on to a beautifully illuminated runway. The pilots reported that they found the burners of great assistance and that they could not have landed without them.

The precision with which FIDO did its job when everything was working perfectly was brought to mind by Jimmy Barclay:

> I recall it as an awe-inspiring sight when in full flow – a noise like a continuous thunder roar, or that of a modern jet aircraft. On a very foggy night when standing at the end of the main runway, it was as if someone had cut a block of fog completely out of the runway and the approach areas (approximately one and a half miles). One could actually look up through the gap and see the stars.

The weather over Britain and much of north-west Europe was appalling for days on end throughout December, and it was under cover of the poor visibility that the Germans launched their Ardennes offensive against American positions in the region on the 16th. For several days it was impossible for the Allied air forces to go to the aid of their army colleagues. A force of 113 3 Group Lancasters was briefed to attack the route centre of Trier at midday on 21 December. East Anglia had been wreathed in fog for over 24 hours; in fact one report says that the whole of England east of Reading was fogbound. Nevertheless the situation was desperate and aircraft took off from any airfield where there was a remote chance of success. By this time 186 Squadron had left Tuddenham for Stradishall and at 12.08 the order was given to light FIDO so that thirteen of 90 Squadron's Lancasters could take off. Visibility at ground level was 1,000 yd, but the radiation fog had built up over a period of windless days to 1,500 ft deep. Wg Cdr Ogilvie led the squadron into the air, vanishing from view in a matter of seconds from leaving the ground. The system remained alight for 40 minutes in case of any early returns and was extinguished at 12.50.

Less than an hour later the order was given for FIDO to be lit again when two machines were reported to be on their way back. It took nearly 20 minutes from light-up to clear the smoke and have the apparatus fully functional, but by 14.00 FIDO was at full blast. Visibility at ground level was improved to 2,000 yd and a substantial tunnel was cleared, though a cross-wind created by the system itself caused the clearance to be the starboard side of the runway. Into view came Lancaster J-Johnnie to make a very heavy landing. Its undercarriage collapsed and the aircraft slid along the runway, coming to rest 100 yd beyond the perimeter track. The crew was unhurt, but the machine suffered category B damage. The second Lancaster landed without mishap. FIDO was doused again at 14.20.

At 16.15 another burn was ordered for the return of the remainder of 90 Squadron. Again, it took 20 minutes for the system to burn clearly, due to faults in three of the burners; but a further 15 minutes at full burn cleared the air substantially, maintained by idling the burners so that visibility was sufficient without countless therms going to waste clearing fog which wasn't there. Eleven Lancasters landed safely, plus one from 15 Squadron. The pilots approved the performance of FIDO, although some complained of the glare. Final shutdown was at 18.20. Altogether, spread over a period of 6 hours, thirteen aircraft had taken off and fourteen landed, for a total petrol consumption of nearly 200,000 gallons. As on 16 November, FIDO spent far more time idling than at full burn. One shudders to think what the petrol consumption figure would have been if it had been the other way round.

Limited aerial activity was possible over the Christmas period, but Bomber Command aircraft attacked communication centres whenever the possibility arose. Sometimes the aircraft were lucky enough to find gaps in the awful weather and could make their flights in comparatively clear conditions; at others, operations were postponed or diversions ordered on their return. FIDO was called for on twenty-six occasions during the last week of the year, countrywide.

As far as Tuddenham was concerned, the last recorded FIDO landings of 1944 took place following a daylight raid by 200 Lancasters of 3 Group on the railway yards at Rheydt on 27 December. Fourteen of 90 Squadron's Lancasters took part. As they streamed homewards with the other Group aircraft, 500 ft of radiation fog lay over most of East Anglia and FIDO was lit at five stations to facilitate landing. One of the problems was that the machines were returning into the setting sun which reflected off the mist and made oblique vision difficult. The fog dispersal system at Tuddenham was lit at 15.50 and during slightly less than two hours all fourteen home-based Lancasters landed safely together with five more from 149 Squadron based at Methwold.

One of the latter, T-Tare, was piloted by Flg Off Jones, whose air bomber was James Woodward. His diary entry for the day reads:

> We were up bright and early and briefed to go right into Germany. Then the whole thing was changed – take-off time put back 5 hours and in the end we just crossed the Rhine frontier to raid the town and marshalling yards at Rheydt. We had to go right round the town on our course away from the target – and what a shambles it was, the whole place was exploding.
>
> We landed away on the FIDO at Tuddenham, but only stayed one night there and are back here again today. We're on again tomorrow. At this rate I'll soon finish a tour of thirty trips!

Tuddenham's ops record book says of the visiting airmen: 'They were interrogated, fed and bedded.' The importance of having FIDO at Tuddenham in a month of 'extensive fog, particularly in the middle of the month, which caused daylight operations to be considerably curtailed', is better understood when the role played by its parent 3 Group is appreciated. The official historians record that '3 Group was at times the only element of Allied air power which could operate during the bad weather at the time of the Ardennes counter-offensive.'

A chance encounter with FIDO is recorded by Dick Sanborn at about this time:

I was a B–17 pilot with the 8th Air Force and landed at Tuddenham one hairy night. My crew of the 94th BG, 410 Squadron, based at Rougham, Bury St Edmunds, and I were returning from a practice mission over France, if my memory serves me correctly. It was some time in December 1944 or January 1945. England was pretty well socked in with low ceiling and fog. We had peeled off above the clouds and let down to break out very close to the ground. It was dark and murky. We were homing in to Bury St Edmunds on a radio beam with the togglier calling out the contours of the land, while we dipped and banked around valleys and knolls. The ceiling was very low and we hedge-hopped between the ground and the low scud clouds. It was getting darker and dirtier and visibility was decreasing – getting kind of hairy. We kept barrelling on.

Suddenly, visibility cleared to about 300 ft as we went screaming across an airfield. I saw firepots outlining a runway; something I'd never seen before. They beckoned me to land and I wasn't about to refuse. We crossed the field and re-entered the soupy weather again as I banked sharply to the left, telling the crew to keep an eye on those firepots as I didn't want to lose them. We were dangerously low, skimming over the rooftops of houses. At one time the nose called out 'Church steeple twelve o'clock high, Chief!' We lined up the runway, dropped wheels and flaps and came in for a good landing. Firepots whipped by our cockpit as we sped down the runway. It was very eerie. It was as if we were landing in Shangri-la, or a dark dreamland. Beyond the firepots it was pitch dark and the fog swirled all about.

It was spooky, but a great relief for the crew of the B–17 '4F-Travelaires'.

1945 began with weather just as bad as that with which 1944 had ended. In fact there was scarcely a day in January when there was no snow, fog or other form of bad weather. On Twelfth Night 90 Squadron was also out as part of a force of 119 3 Group Lancasters detailed to attack the town of Neuss. Nine Tuddenham aircraft took off, Wg Cdr Alan Scott leading 'B' flight. Recalling the return from such raids he considered that:

. . . so far as landing was concerned, the heat did clear the fog from immediately above the runway surface, but the great advantage to my mind was that from a few thousand feet above the airfield, looking vertically downwards, one had the visual outline of the runway.

Returning aircraft were stacked overhead at 500 ft intervals and descended as the one at the bottom of the stack landed. One therefore merely let down in the stack until it was one's turn to land and then did what was virtually a visual circuit. On the final part of the approach there was always a sort of heat shimmer and when flaring out for landing, one had to allow for a little more floating due to the additional lift from the heat of the FIDO burners; but this presented no great problems.

I recall one night [probably 6 January], while returning from the Ruhr and about to cross the Dutch coast, noticing a glow on the clouds ahead. This turned out to be from our Tuddenham FIDO, and I have since calculated that it must have been visible for about 150 miles from 20,000 ft, and through a depth of some 5,000–6,000 ft of cloud. . . . I don't think that we had incidents of any kind while using FIDO. What is absolutely certain though is that it enabled us to operate in weather conditions which would have been quite impossible without it.

Eric Wannop, flying U-Uncle, was also on the Neuss raid. For him and his crew it was their second attempt to complete their first op, an engine on fire having put paid to the previous day's sortie. Following the expected tensions of a first raid over enemy territory which they accomplished unscathed they departed the scene at greyhound speed. Eric was looking forward to his post-operation meal when the wireless operator interrupted his thoughts: 'Skipper, from Bob. Just had a message stating heavy fog over base. FIDO will be in use.' At least they would not be diverted:

We crossed the coast near Harwich at 8,000 ft and as we approached base I saw a dull orange glow through the fog. Not unlike the scene at Neuss, but without the flak and searchlights. Before requesting landing permission I flew directly over the 'drome and looked down into the glare. The runway was clearly visible. Down either side, petrol was being forced through very small holes in two parallel pipes. I knew that only 10 minutes after lighting when flames were leaping three feet into the mist-laden air, visibility would have increased to nearly four miles.

At the time FIDO was lit, 19.45, it was in fact down to less than 1,400 yd. The approach box was ignited and a few burners on each side of the runway, which soon cleared the air for a safe landing:

It was a most comforting sight to behold. My turn to land came round. I slowly descended from the clearness above into the grey mass of fog . . . nature's own blackout. It was total darkness as I switched to instrument flying. Never had I appreciated so much the endless hours spent under the 'hood', practising on instruments. At about 200 ft the fog dramatically cleared. Ahead lay the airborne fiery furnace. It looked like a scene from hell. My approach speed was higher than usual to counteract the effect of the rising hot air. The aircraft bobbed about like a cork at sea.

At touchdown it floated more than usual, supported by the warm air, and I began to think that we would overshoot the end of the runway. The fog was so dense that taxiing back to dispersal was a hazard, despite the assistance of a small transport vehicle leading the way . . .

The following day I watched with pride as the Flight Commander put the figure 1 against my name. Only another twenty-nine to go!

Krefeld was the 3 Group target on 11 January 1945. Sixteen Lancasters from 90 Squadron were part of a force of 152 which conducted a daylight raid there. Ten-tenths cloud was experienced in the target area when they bombed at about 15.15, and things did not improve as the squadron made its way home. By 16.00 a 300-ft blanket of fog enveloped the airfield at Tuddenham with visibility of a few hundred yards. This was tolerable on the ground but hazardous in the extreme when feeling one's way down.

FIDO was lit and in the space of 20 minutes cleared the air over the runway, although it did not clear the snow from its surface. Being 50 yd back from its edge it seldom did. All sixteen crews were safely down, de-briefed and ready for a good meal by 20.00, rating FIDO 'a valuable aid for lining up the runway in view of the poor visibility and snow-covered ground'.

This operation completed Wg Cdr Alan Scott's second tour. With him were a number of others busy clocking up the ops. Air bomber Tom Saunders in E-Easy recalled: 'The sight of that double row of flames marking the runway was so welcome as we crossed the coast, and not a little frightening as we neared touchdown; a not-so-easy operation, since the rising hot air tended to keep the old Lanc in the air when she should have been on the ground. The sight of others landing silhouetted through the flames and fog while taxiing to dispersal was also a scene which remains in the mind.'

Mick Smith, Tail-end Charlie aboard Lancaster PD430, remembered that:

the fog was really thick, and listening to the dialogue over the intercom, I could appreciate how welcome a sight such an invention was to pilots who, coming in to land and breaking through the fog, could visually see the length of runway.

This trip had an amusing ending. Eventually getting back to dispersal we were informed that no transport was available to come out and pick us up 'due to the fog'. As we could see the glow of FIDO we knew where the runway was and the approximate position of the interrogation room. Unfortunately, we were one of the last to land and FIDO was extinguished when we were only halfway there, leaving us lumbering around in full flying kit for nearly an hour before we got to de-briefing!

A month went by before any further record of FIDO appears. The weather was cloudy, with poor visibility all day on 16 February. Six of 90 Squadron's Lancasters formed part of a 3 Group force of 100 aircraft raiding Wesel just north of the Ruhr. As they made their way home at about 17.00 with not much more than 1,000 yd vision at ground level, it was deemed advisable to light their way with the fog dispersal system. In a short time the whole runway length was cleared of fog, and over the next hour or so five of Tuddenham's machines landed back safely, one electing to put down elsewhere. Just before closedown at 18.25, a stray Liberator landed, lost and attracted to the flames like the proverbial moth to the candle. Just short of 88,000 gallons of petrol were consumed during the burn, almost 1,000 gallons per minute!

On 19 February 3 Group returned to attack the railyards at Wesel, 168 Lancasters taking part. Ten aircraft of 90 Squadron formed part of the force, which suffered considerable damage during the raid, one, piloted by Wg Cdr Peter Dunham, being shot down. At least two others lost engines, and to aggravate matters visibility in the twilight hour around 18.00 was below 1,000 yd. In view of this, FIDO was lit and runway-length clearance was obtained.

One of the damaged machines was Lancaster U-Uncle with Bill Ingham as flight engineer:

We lost two inner engines and suffered structural damage over Wesel. We returned to base helped by another Lancaster as our radio and audio connections were u/s. The weather on our return was dusk and misty and FIDO must have been already lit and used by the rest of the squadron who had already landed. We knew that we would have only one shot at landing with our two outer engines, and our pilot, Flt Sgt K. Clarine, was helped a lot by FIDO as he had no contact with the Control Tower. As it was, we landed rather fast and well down the runway and went beyond the end, but pulled up eventually. FIDO was a great help that day.

Heavy raids were carried out on Essen and Gelsenkirchen on 23 February, 133 aircraft of 3 Group taking part in a daylight attack on the latter; 90 Squadron supplied eleven Lancasters, which sustained no casualties. Prospects for an easy return diminished on the way home, however, and by 16.00 the cloud base had fallen to only 400 ft, with ground visibility of 1,000 yd. FIDO was lit at 16.30, and in just under an hour all eleven Tuddenham machines put down safely, together with five cuckoos (two Lancasters and three Fortresses). The cost to the taxpayer was 44,000 gallons of petrol.

The last fog dispersal report for Tuddenham covers the daylight raid on Dortmund by 1,108 Lancasters, Halifaxes and Mosquitos on 12 March. Twelve of the Lancasters were from 90 Squadron. With the large number of aircraft involved and fading light, it was thought wise to order the lighting of FIDO against any widespread diversions which might be ordered. As vision decreased below 1,500 yd at 18.30 the system was ignited. Within half an hour the twelve Tuddenham Lancasters landed without mishap, plus another and a Liberator looking for any port in a fog: 10,000 gallons of petrol were consumed. With an Englishman's sense of humour, Mick Smith says that he remembers the Dortmund raid well – he was in jail there, having been shot down on 9 March during the final trip of his tour!

It is difficult to establish exactly how many aircraft and their crews took advantage of FIDO at Tuddenham during the eighteen months between its first and last recorded use. A Bomber Command report estimates the figure at 250, but the writer has evidence of 225 landings and 47 take-offs, a total of 272. If fog dispersal reports no longer surviving could be taken into account the number might be even higher.

EIGHTEEN

Woodbridge

. . . a home from home in bad weather

Wg Cdr McGlinn, Station Commander

As was mentioned on p. 8, Gp Capt Basil Embry had established the practicability of an emergency runway in 1941, by the extension of the aerodrome at Wittering. At a meeting held at the Air Ministry on 5 August 1942 it was formally agreed that three such runways should be built at 'Woodbridge, Bridlington and Canterbury'. The last two were later more accurately defined as Carnaby and Manston.

To the pilot of an aircraft in distress, whether from battle damage, crew injury, fuel shortage or malfunctioning of engines or controls, the sight of a huge, well-defined, uncluttered runway would be a great relief, and all three emergency airfields sought to provide just this. Michael Bowyer points out: 'The site chosen for RAF Woodbridge was almost ideal, as it was nearly fogfree and had no obstructions for miles. It was, however, in the middle of Rendlesham and Tangham Forests, and before construction could commence, more than a million small trees had to be cleared, which much displeased the local population.' Viewing the area following the storm of 1987, when another half million, this time full-grown, trees were destroyed, one can imagine their feelings.

As first envisaged it was intended that Woodbridge should have a massive 3,000 yd long runway, 250 yd wide with a 500 yd undershoot and overshoot. The runway was aligned due east–west with unhindered approach from either end. At the western end of the runway proper it was proposed to construct 420 yd diameter dispersal loops to right and left to accommodate sound aircraft. Machines with collapsed undercarriages and the like were to be lifted, dragged or bulldozed clear of the runway via a series of exit points on either side of the airstrip. The idea of loops was not proceeded with as it was feared that there could be congestion at the exits, and that aircraft thereabouts could prove a hazard to machines landing from west to east. In the event, exit points were built on the south side only, which avoided cutting down more trees than necessary. Plans were changed several times in as many weeks, which did not please the airfield contractors any more than cutting down the plantations had pleased the locals.

It was optimistically expected that the runway would be completed by October 1942, a date which was very soon amended to January 1943. In fact, construction took far longer than expected, for the bitumen-and-sand surfaced runway alone covered 160 acres. The main concourse of the airfield was divided into three lanes for emergencies, indicated by coloured lights at night: 'The south lane is coloured green by night and marked by white painted lines by day; this is the emergency lane on which aircraft can land without contacting Flying Control. The centre lane is coloured white and the north lane yellow by night, the line of light installations clearly defining the lanes by day.'

The first FIDO installation, at Graveley, was still at the drawing-board stage when the PWD got to hear of the Woodbridge project. On 24 October 1942 Technical Director A.C.

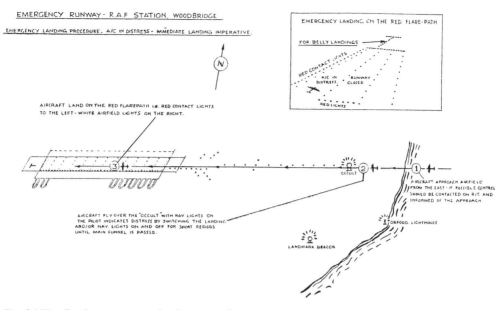

Fig. 24 Woodbridge, emergency landing procedure

Hartley noted in his diary: 'Just on leaving Staines met Wooldridge. Went back with him. Discussed his visit to Woodbridge yesterday where the landing ground 4,000 yd long with three miles of open country beyond it is being constructed. This runs through a fir tree plantation, most of which would have to be cleared for the installation.' Wg Cdr Wooldridge, Bomber Command's and PWD's liaison officer, talked it over with Pathfinder chief Gp Capt Bennett, and paid another visit to Woodbridge, whence he returned with a flea in his ear, reporting to Gp Capt Bennett that 'the people at Woodbridge are very Bolshie that the system had been changed so often,' and could do without further upheaval.

Not until April 1943 was Woodbridge again examined as a likely site. On the 13th it was considered that 'The installation of FIDO apparatus would be a considerable undertaking, but is a practicable proposition.' When a list of the next airfields to be equipped with fog dispersal was drawn up at the end of the month, however, Woodbridge was not among them.

FIDO achieved its first operational success at Graveley in November 1943, almost coinciding with the official opening of RAF Woodbridge. This was followed soon after by landings at Fiskerton and Downham Market, whereupon Bomber Command requested that sites be chosen for another group of airfields to be so equipped. The first of these was Woodbridge, designated Station X.

Work began early in January 1944 on what was to be the biggest FIDO project so far undertaken. With a 250 yd wide runway, and the burners set another 20 ft further back on each side, a single row of burners, no matter at what pressure they might be operating, was not going to be powerful enough to heat the vast quantity of fog which would gather under certain conditions. Therefore, as can be seen from the plan (Fig. 25) a double row of Mark IV burners (see Fig. 5) was installed on each side of the runway. When it was necessary for the burner lines on the south side to cross the exit points, the inner row was fitted with very short burners and the outer row had IRBs (see Plate 22) sunk into a trench. A quadruple cross-line was placed halfway along the undershoot and an entrenched Rapex burner (see Fig. 9) installed about a mile down the runway. This would effectively have sealed the runway completely but was not welcomed by aircrew, although experiments showed that it could in fact be extinguished within a few seconds. Such a system could, in an extreme case,

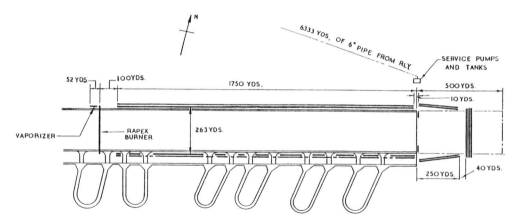

Fig. 25 Woodbridge, FIDO layout. See Plate 66

involve the consumption of nearly a quarter of a million gallons of petrol in an hour. In fact, this was never required, although, as will later be seen, prodigious amounts were burned. To fuel the lines, four enormous steel tanks were erected by Royal Engineers on the north side of the approach box, each one with a capacity of 10,000 barrels (approximately 350,000 gallons).

Up to the time of the Woodbridge contract, the petrol for storage tanks had been delivered from the nearest depot or railhead by convoys of road tankers, each of which probably carried about 3,000 gallons. To attempt the same thing at Woodbridge would have choked the roads for miles around. Therefore a railway siding was built at Melton, nearly 4 miles away. Tanks with limited capacity were built alongside and the fuel pumped along an underground pipeline to the airfield tanks. The layout of the siding and its equipment would have been similar to that shown in Fig. 19 and Plates 49–52. The railway siding was in fact the main stumbling-block to progress with the installation. Contractors William Press were handicapped by a shortage of labour at their factory, which put the supply of burners behind schedule. There was also difficulty in transporting men to the airfield as no billets were available in the vicinity. When to these problems was added the tardiness of the railway company in even producing plans for the siding, February 1944's progress report was not very encouraging. At that time it was hoped that the system would be fit to use by the end of April and completed a month later; rather a daunting task.

Things did improve, however, and towards the end of April, most delays and difficulties had been overcome:

> The first trainload of gasoline was brought into existing sidings at Melton on 16 April and was discharged through a temporary header and pumped direct to installation tankage. On 17 April initial tests were made on the airfield installation itself, commissioning a pumphouse and the main control house. The feed main on the north side was filled up to the end of the 10 in section and the first four burner units were lit [about 200 yd]. The operation was quite satisfactory and tests of burner units are being continued as gasoline stocks permit.
>
> About 800 tons of gasoline should be delivered by 29 April [by which date] it is anticipated that the whole of the burners along each side of the runway, together with the cross-burners at the touch-down end, will be completed. The wing burners [IRBs] may not be completely operational.
>
> The special rail siding will not be completed until 6 May, after which it should be possible to bring in a trainload of gasoline per day, completing the filling of the installation tankage by abut 25 May. The system can be made operational for a certain length of time from 29 April.

Mr G.L. Pope recalled quite a startling occasion from FIDO's early days (or nights) at Woodbridge: 'One evening, when standing on the top of Snape Hill, a large area of fir tree forest to the south appeared to ignite. No one could – or would – explain it, and it was not

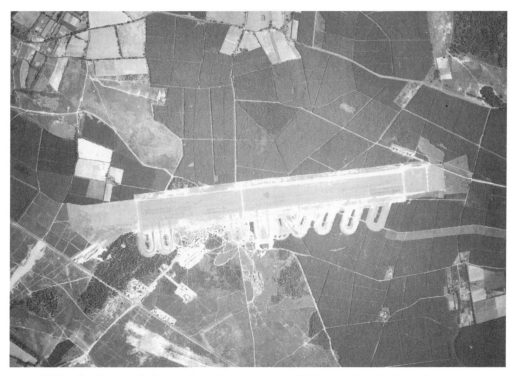

Plate 66 Woodbridge aerial. Approach on due west course, 270° or reciprocal. Rapex burner crosses two-thirds along runway. Storage tanks north of approach box. Also see Fig. 25 (Crown/MoD)

until after the war that the cause of the blaze came to light (if you will pardon the pun). It was a trial being carried out at Woodbridge air base, which at that time was used for damaged planes returning from Europe.'

Mr J.W. Gosling recalled that when FIDO at Woodbridge was alight and at full blast you could not hear yourself speak, and the heat was enormous. By night, small print could be read with ease half a mile from the base. Then, he added:

> After it had been alight for half an hour or so it rained! It did, however, clear the fog from around the runway and aircraft could land between the two lines of fire which of course they were able to see from some distance as they crossed the coast.
> When they started up FIDO they turned on the main petrol supply and primed each pair of fixed pipes with small hand-pumps. A chap or two then ran down the lines of pipes, and as the petrol began to come out of the many small holes drilled in them, flung a light down below. When both sides were burning, more powerful pumps were brought into use at the big tanks, and the petrol fed at pressure to each side of the runway.
> It was quite a sight to see the flames mounting into the darkness and fog, and hear the roar of that great mass of fire.

Within a week of the D-Day landings the first flying bombs were launched against London and southern England, and the Allied air forces had to divert part of their efforts to dealing with launching sites and stores, particularly in the Calais region. It was in this connection that the first operational use of FIDO at Woodbridge is recorded. 'On the night of 23 June 1944,' recalled Flt Lt (later Air Cdre) Brian Frow, then of 7 Squadron:

> I was returning from a raid on V1 installations in the Pas de Calais area, when I was involved in an engagement with three German night-fighters, two of which were destroyed and one damaged.

However, my Lancaster received severe damage, as a result of which it was very difficult to control, and the hydraulics had failed. It was a very dark hazy night with medium cloud at about 10,000 ft. I ordered an SOS to be sent by W/T and called *Mayday* on R/T. Manston replied to the latter, but as our position was about 75 miles east of Southwold, I asked for Woodbridge to be illuminated.

I could see the flames on the runway as I broke cloud about 30 miles from Woodbridge. I was unable to manoeuvre the aircraft more than by very slow unbanked turns as one aileron had been shot away and the other badly holed. I decided to attempt a straight-in approach at high speed to ensure controllability, descending slowly, using throttle, and eventually crossed the first bar of flames at about 500 ft and 150 knots (normal was 85).

Using the emergency air I attempted to blow the undercarriage down, but nothing happened. I eventually belly-landed at about 100 knots halfway down the runway and skidded to a standstill. No one on board was hurt. We owed our lives to FIDO.

A fortnight later FIDO was again in use at Woodbridge, following a raid on V1 launching and storage sites by 542 Lancasters, Halifaxes and Mosquitos on 5 July. Robin Craw (RNZAF) was captain of Lancaster C-Charlie of 7 Squadron from Oakington:

. . . we were halfway across the Channel when we were attacked by, we believe, a Ju88 and our starboard inner engine was hit and set on fire. The fire extinguisher was used and the fire was put out. The fighter continued his attack for some time and during the violent evasive action the top came off the ammunition tanks for the rear guns, leaving them inoperable, and a lead came unstuck from one mid-upper, leaving us with a single .303in for our defence.

I decided to use Woodbridge with the knowledge that it was possible our landing gear under the u/s engine had been damaged. I also knew that large areas of fog covered parts of the low country. We duly landed on three engines at Woodbridge using the FIDO system. I recall thinking as we came into land that I hoped we would not pull up over one of the cross pipes busily burning fuel. If I remember correctly, the runway was grass, or perhaps we landed to one side on grass.

The violent evasive action had opened a parachute, and oil and charts etc. were everywhere and ground crew asked us if we had been looping the loop. Our aircraft had to be repaired and we were picked up by a spare crew from Oakington. We had a strip torn off for landing away, but the crew were happy and on top of the world, having survived a fighter attack and fog with no injuries.

Over 800 sorties were flown by Bomber Command on the night of 26/27 August. In particular, a force of 382 aircraft raided Kiel and 174 Lancasters attacked the Baltic port of Konigsberg.

At 06.29 Lancaster K-King of 97 Squadron approached on its return very short of fuel. Its captain, Flg Off Simpson, had been given a diversion from his home base of Coningsby, but had elected to head for Woodbridge. The clouds were on the ground with visibility of only 150 yd. The ground crews were in a dilemma, for the initial light-up of FIDO would have worsened the vision available to the pilot until the smoke cleared – and it was throught that he didn't have that much time to spare. Before any action could be taken, however, Flg Off Simpson took the decision out of their hands. Making an initial practice run, unseen from the ground, he touched down safely – still unseen!

Stirling aircraft M-Mother, flown by Plt Off R.J. Goggler of Wratting Common, had occasion to call for FIDO late on 22 September in conditions of absolutely freezing fog. The system was alight by 20.55 – perhaps not for him alone. Plt Off Goggler later reported that at the time of his initial approach his controls were badly iced up and that it had been impossible to see through his front windscreen:

The aircraft was diverted here as its base was unfit. The windscreen was iced up and right bank could not be put on due to icing. The pilot flew over the installation for 5 minutes at approximately 1,300 ft and cleared the ice. He approached at 10 to 15 mph faster than normal and experienced no bumpiness, although there was some dazzle, making instrument reading difficult. It was the pilot's first landing with FIDO and he was most enthusiastic.

It was also the first time that a Stirling had landed at Woodbridge.

Plate 67 Test burn of FIDO at Woodbridge. Part of the double row of burners on the south side of the runway is alight. The vast width of the concourse can be appreciated from this photograph, and the enormous quantity of petrol required to keep it clear of fog (Sir Donald Banks)

Plate 68 Control point, pressure gauge and telephone for double line of burners at Woodbridge (PWD)

Plate 69 The distortion caused by prolonged periods of burning can be seen from this photograph of the double row of burners at Woodbridge (IWM)

Stirlings were considered ungainly birds, but they seemed to come to roost at Woodbridge with no difficulty, as did C-Charlie of 138 Squadron early on 16 October. One of two machines on Resistance operations, LK145 flown by Flg Off W.P. Moffatt was unable to return to its base at Tempsford and was diverted to Woodbridge. There, radiation fog in patches 100 ft deep was being experienced, and FIDO was lit to clear it at 02.50. Visibility at that time was down to 200 yd and FIDO personnel were doubtful whether the system would operate effectively, as 800 yd of the piping needed repair, and no maintenance had been possible for three weeks. When it was borne in mind that at that time about seventy emergency landings per week were being undertaken, this is perhaps not surprising. However, the remainder of the system stood up well. Flg Off Moffatt reported that he had to descend through 500 ft of stratus to enter the cleared air over the runway, and that a pillar of mist had formed between the flames at the western end of the airstrip – shades of Moses! After two dummy runs he made his final approach and, says the station report, 'made a perfect touch-down'. C-Charlie landed at 03.17 and five minutes later the silent, eerie, clammy fog was stealing back again across the 'drome.

FIDO did not get much of a respite for maintenance before it was in use for a sustained period on 26 October. Bomber Command and the US 8th Air Force flew hundreds of sorties during the day in far from ideal weather, and as they made their way homewards many diversions were called for. There was radiation fog 200 ft deep over Woodbridge, with horizontal visibility only 300 yd and not much better than that elsewhere in East Anglia. FIDO was lit at 16.55 and burned continuously until 22.05 at varying pressures to accommodate the arrival of a variety of aircraft.

First came B–24 No. 385 piloted by Lt Bright, returning from Special Duty ops with its port outer engine u/s, followed by Stirling LJ617 on similar ops with port inner engine u/s.

Both pilots made good landings, though the air was so wet that they made vapour trails on their final approaches. Flt Lt Austwick, the Stirling pilot, was well pleased with his welcome, 'Marvellous, will come again if in any trouble.'

Shortly after they landed, it began to rain, and the system remained alight against the possible diversion of 3 Group Lancasters which had been raiding Leverkusen, and nearly 1,900 US bombers and fighters returning from attacks on industrial and communications targets. Few of them opted to land at Woodbridge, but over a period of nearly 5 hours two Wellingtons from RCM patrols, two B–24s, a Mosquito, a Stirling, an unspecified number of Tempests from Bradwell Bay (itself a FIDO airfield), another B–24 and finally a Hudson, home from a Resistance operation, landed without incident; at least a dozen machines, at what cost in petrol consumption can only be imagined.

Moving into November, FIDO was called for in conditions of decreasing visibility on the 3rd. At the time of the initial stand-to, horizontal vision was 1,800 yd, but by the time of light-up it was down to 500 yd. The system was ignited at 08.50 and further deterioration was arrested – in fact, it increased to 2,800 yd as the advection fog was evaporated faster than it arrived. At 09.10 the first divertee arrived, a B–17 from Bassingbourn, to be followed in the space of a quarter of an hour by Spitfires A-Able, E-Easy, R-Roger and S-Sugar from Matlaske, mission unknown. By half past nine all had groped their way to dispersal and everything was once more enveloped in fog. Miles Tripp described it as 'existing in a roll of poorly developed film taken by an unfocused camera'.

Hess Bomberger of the 361st Fighter Squadron US 8th Air Force Martlesham recalled making an emergency landing at Woodbridge two days later:

My P–47 had taken a flak hit over Koblenz on the way in. My wingman could see no damage, but I was getting smoke in the cockpit. However, it went away and I completed the mission. When we got

Plate 70 Night burn of Mk IV burners at Woodbridge. Pipelines are 20 ft apart (IWM)

back to Martlesham Heath my flaps 'milked' back up as I was turning final. Then I found my
hydraulic pressure gone; went to Woodbridge. I don't recall the weather being particularly grubby
that day. . . . However, I do remember landing when FIDO was working . . . The memory is fairly
vivid.

First of all the distance one could see the FIDO through fog was quite amazing. The other thing I
remember is the 'ballooning' one got when one crossed the threshold and how clear it was within the
strip's boundaries. The FIDO of course generated considerable heat which made the bird rise a
couple of hundred feet on crossing the field boundary and similarly made the air within the
boundaries rise, and the fog with it. I can't seem to remember, but I thought that they didn't light the
gasoline across the threshold; but why would I have 'ballooned' on approach?

Another 361 Fighter Squadron veteran, John Lindsay, recalled those murky days in late
1944:

Probably the most memorable was a return from Germany leading a flight of four Mustangs, when
the fog was quite thick and heavy. As we approached the English coast we were flying above the fog
at about 5,000 ft when we received word that the FIDO was being lit at Woodbridge and we were to
land there. Shortly, we saw the bright glow from the strip and we started our descent with the outline
of the runway in clear view from the FIDO. I called the strip on radio for landing clearance and
instructions and was advised to land straight in; all four ships in formation. As we approached to
within about a mile to a mile and a half, the heat of the fire had thinned the fog to an almost clear
day and our landing on this huge, very wide, long runway was strictly routine. At the time the fog
over the area was severely restricting vehicular traffic – visibility near zero.

An extremely busy day for Bomber Command and the US 8th Air Force was 16 November.
In order to cut communications behind the German front line, 1,188 British aircraft attacked
Düren, Jülich and Heinsburg, and 1,243 B–17s and B–24s escorted by 282 P–51s attacked
gun positions east of Aachen as the prelude to an Allied ground offensive. Casualties were
not heavy, but visibility deteriorated seriously as the forces made their way home, and
widespread diversions were the order of the day. 'DBX – you are diverted to . . .' was heard
by many radio operators that day.

To cover all operations, including early returns, instructions were given for FIDO to be lit
at 11.35. Even before the initial smoke had cleared, the first enforced diversion had landed,
Halifax P-Peter of 192 Squadron from Foulsham with ABSI u/s. Over the next 7 hours no
fewer than eighty-five aircraft landed safely, all but two of them from operations. Landing
conditions were not easy, for the SBA system was not working and quite a barrage of Verey
lights was visible at times. Apart from the early returns, the B–17s from 493 Bomb Group
were the first to land, being diverted from their base at Debach (which any local will tell you
is pronounced Debbidge), only a few miles away. Between approximately 14.00 and 15.00
thirty-three of them landed safely (see Pl. 72). Describing the occasion the Bomb Group
history says that the Flying Fortresses

. . . found they were unable to land due to very low visibility. The RAF in cooperation with the 8th
Air Force immediately made available an aerodrome equipped with a fog dispersal unit. Hundreds of
feet of pipe similar to a truck gardening sprinkling system, burning gasoline instead of sprinkling
water, lined both sides of the runway at the RAF field. The tremendous heat generated literally
burned the fog away, showing a landing strip visible in the air for miles.

In addition to the B–17s, fourteen P–51s, some B–24s and a P–47 Thunderbolt flown by
'Lieut A. N. Other', sixty American aircraft all told, sought haven at Woodbridge over a
4 hour period, several of them with battle damage.

Scarcely had they been herded to all corners of the airfield than their British counterparts
made their return. Whenever visibility looked like being stable for a reasonable period,
FIDO had been turned down to idling, the outer line only being used for an hour or so. Most
of that time was in the late afternoon, from about 16.50 to 17.40, when twenty-one Lancasters

Plate 71 Light-up of FIDO at Woodbridge, 16 November 1944. See p. 198 (Smithsonian)

Plate 72 With inner props still, a Fortress of 493rd BG manoeuvres through the exit point at Woodbridge, 16 November 1944 (Smithsonian)

and Halifaxes diverted due to the weather, and several non-operational machines made landings without mishap. Most of the operational aircraft were suffering from a variety of defects – hydraulics u/s, elevator and rudder u/s, two engines u/s, navigational aids u/s, and so on.

One was Halifax H-How of 434 Squadron based at Croft in Yorkshire. Captained by Flg Off Kowalchuck (RCAF), it was part of the force which attacked the route centre of Jülich in western Germany. On the way home the oil pressure in the port outer and starboard inner engines fell and it became necessary to feather both propellers. Ken Windle was flight engineer aboard H-How: 'Many miles out to sea we could see this glow in the sky and thought Jerry must have given Ipswich a pasting, but on coming in to land, firing red Very cartridges for an emergency landing, we realized that it was FIDO, lighting our way on to the runway. As we touched down, a Lancaster also came down at the side of us and went careering along the runway like a bat out of hell, presumably with his hydraulics shot up.' Ken's memory has served him well, for the Lancaster in question, Y-Yoke, from 431 Squadron also at Croft, was indeed in trouble, with two engines u/s and hydraulic system out of action, and needed all the runway and a sizeable portion of overshoot before it came to rest.

Shortly afterwards, a batch of 218 Squadron's Lancasters from Methwold turned up, 'weather BFX'. They had been on the Heinsburg raid and appear to have been free of battle damage, but Methwold could not take them. First to arrive was J-Johnnie, flown by Flt Lt John O'Brien. His rear gunner was Rowland Mason:

> I was always happy in the old tail end (position-wise that is), but I must admit that after being in the complete dense fog for so long it became a bit claustrophobic and I was pleased to hear that we were being diverted to Woodbridge. This being the first, and in fact the only occasion when we were to put FIDO to the test, I think that we were all a little apprehensive. I recall that from utter darkness and nil visibility we went to seeing a faint glow and then, lo and behold, joy at seeing the runway stretching out before us – or in my case behind us – as we circled and prepared to land.
>
> I recall, as we were landing, seeing the roaring flames on either side and also damaged and crashed aircraft that had been pushed to one side. I don't remember much else about the landing, although I have a vague recollection that for some reason or other we were all inoculated!

The sum total of FIDO's efforts for that day was that eighty-five aircraft landed in safety between 11.35 and 19.40 at a cost of 717,544 gallons of petrol. The inner lines of burners were operating for the whole 8 hours, suffering severe fouling of the jet holes and three fractured burners in the process. The outer lines were lit in addition for an hour. Minister for Petroleum Geoffrey Lloyd was highly delighted at this achievement and wrote to the prime minister:

> Fog and haze came down on many airfields yesterday, when our aircraft were returning from the continent. Altogether 161 aircraft landed with the aid of our fog dispersal apparatus. The great emergency runway at Woodbridge was kept clear for 8 hours while eighty-four aircraft with 100 aircrew landed there. There were sixty Fortresses, Marauders and Mustangs of the 8th Air Force. The Americans were thrilled and said, 'Without it we would have had it!'

Although a safe landing was all-important, the technicalities of the landing itself sometimes took second place to the aftermath. C-Charlie of 622 Squadron, based at Mildenhall, homed in at 17.38 with starboard inner engine feathered and hydraulics u/s. Flown by Tony Waigh, Steve Briggs was navigator. Steve:

> . . . can't help thinking that poor visibility was also involved as, although I had heard of FIDO and its purpose, I recall how surprised I was at the height of the flames and the noise of the jets.
>
> Further, there was a very long wait until a crowd of us left in convoy in the early hours of the following morning, stopping somewhere in Ipswich for an early breakfast (about 5.30 a.m. I think) in what was I believe a church hall being used as a dining room for an army establishment.

We were all very tired and hungry and I distinctly recall that we had bacon on a slice of fried bread, a slice of bread and jam and a mug of tea. I am lucky enough to have had plenty of marvellous meals over the years, but few have been as memorable as this one. Our army colleagues certainly did us proud that morning and I often wonder what they themselves had for breakfast later that morning – only the bread and jam probably!

FIDO was very active from morning till night on 26 November. Apart from RCM patrols, Mosquitos were the only Bomber Command aircraft out on the night of the 25/26th. One of them was P-Peter of 105 Squadron flown by Flt Lt J.A. Ruck, who was forced to return from ops with bombs still on board and only one engine functioning. In conditions of poor visibility he made a good single-engined landing at 00.49. At 04.42 a B–17 from Alconbury piloted by Capt K.I. Menzies 'landed direct, with its port engine on fire. This was extinguished by the ground crew.'

At 13.55 Mustang OC-Q flown by the ubiquitous A.N. Other from Martlesham 'made a fast but good landing with half of its starboard wing shot off by an enemy aircraft'. It had been part of the escort to a force of 1,137 American bombers attacking rail viaducts, marshalling yards and oil installations in the area of Misburg, Bielefeld and Hamm.

With many combat aircraft still homeward bound, the system was lit again when visibility fell to less than a mile at 15.40, but the only machines to set down were two Fortresses and a Liberator on communications flights. The same thing happened at 16.50 when 3 Group aircraft were returning from operations over Fulda. No diverted aircraft were received from this force, but another B–17, JW-Q, of the 92nd Bomb Group landed with FIDO's aid.

The landings of the American aircraft were observed by Alan Firth and Charlie Maughan of Tim Donelly's crew aboard Albemarle K1554, flying a cross-country exercise from Ashbourne in Derbyshire. 'Upon returning to base,' recalled Alan, 'the area was enveloped in a severe snowstorm, a wall of white all round, and consequently we were diverted to Woodbridge.' Adding his recollections, Charlie wryly commented:

Albemarles were a little-known twin-engined general-purpose bomber; so little known in fact that both sides used to shoot at them!

Although flying above the fog, or rather, low cloud, we had no trouble getting to Woodbridge. We joined the circuit in the usual manner, with the ground below visible from 1,000 ft and the glowing rectangle of flame showing through the haze. As we flew downwind we were instructed to hold off for one more circuit to allow a badly shot up B–17 to land, wheels up. This we witnessed, with the ambulance and fire trucks homing in as the Fortress slid along the runway. By the time we had gone round again the Fort had been dragged off and only foam on the runway indicated where it had come to rest. We received the go-ahead to land 'well up the runway', turned into the wind, throttled back to lose height and with a bump came into the clear vision box inside the FIDO system. We touched down in clear air, looking at walls of fog on each side, and received radio instructions to keep taxiing to reception PDQ – and we did!

A Fortress which followed us in had been on a day trip over the Reich, and parts of its fuselage looked as if it was made of chicken wire, but there was not a scratch on any of the ten to fifteen crew who seemed to get out.

Then came a Mustang with a flat tail-wheel and a neat hole from a cannon shell through one blade of its propeller. The pilot was unhurt and most concerned to get back to base for a date that night.

At 16.35 the next day, 27 November, FIDO was in demand again to cover the return in poor visibility of Lancaster G-George flown by Flt Lt R.A. Pickler of 514 Squadron. The machine had suffered heavy flak damage during a daylight raid on Cologne. Its rear turret was u/s and elevator trim cable cut through. As soon as clear air had been obtained over the runway, Flt Lt Pickler was given clearance and made a direct approach and landing.

At 21.55 it was necessary to light the system again when visibility was down to 1,500 yd. A number of aircraft were reported returning from ops, short of fuel. Two hundred and ninety bombers had raided Neuss and another 341 had attacked Freiburg, while eighty-six Mosquitos had been to a variety of other targets, including Berlin. Mosquito B-Baker of 105

Squadron homed in with one engine u/s. She touched down safely, having been plotted when still 100 miles out to sea, but then ran wildly off the runway, damaging two of the FIDO burners at the western end. There is no report that the particular burners were alight at the time. Mosquito O-Oboe of 109 Squadron, Halifax O-Oboe of 425 Squadron and Halifax X-X-ray of 429 Squadron, both in 6 Group, landed safely during the next hour.

Moving on into December, the intensity of operations by Bomber Command increased as the quality of the weather decreased. Similarly, the US 8th Air Force continued its daylight harassment of troop and munition movements and attacks on oil production plants. On 6 December, 818 B–17 and B–24s, escorted by 813 P–51s and P–47s raided oil installations and rail targets at Merseburg, Bielefeld and Minden. The majority of both fighters and bombers returned to their own airfields without difficulty, but the Mustangs of 356 Fighter Group, comprising 359, 360 and 361 Squadrons, based at Martlesham, between Ipswich and Woodbridge, found their flights ending in conditions of industrial smoke which reduced visibility to only half a mile and angular vision to considerably less. They were accordingly diverted to Woodbridge.

It was realized before the order to light up was given at 14.00: ' . . . that the FIDO would have little effect in improving visibility on the runway, but the intention was that the burners should act as runway markers. Alternate inner runway burners only were lit, which achieved the desired result.' The 'desired result' was that visibility improved to 1,300 yd within a short time, and remained so for the best part of two hours. The Group was led home by Major Jim Wood in PI-V at 14.25:

> I can recall being concerned about the weather at Martlesham as we approached the English coast. It was welcome news when we were directed to Woodbridge because of its long, wide landing strip. As we approached Woodbridge it was most pleasing to see the somewhat improved visibility, probably due to FIDO, but even more important the clearly outlined airstrip due entirely to FIDO. I was even more thankful as I observed the many members of our Group who landed after me.

'Many' was certainly the right word, for within the space of 40 minutes, forty Mustangs landed safely. One of them was in fact Lt Rex Burden in QI-A (361 Squadron), at 15.03: 'We flew tight formation in zero visibility to about 5,000 ft. From that altitude we could see the glow of the field as we proceeded with our descent. The fog over and around the field was lifted to about 500 ft. We all made normal landings and returned to Martlesham by truck.'

In addition to the P–51s, eight Fortresses, a Liberator and a Lancaster made use of the amplified flare path that day – fifty-one machines in all. During a total burn of 155 minutes, 124,864 gallons of petrol were consumed – and that was with only half of the inner line of burners alight. The station commander concluded his fog dispersal report by saying: 'The use of FIDO in conditions which are not impossible for flying is perhaps not strictly in accordance with its original conception. However, it was the only way to get aircraft down quickly and with the poor weather giving prospects of more to come, it was a good decision to burn it. No aircraft had to make a second circuit.' The aftermath of this burn was also quite exciting. Rex Burden recalls that: ' . . . the planes were partially refuelled that night and we came back early next morning to return our planes to our home field. We lined up, forty planes abreast and took off across the runway, peeling off and returned home in trail. Quite a sight!'

On 16 December, when conditions were at their worst, Field Marshal von Rundstedt launched his counter-attack, the Ardennes offensive. For several days his advance against American troops made substantial headway, for it was impossible for Allied air forces to operate in their support. Not until the 19th were they able to intervene over the continent.

Meanwhile, Bomber Command's other operations continued. They included a raid by 236 Lancasters of 5 Group on the Baltic port of Gdynia on 18/19 December. One of the squadrons involved was 630 from East Kirkby. The raid was carried out at extreme range, aircraft being aloft for approaching 11 hours. As if that was not bad enough, by 03.00 on the

19th much of Lincolnshire was enveloped in fog. Ted Watson was flight engineer to Flg Off Jerry Monk in Lancaster G-George, and recalled:

With a bombload of 10,420 lb we took off at 16.40 hours; our route over Denmark and Sweden, then down to Gdynia, returning home low level, a duration of 10 hours 55 minutes. Approaching England, G-George was notified by wireless of widespread fog, with instructions to divert to Woodbridge.

Normal night landings were hairy enough; this was to be a new experience. In my crew position alongside the pilot and assisting him we had a grandstand view and both felt really apprehensive about it. I recall flying above the fog and at a distance of about 10 miles from Woodbridge being able to see the glow of FIDO. It was reminiscent of a bombing raid through cloud.

Upon instructions by R/T from the Control Tower to join the circuit, the centre of the glow was judged to be the airfield and Jerry eased the aircraft down into the flowing mass. Our eyes having been subject to the intense darkness now began to smart and ache. We entered what appeared like dense, bright, steam-like fog with nil visibility, hoping that Tower had complete control of all aircraft positions.

As we decreased in height, the glare became more and more intense, the aircraft began to bump around and we could feel the heat inside the aircraft. The glare through the cockpit windows was similar to being coned by searchlight. Jerry and I opened our hinged side windows hoping to be able to see more clearly. Great difficulty was being experienced by Jerry in maintaining a good circuit. Our eyes would normally be scanning outside the aircraft with an occasional check of the blind flying panel inside the cockpit, but the reflected glare made this impossible.

With a lot of guessing by Jerry, and on his instructions, I lowered the undercarriage and flaps and adjusted the rpm at different parts of the circuit. Commencing the final, very bumpy approach at about 500 ft, the two great walls of flame on either side of the runway seemed to be sucking the aircraft down. Bill Whenray, our navigator, commenced calling our air speed, and upon command from Jerry I cut the throttles a few feet above the runway. It was not a good landing, but we were all thankful to be on terra firma. I would guess that something like twenty aircraft landed at Woodbridge that night.

New Zealander H.A. Ramsey, also of 630 Squadron, brought to mind his own experience in Lancaster JB290 on the same occasion. They were initially diverted to Fiskerton because of fog at East Kirkby, but on arrival found that a Lancaster had bogged down by the runway and were re-diverted to Woodbridge instead: 'We were impressed at the speed with which a damaged Lanc was picked up and towed away. Later, a Fortress belly-landed, the crew leaving all their gear behind. Out came two bulldozers and just scraped the aircraft off the runway. Quick, but wasteful!'

The station commander had a right old bleat in his monthly report: 'With a total FIDO crew of 31 it is impossible to control smoking of the burners. The numbers available are never more than twenty.' Remembering the dozens of control points to be manned when a full burn was required, the needs of pumphouse personnel, and the thousands of jet holes to be pricked out after prolonged burning, he certainly had a point.

The position was aggravated on the evening of 22 December. One hundred and sixty-six aircraft from 1 Group with two Mosquitos from the PFF had carried out an attack upon the Mosel railway yards at Koblenz. At the same time 106 aircraft of 4 and 8 Groups raided the marshalling yards at Bingen. Considerable fog had accumulated over East Anglia as they approached home and FIDO was lit for those who had to be diverted. As they descended into the ever-increasing gloom, with fuel and altitude gauges falling in unison, eyes anxiously sought a sign of FIDO's presence. Visibility was only 800 yd, with radiation fog 50 ft deep, and there was a cross-wind from the north of 10–15 mph. FIDO was ignited at 19.25, but was soon in trouble. The wind had not been from the north for a long time, so that the ground south of the burners had not been dried out. Consequently, on light-up, the grass south of the burner lines gave off dense smoke which took a long time to clear. In addition to that, distorted and leaking pipes reduced FIDO's efficiency; and the operating crews complained that they could not hear their instructions over the Tannoy system because of the noise of the burners.

Nevertheless, by 19.40 the apparatus was going full blast, first at 80 lb per sq. in, then gradually reducing to 30, as the fog evaporated and was held at bay, with occasional bursts to keep it that way. From a glow to a finger, from a finger to a flame-lined gouge in the fog the runway was gradually defined. One Mosquito had returned before the burners were even lit, another landed the moment the runway was clear, and then from 20.34 until 22.07 forty-two Lancasters from 1 Group landed without incident. Fifteen of them were from 101 Squadron, based at Ludford Magna. Ludford was equipped with FIDO, but conditions there were often such that it could not clear the low stratus cloud which enveloped the airfield, and this was one more occasion. Polish squadrons 550 and 300 made up most of the other machines to land, and Woodbridge Flying Control did very well to record names such as Wilmicki, Zarebski, Liefooghe, Wyganowsk and Mykietyn before FIDO was extinguished at 23.05. Three and three-quarter hours of fog clearance set the taxpayer back the cost of 308,361 gallons of petrol.

Christmas Eve 1944 at last gave the opportunity for maximum effort by Bomber Command, and the US 8th and 9th Air Forces. A high-pressure area extending across Western Europe brought clear skies and allowed the 8th Air Force in particular to launch the largest air strike of the war. A force of 2,046 heavy bombers escorted by 853 fighters attacked over thirty airfields and communications centres. Freezing conditions and ground fog caused numerous take-off accidents. So numerous were the early returns and diversions that, to quote three participant sources, at Woodbridge, 'the refugees from the gathering mists outnumbered the resident aircraft'; 'it looked as if half of Bomber Command's aircraft had arrived here'; and 'around Christmas 1944 Woodbridge reached overflow'.

The same conditions prevailed on the following day. An appraisal of Christmas Day's weather in 1944 comes from USAF Staff Sgt Edgar Matlock's diary: 'It was cold this morning, the ground was frozen and the fog which moved into our area during the morning of the 19th continued throughout the day in undiminished intensity. . . . During the afternoon some combat personnel came back to the base in trucks from the bases at which they landed yesterday. Skeleton crews were left with the airplanes to return to the base if this infernal fog ever lifts. . . . Low temperatures today, 17 degrees F.'

Many of the 8th Air Force's aircraft were still far from home on 25 December following massive diversions the day before, but a moderate force of the 2nd and 3rd Bomb Divisions returned to the general area of the previous raids. One of nine B–17s targetted at Bad Münster railyards was 525 of the 95th Bomb Group with Bob Hastie in its crew:

> On arrival over East Anglia fog was rapidly rolling in over our air bases. I do not recall if any of our Group landed, but *we* were diverted to Woodbridge. At that location fog was over 1,000 ft thick and a large rectangle of black smoke was visible. Mortar type flares were arching up through the soup at one end of the smoke pattern. We aligned ourselves with the flares, checked altimeter setting, lowered landing gear, set 15° of flaps and pulled the power back.
> We settled gently into the fog bank. At about 2–300 ft the ground and airstrip, framed in flames, came into view, so with full flaps and flare out we made an easy landing. The unit provided a welcome cup of rum and tea. Trucks despatched from Horam returned us to base by midnight through fog and beautiful hoar frost. No Christmas dinner. We returned to Woodbridge and flew the plane home the following day. FIDO worked!

On 26 December, records Martin Middlebrook: 'The weather at last improved and allowed Bomber Command to intervene in the Ardennes battle. 294 aircraft . . . of all Groups except 100 were able to attack German troop positions near St Vith. This was the first time since mid-October that aircraft from all groups had joined together in one raid.' Roger Freeman writes: 'The USAF bomber effort on Boxing Day was even smaller than at Christmas – some 150 sorties. Winter now had most of Western Europe in an unusually icy grip. Freezing fog clung to the East Anglian countryside. Even at midday the sun was unable to diminish its persistence.'

Widespread diversions were the order of the day for machines of both air forces, and FIDO was lit at all three emergency airfields as well as at Downham Market and Graveley as they returned home. It was a calm afternoon in the Woodbridge area but at about 13.00 a thick fog began to roll in from the sea. As it proceeded in a westerly direction, half of the runway was blotted out while the other half was still clear. A P–51 hove into view with the intention of landing on the clear half, but as the pilot did so it vanished before his very eyes. Pulling up above the 2–300 ft blanket of fog he called up on R/T, to be told to circuit the airfield while FIDO was lit, since no neighbouring aerodrome was clear. So thick was the fog that even with all burners going, visibility on the runway could only be raised to 100 yd. Throttling back as much as he dared the pilot of LC-E of the 20th Fighter Group could only pick out the burners when he was directly over them, by which time dropping down was too late. However, after going round a total of six times he was eventually able to judge things correctly and landed safely on the seventh. Shortly afterwards two machines which had been marooned at Woodbridge overnight took off to return to base.

Wg Cdr McGlinn took the opportunity to complain about the condition of the FIDO burners, which were emitting far too much smoke, and the shortage of crew. Nine joints had failed and numerous pipes were badly distorted due to the extremes of cold and heat being experienced. It should be borne in mind that every burner out of action meant 45 yd of runway unprotected. Said Wg Cdr McGlinn: 'I appreciate the demands for trained men for this work elsewhere, but I do feel that we should be allowed to build up an experienced team at this runway. Good FIDO is essential, especially as we tend to be a home from home in bad weather.'

The weight of the Allied air offensive increased on 28 December, although conditions were far from ideal. A force of 1,275 Fortresses and Liberators, escorted by 606 Mustangs, attacked rail and road bridges at Kaiserslautern, Koblenz et al, while in a series of night and day raids, Bomber Command attacked Opladen, Cologne, Mönchengladbach and Bonn. One of the P-51s was flown by Robert E. Cope, White flight leader of 361 Fighter Squadron in QI-I:

After a successful mission we reached the Channel with only a few clouds below. . . . Then we hit a fog bank as we reached the English coast at around 8,000 ft. . . . We were in tight formation and in the fog all I could see were the wing-lights on each side of my canopy, only a few feet away. . . . Our homing section which never received credit for the many planes they brought down safely, said that they would vector us to Woodbridge emergency landing strip about 5 miles north-east of our base, explaining that the FIDO system was in operation. . . . He also explained that it was an east to west runway and the good old English saying, 'You cawn't miss it!'

It is not possible for many to know what it feels like to be flying blind with the responsibility of three other pilots riding your wing and your directions. Checking my times and altitude constantly, nothing ever looked better than seeing the big red glow in the heavy fog and clouds at around 1,500 ft. . . . With my stomach in my mouth and the adrenalin flowing fast, we changed to an echelon formation and proceeded with our let down. . .

On our final approach the red glow grew brighter and around 75 ft we broke out of the fog, and I have never seen a more beautiful sight of a runway right in front of us, as any normal type of landing. . . . We all touched down at the same time and taxied to the service area. . . . Needless to say, after shutting down the engines there was a very long delay – time to give thanks to the Almighty, and all the people who helped bring us back safely.

Communications centres were again the targets for Bomber Command and the 'Mighty Eighth' on 29 December. Two separate RAF forces attacked railyards in Koblenz, one of the main centres serving the Ardennes battle front, while 827 USAF bombers, with a fighter escort of 724, raided similar targets in Frankfurt, Bingen et al. Flying conditions for all aircraft operating were appalling and there was fierce opposition from enemy fighters.

On Boxing Day, the station commander had said that Woodbridge tended 'to be a home from home in bad weather', and it was certainly the case on this occasion. With visibility down to 1,000 yd for most of the day a steady, or perhaps unsteady, stream of battle-damaged B–17s, B–24s, Lancasters and Halifaxes made their way down through the clag, together with a batch of 149 Squadron that had been unable to land at their home field at Methwold. Ten East Anglian airfields were represented, together with a couple of B–17 communications aircraft, lost and attracted by the flames. Of the total of twenty-six machines which descended between 10.48 and 17.40, only J-Johnnie from Tuddenham had to make a crash landing. Total petrol consumption for the period was just over half a million gallons. The poor conditions were widespread and FIDO was used at six airfields all told, receiving eighty-eight aircraft.

At 09.15 on 30 December a B–17 from 375 Bomb Group at Framlingham was reported caught out in fog 2–300 ft deep, with its wireless and homing devices u/s. The machine had experienced severe icing conditions above low clouds and it had apparently taken the Royal Observer Corps half an hour to track its erratic whereabouts and inform Woodbridge of its predicament. The burners at the eastern end of the runway were lit as amplified flare path markers, on to which the pilot soon latched and made a safe descent at 09.50, to be followed by a B–17 communications aircraft 5 minutes later.

Before the night was out, FIDO was used for the last time in the year, following a raid on the Kalk-Nord railway yards in Cologne. The weather conditions are uncertain, but at 23.15 Halifax X-X-ray of 77 Squadron, flown by Flt Sgt Kerslake, made an emergency landing with fuel-line cut by flak, and at 23.37 WO Adams in Mosquito E-Easy of 692 Squadron returned, 'aircraft unable to maintain height'.

This brought 1944 at Woodbridge to an end as far as FIDO was concerned. During the year just over 2,600 aircraft had made emergency landings there, the reasons almost equally divided among battle damage, technical trouble, fuel shortage and weather diversions. Of the last group, into which FIDO usually fell, 262 occurred in December. Woodbridge's records are incomplete, but PWD records estimate the December FIDO landings at 145, with a total petrol consumption of over 1.3 million gallons. We incline to think that these are underestimates.

The massive air offensive continued into the new year, despite consistently bad weather. Roger Freeman wrote: 'The winter weather of 1944–5 was exceptionally bad in England. The frequent rains of the autumn were followed by many days of persistent fog – some of the worst this century – which gave way to freezing conditions and several weeks of snow, thaw and snow again during the New Year. The lot of the ground crews was miserable and the whole effort to sustain operations made extremely difficult.'

Even so, US air forces maintained massive attacks on communications and rail targets as weather conditions permitted. Over 800 B–17s and B–24s of the 1st, 2nd and 3rd Air Divisions escorted by more than 600 P–51s and P–47s carried out raids, supported by Ramrods, to Cologne, Koblenz and Worms on 6 January. Visibility closed in as the fighter escorts left their charges on the last leg of the homeward flight, and groups from Framlingham and Martlesham were alerted to the likelihood of diversions. When it was impossible to see more than half a mile on the surface, and the fog anything up to 100 ft deep, FIDO was lit at 12.35.

Aircraft of the 356th Fighter Group based at Martlesham, being appraised that their own airfield was fogbound, began to arrive 50 minutes later; a P–47 and two P–51s at 13.23, followed between 13.33 and 13.53 by another fifteen Mustangs. First man home was Lt Eugene Turner in PI-A 'Dotty', named after his wife. Some way further back came Lt (later Maj Gen) Wayne Gatlin in PI-L. Writing home in as much detail as censorship would permit, he told his mother: 'I flew today, but the mission was pretty dull until we got home and found the visibility down to less than half a mile and in spots just plain nil. Boy, what sport! First we landed at a bomber strip [Woodbridge] and then took off for home again. My traffic pattern was about 100 ft off the ground and I was able to hit the field by luck.' To the author,

General Gatlin recalled: 'When we all got down we checked the weather at Martlesham by telephone. Apparently the weather there looked promising, for we all took off for what was about a 30-second flight. That was the mistake of the day, for getting down at Martlesham was one hair-raising experience. There were even attempts to land on taxiways.'

In fact, two pilots, Lts Rensch and Rudd, gave up trying to land through the conditions at Martlesham and returned to Woodbridge, where they landed for the second time at 15.01 and 15.03 respectively. Their re-arrival confused Flying Control and they were logged in as Lts A.N. Other. Following their landings, nos 19 and 20 for the day, the system was turned to idling for over an hour until the first of the B–17s from Framlingham began to assemble at 16.09. Twelve of them set down in 25 minutes and then another two P–51s, after which FIDO was extinguished, with twelve bombers and twenty-two fighters to its credit. As the effects of FIDO died away, along with the staccato crackle of engine exhausts, the all-pervading mist resumed its blanket over the scene.

At 18.10 on the same day, 3 Group called up with a request for FIDO to be lit to receive two of their Hudsons from 161 Special Duties Squadron at Tempsford. Flown by Flt Lts Ferris and Webb, they had been engaged on an Air Sea Rescue search and had made a sighting which entailed circling the dinghy while surface craft hastened to the spot. Meanwhile, the whole of 3 Group area was becoming unfit due to the fog. As it was known that both Hudsons had plenty of fuel left, FIDO was not re-lit until the first aircraft called, clearing something like 100 ft of low stratus from the runway. There was quite a delay before the second machine put in an appearance, for Flt Lt Webb had returned to Tempsford, only to be diverted back to Woodbridge. Both were eventually landed safely, fed and watered within the hour.

Two hours later the FIDO crews had to stand to again in conditions no better than before, runway visibility being down to 300 yd. A force of 482 RAF bombers had attacked the rail junction of Hanau and two, in distress, were directed to divert to Woodbridge. To cover their return, and that of any others which might be in difficulty, FIDO was lit well before they were due. At 21.15 Halifax U-Uncle of 427 Squadron landed with its starboard tyre burst and air-bomber injured. Although its passage down on the runway was erratic to say the least, it was brought clear and its crew members disembarked without delay. Twenty minutes later Halifax Y-Yoke, short of fuel and battle damaged, set down safely. 'FIDO was visible from the French coast – as good as daylight', said Uncle, while the pilot of Y-Yoke reported that he had seen FIDO while still 10 miles inside France. 'It was most useful as a beacon,' he reckoned, 'because GEE was unserviceable.' Finally, at 22.00 FIDO was extinguished for the night, with thirty-eight aircraft to its credit, for the expenditure of some 90,000 gallons of petrol. There was just time for the crew to get to the NAAFI before lights out – if only they could find it in the fog!

Almost 1,500 bombers and fighters from all three 8th USAF divisions took part in raids on the marshalling yards and Rhine railway bridges at Bischofsheim, Maximiliansau, Rudesheim et al. on 13 January. Flying conditions were atrocious with considerable icing and extensive cloud over the continent. It was not foggy over England as the force made its way home, but a cloud base of only 600 ft was common over East Anglia, reaching up to 5,000 ft. It became very difficult to control the large number of aircraft being diverted with that depth of cloud between them and clear air below. Instructions were therefore given for FIDO to be lit at Woodbridge in an endeavour to lift the cloud base rather than disperse fog. First light-up was at 14.45 and after a while there was 1,000 ft of clear air above the runway.

The prevailing wind at the time was gusting up to 25 mph from the east, a tail-wind, so it was ordered that all landings were to be made from the west. Fortunately, everybody got the message, and the aircraft captains found that as lit, FIDO made an excellent marker for the starting-point of their descent from the west. They were actually able to make wide circuits in formation when their turn came to break cloud at 500 ft. Because of the west to east landings, the sodium lamps and cross-lines at the eastern end were not used, but this proved no handicap to the pilots, who descended in droves.

Several machines landed before the apparatus was burning clearly; but then, from roughly 15.00 onwards, the lowering skies and the runway reverberated to the sound of Pratt & Whitney engines as eighty Flying Fortresses, five Liberators, eleven Mustangs, with their staccato Merlins, joined by three Lancasters, made their circuits and approaches. Ninety-nine aircraft set down by 17.45, the great majority within the space of an hour and 40 minutes, with no mishaps on approach, landing or dispersal. Thirty-nine of the B–17s were from 384 Bomb Group at Deenethorpe (Northants) and another twenty-six from 457 Bomb Group at Glatton (Hunts). A total of 171,827 gallons of petrol had been consumed to good effect. Within half an hour of extinguishing the burners, the cloud base was down to its original 600 ft level again.

Bomber Command flew over 1,200 sorties on the night of 14/15 January 1945. As far as Woodbridge was concerned, two 100 Group aircraft sought refuge early on 15 January: Mosquitos W-Willie from Swannington and Y-Yoke of North Creake, returning from intruder and RCM patrols respectively. Smoke mingling with very low stratus had made visibility below a mile and less than 200 ft ceiling. When FIDO was lit, the system was in very poor condition. Nine welds had burst on the north side, which either put the burners out of action or created additional smoke, and forty-two spreaders were no longer spreading the pipes, but allowing them to resemble a scenic railway, spewing petrol all over the shop. Despite this, sufficient clearance was obtained to bring both aircraft home without mishap. The fog dispersal report says that five burners on the north side were damaged by aircraft, but it does not say that it was by these particular machines.

The US 8th Air Force planned a major strike at oil and industrial targets in Germany on 16 January. Weather conditions were very bad, and there were recalls and cancellations for some of the bombers and many diversions for bombers and fighters on the return flight. Diversions to Woodbridge began as early as 10.25, with a number of P–51s between then and 11.50. Soon after that advection fog which had been present all morning thickened in a WSW wind of 10 mph until visibility was only 1,200 yd, at which point it was considered advisable to light the fog dispersal apparatus. It was in a parlous state due to extensive burning and minimum maintenance, with twelve fractured pipes, forty-five broken spreaders and four concrete securing blocks lifted. Nevertheless, from 12.35 FIDO managed to raise visibility to 2,500 yd and hold it there until 14.00, during which time about sixty more aircraft landed. No less than thirty-nine of these were P–47s of 56 Fighter Group from Boxted in Essex, which had been engaged in an offensive sweep.

In mid-afternoon the approach of a warm front caused a marked deterioration, with the cloud base descending to only 500 ft. Petrol pressure was increased from 60 to 75 lb psi but by 16.00 the clouds could be kept no higher than 300 ft. The number of aircraft landing grew fewer and fewer. Petrol pressure was increased again to its maximum of 90 lb per sq. in, but with the onset of drizzle, landing became increasingly hazardous. Several machines slipped in under the blanket of cloud even so, but finally at 18.00 defeat had to be admitted and the remaining aircraft aloft were given alternative diversions. From start to finish, including the half dozen pilots who squeezed in before FIDO was lit, eighty-three aircraft made emergency landings – thirty-nine Thunderbolts, twenty Mustangs, eighteen Fortresses, three Liberators and a Cessna Crane.

Following this date, American operations dwindled, and from 24 to 27 January no offensive operations are recorded. Bomber Command records also show that few sorties were flown over the same period. Prolonged bad weather was the principal cause of this. Even so, enough aircraft were airborne on the 24th to require FIDO's services on three occasions. The first stand-to came at 07.45, when visibility over the East Anglian countryside was down to 100 yd; 'in the grey of the dawn as the mists uprose from the meadow,' as the poet might have perceived it. Two B–17s, 158 from Eye and 370 from Snetterton, were caught out and requested FIDO-assisted landings. So thick was the fog that the ground crew could almost have done with FIDO to find their control points along the vast featureless airstrip. They managed it, however, and the burners improved runway vision to 1,200 yd, sufficient for the pilots to descend in safety.

Before the burners could be extinguished, a call came through for them to be kept on for a Met Flight (1409) Mosquito which had been recalled, ETA uncertain. This machine duly arrived, but again, before the system could be doused came another request. As visibility was still not above 800 yd and the fog 100 ft deep, part of the system was put on full burn, and between 09.40 and 10.50 five of 36 Bomber Squadron's Liberators, which had been on RCM sorties, landed in safety – P, E, M, L and F from Chediston. At 18.23 a last call was made, with a 50 ft deep radiation fog prevailing widespread. A few burners on each side of the approach end of the runway were lit as a marker, whose glow penetrated the shallow fog. Within a quarter of an hour two Mosquitos from Ford in Sussex, lost and far from home, effected good landings; a bag of ten for the day.

Before summarizing January's activities mention must be made of a remarkable incident on an unspecified date, recorded in the *Emergency Runways Bulletin* for that month. A Flying Fortress landed at Woodbridge during a FIDO burn, and after touching down it was noticed that its back was broken and its tail-wheel and rear turret were missing. When the pilot descended from his machine he revealed that he had attempted to land at his own base but struck the ground so heavily, tail down, that the rear turret and its gunner had broken away. Several of the crew had actually seen the turret rolling merrily down the runway for two or three hundred yards after impact. Subsequent enquiries elicited that apart from a small cut on his forehead, the gunner was uninjured and was back in the mess hall long before his diverted shipmates were.

A grand total of 554 emergency landings took place at Woodbridge during January 1945. At least 250 of these were achieved with the aid of FIDO. Summarizing, the station commander said:

> The number of landings for this month established yet another record, FIDO being responsible for a great number of them. Snow threatened to be a problem at times. The severe frost caused great difficulty with the installation for delivering FIDO petrol, caused, it is thought, by a high percentage of water in the spirit, which resulted in pipes becoming blocked with ice. It was lucky that this occurred while FIDO was not in extensive use. Had this not been the case, it would have seriously impaired the efficiency of the runway. On one occasion 950 aircrew were received over a period of three hours.

Martin Middlebrook records that the weather started to improve at the beginning of February and that Bomber Command commenced an almost unbroken period of operations which continued until a halt was called to the strategic bombing offensive in April. The first round of raids, however, was hampered by bad weather.

On the night of 1/2 February nearly 1,300 sorties were flown, with main raids on Ludwigshafen, Mainz and Siegen. Among supporting operations was one by a group of four Oboe Mosquitos detailed to drop dummy target indicators on Mannheim. Wg Cdr Bill Simpson, RNZAF, of 109 Squadron flew one of them:

> I had lost one engine and was instructed to land at Woodbridge as the weather was bad everywhere with fog and low cloud. We made a direct approach in cloud from over the North Sea and suddenly, at a few hundred feet, the full red glow of FIDO emerged ahead – a most reassuring sight. There was some turbulence when we entered the area of heat and smoke generated by the burning fuel, but the runway was relatively clear, and it was a relief to make a safe single-engined landing.
>
> When we coasted to a stop, being unable to taxi on one engine, I stopped the live motor and called for a tractor. No sooner had I done this than I heard a roar of engines and the dark shape of a

Lancaster rushed past, its port wing flashing across our canopy and missing us by what seemed to be only inches. This made me realize that sitting in a stationary Mosquito on the Woodbridge runway in the dark beyond the FIDO fires was not a good place to be. I could visualize masses of other bombers coming down the glide path and churning into us, so it was a very relieved crew who were towed away shortly afterwards.

Karlsruhe experienced its last major raid of the war on the night of 2/3 February. Ten 627 Squadron Mosquitos were markers for the force of 250 Lancasters, fourteen of which were lost. Considerable cloud was experienced by the raiders to this and other targets, and on their return flight conditions were not any better. Pilot F.A. Saunders, of 627 Squadron, flying from Woodhall Spa, with Flt Sgt G.T. Swales as navigator, was ahead of the main force:

A faint glow on the horizon ahead warned us that it was time to begin our descent from operational height. The noise of the Merlins muted as I eased back on the throttle to lose height. It was necessary to watch for any icing layer. Met didn't mention any but it was as well to keep looking for it. Engine temperature and fuel gauges had also to be watched as we reduced air speed.

Given our final instructions we prepared for the landing procedure. At 2,000 ft we entered the thick swirling mass and could see nothing outside except streams of fog flashing past the blue flames of our own exhaust pipes. The glow on the horizon had gone. Nothing but flickering orange opaqueness all around us. On the last run in, the aircraft was buffeted by rising warm air. At 800 ft we could still see nothing. I increased throttle to give a little extra speed to counter the heated air. The fog took on an orange hue at 600 ft. By 400 ft we were in landing attitude, and suddenly we found ourselves flying in a clear atmospheric tunnel, with a line of fire stretching on both sides of us. No sight of the runway except a black void where it ought to be. A bump as the two huge tyres hit the ground, followed by the tail-wheel. Then we were speeding down the fiery lane, nicely straight, with speed dropping fast.

We radioed control, 'George-Baker clear of runway', and received the order to follow the van which carried an illuminated sign 'Follow me' to dispersal. . . . After handing over our Mosquito to

Plate 73 Liberator of 491st BG landing in daylight fog at Woodbridge, February 1945. Single line of burners on south side alight. North side may be the same (IWM)

the ground crew I glanced back to see its beautiful lines silhouetted against the flames of this unique runway. Strange how humans can get sentimentally attached to inanimate objects. Sad that it is a machine of war.

For the third day in a row the US 8th Air Force sent over 1,000 bombers to oil and rail targets in west Germany on 16 February. On each day the weather had been successively worse, and although we do not have evidence of any diversions to Woodbridge on the first two days, 'extremely poor visibility forced returning bombers to be diverted to continental or west of England airfields' on the 16th.

Weather conditions were of low cloud rather than fog when Liberators 614 and 958 asked for assistance at 15.30. Skipper of the first machine, Lt Rosholt, reported:

> There was 10/10 cloud from 200 ft up to 1,500 ft. We used the GEE box for homing until we had contact with Woodbridge on 6440. We let right down to 200 ft but still could not find the means of homing into the field or contacting them at any distance. However, the fires proved very good, and the circle lights pretty good, but a *Buncher* on the field would be of great help and frequency given to all ships.

Both aircraft landed safely, and as a safeguard against any other planes diverted their way, FIDO was kept idling until 18.30.

The weather was no better on the 17th. Before the main forces took off, USAF weather reconnaissance Mosquitos surveyed conditions to and from rail and synthetic-oil targets in western Germany. Two of them were victims of the weather they were trying to predict and sought asylum at Woodbridge. Cloud was 10/10 below 800 ft, and Mosquitos NS634 and NS708 were unable to make their own 25 Bomb Group base. FIDO was lit for them at 06.35 and within half an hour both were safely down. We do not know if their report was heeded, but the whole of the 1st and 2nd Air Divisions, 550 bombers, were recalled before reaching Germany and 'the weather was so bad that some aircraft controls froze and several had to jettison their bombs during assembly'.

Bomber Command's 3 Group carried out a daylight attack on the railway yards at Wesel during 19 February. By 17.30 the Lancasters were streaming home. Meantime the ever-present mist had thickened, with horizontal visibility below a mile and oblique vision very difficult. FIDO was requested to cover the return of the bombers; first of all three burners on each side to act as a marker, by which Lancaster KB-Y landed, and one other, unidentified machine. Then P-Peter of 186 Squadron, flown by Flg Off Beck called up, requesting an emergency landing due to battle damage. Six burners on each side were brought in and by their light he was able to line up the runway, shoot along its length and come to rest in a bellylanding on the overshoot.

On 22 February the American 8th Air Force began Operation Clarion, a major assault on German road and rail communications, widening as the month continued to include synthetic-oil plants as well. For ten days in a row, never less than 1,100 bombers set forth, with anything from 600 to 800 escorts. On 23 February, 1,274 B–17s and B–24s, with an escort of over 700 P–51s, raided Ansbach, Plauen, Paderborn and others. The weather was poor for their take-offs, and remained so throughout the morning, with the additional impediment of rain. At about 10.50 two early returns contacted Woodbridge for runway clearance, a B–24 and a P–51 of the 2nd Air Division. By this time there was 10/10 cloud from 600 up to 2,000 ft. Lt Fox, the Liberator pilot, asked where he might find broken cloud thereabouts, but was told there was none. He reported that his instruments were all u/s and agreed to stand by while FIDO was lit, which was achieved by 11.00 – all the inner lines at nearly full pressure. US–S then began a gentle descent through the cloud, emerging over the River Deben, at which point Lt Fox could see the glow of FIDO quite clearly, though ground details were very blurred. From thence he was able to circle and land without difficulty. The P–51 was in a different position. It had no flaps and was difficult to control. The pilot made a straightforward run in, but was hard put to it to keep his machine on the deck as it made its way down the runway.

Conditions were almost the same as the main force proceeded homewards three hours later. FIDO was lit to cover their return, which extended over another 3 hour period. During that time twenty Fortresses, fifteen Mustangs, five Liberators, a Lancaster and an Oxford landed without mishap, with visibility never above 800 yd and constant drizzle. Lastly, at 22.10, a Mosquito requested direct landing with one engine out of action. At this time there was 6/10 cloud at 600 ft, and it was only necessary to light six burners, say 300 yd, on each side of the runway at the approach end to mark the Mosquito's path as it touched down. Total for the day, forty-five aircraft.

Bomber Command's level of operations reached a crescendo in March as its strategic offensive came to an end. Over 500 heavy bomber sorties per night were being flown. Although the weather was still a hazard to be contended with, there were not many calls on FIDO countrywide. Only one occurred at Woodbridge during the first half of the month. Following a 5 Group raid on Lützkendorf on 14/15 March, Lancaster C-Charlie flown by Flg Off Ledeboer of 57 Squadron requested landing clearance at about 03.30 as his hydraulic system was u/s. Visibility was only 800 yd, and when FIDO was lit at 03.45 it only improved to 1,000. A grinding belly-landing was anticipated, but to everyone's surprise the undercarriage came down and locked satisfactorily, enabling C-Charlie to land without mishap. When questioned afterwards the flight engineer revealed that he had ensured the undercarriage would work by topping up the hydraulic fluid with Elsanol toilet mixture!

On 28 March the last recorded wartime use of FIDO at Woodbridge took place. USAF weather Mosquito NS740 flown by Lt Harrington had been diverted and re-diverted in conditions of low cloud only 200 ft from the ground. He was very short of fuel. At 05.55 Harrington sought permission to land, and within 5 minutes the FIDO burners were well alight. He used GEE on his run-up to the glow through the cloud, and throttled back on the runway, coming to a standstill with only 20 gallons of petrol left. At 13.40 on the same day FIDO was lit again for Fortress 911 to land.

From the time of its establishment in 1943 until the end of the war, it is estimated that 4,000 aircraft made emergency landings at Woodbridge: 770 because of damage by enemy action, 880 because of fuel shortage, another 1,090 due to technical trouble and 1,170 due to weather diversions. Not all of the last group required the use of FIDO. A bald statement in Bomber Command document Air 14/1414 says that 547 did so, which accords quite well with our estimate of 555. In a number of cases, however, where there is no documentary evidence, an aircrewman may have remembered his own landing in detail, but had only been able to hazard a guess as to how many other machines may have landed on the same occasion. There is therefore a strong possibility that the overall total is higher. Records of emergency landings at Woodbridge continue through to the end of 1946, by which time an Air Historical Branch List estimates that there had been a grand total of 4,270 landings of one kind or another.

Tom Lambert reminds us that Woodbridge closed in 1948 but was taken over by the US Air Force in 1952 and has continued under its control ever since. A landing chart of 1954 shows that only the centre 150 ft wide strip was in operation and that the approach lighting encroached 1,800 ft on to the runway, leaving 7,800 ft of landing room. Runway repairs were carried out in 1958 and it is likely that any remnants of FIDO which might have existed would have been removed then. In 1970 the base became the headquarters for the 67th Aerospace Research and Recovery Squadron, flying Hercules HC–130 aircraft and HH–53E Super Jolly Green Giant helicopters. It was also home to the 81st Tactical Fighter Wing. Both units departed in September 1993 when Woodbridge was handed back to the Ministry of Defence.

Even when FIDO was not in operation, it frequently figured in station ops records and the recollections of former servicemen, usually as the victim of an errant aircraft making an emergency landing. Although such incidents occurred at all FIDO stations, at no airfield was it more prevalent than at Woodbridge. This example must serve to typify all the others.

Liberator UH-R of Attlebridge, 2nd Lt P.F. Evans commanding, carried all before it when returning from ops on 11 August 1944. Its port and starboard inner engines packed up after Evans had turned in on his final approach. His port outer engine cut out and swung the aircraft over to the south side of the runway immediately he touched down, whereupon UH-R charged through the FIDO pipes, carrying away a considerable length thereof. Not satisfied with that, its starboard wing sliced through the trees bordering the airfield, and, changing direction violently, it demolished the airfield control van and a few seconds later a Forestry Commission van. But all was not yet over. The plane's wing then tore the body from a contractor's coach, while the starboard mainplane completed the performance by tearing down the nearest Tannoy tower. The aeroplane came to rest on its nose in No. 8 loop. The only casualty was the Forestry Commission agent, who was slightly cut. Poor chap. He was probably only having a quiet smoke! On the same day the station ops record book logged the thousandth emergency landing at Woodbridge.

NINETEEN

Epinoy

... a couple of enterprising Air Traffic Controllers flogged the steel pipes

AVM Edgar James

The French region of Picardy was occupied by advancing German forces in October 1914 and remained in their hands until the last few weeks of the First World War. Epinoy was one of a number of front-line aerodromes established by the Germans near Cambrai and for a while was the home of 'le triplan du Baron Rouge' when Manfred von Richthofen was squadron commander of Jagdeschwader I in 1917.

After the war a considerable period of inactivity ensued, during which the area was largely returned to agriculture. In 1939, however, the aerodrome was reactivated and enlarged under Commandante Fred Geille, only to be overrun again by German troops of the 7th Panzer Division under the command of General Erwin Rommel in May 1940. Three concrete runways were built at Epinoy in 1941–2, when the airfield became the base for units of the veteran Kampfgeschwader 2 (Bomber Group 2), commanded by Major Kriepe.

During the summer of 1944, Allied land forces advanced across France, and Cambrai was liberated by units of the American 79th Infantry Division on 2 September. Epinoy subsequently became a 9th USAF base under the command of Col Harold Mayers, and 138 Wing of the 2nd TAF from Hartfordbridge, renamed Blackbushe, took up residence on 17 November 1944. They continued there until the end of hostilities, flying their Mosquitos on a variety of raids and interception patrols.

'Following an indifferent summer, October had heralded a period of some of the worst Autumn weather in many years, and flying was soon affected, operations being curtailed dramatically,' records Christopher Shores. Fortunately, as related on page 36 and in accompanying Plate 26 and Fig. 10, the necessity for aircraft to operate from a captured aerodrome with minumum facilities under adverse conditions had been anticipated. Elaborate systems were out of the question with the rapidly moving conflict, but the portable installation Haifox was already in an advanced state of preparedness back in England.

The equipment was ferried across post-haste, but a variety of hold-ups by the weather and delay with subsequent supplies meant that there was no opportunity for full-scale tests until February 1945, when the weather determined that a burn in clear skies on 14 February was followed by one in fog 24 hours later.

The first recorded operational use of the Haifox system occurred on the night of 5/6 March 1945. Twenty-four Mosquitos of 138 Wing were detailed to attack road and rail movements east and north-west of the Ruhr. Eight of them were subsequently withdrawn. The weather was very bad over the target area and results were hard to observe, three machines abandoning their attempts. They were diverted to Manston, one crashing en route. The remaining twelve pressed on. As they returned, the cloud base was at 600 ft, with patches drifting across the airstrip in winds of up to 15 mph. Markers only at the head of the runway were lit and three of the Mosquitos landed safely. Records do not show where the others went. All the pilots expressed approval of the marker burners. 'One pilot who was diverted to us was particularly warm in his praise and stated that without the assistance of the marker burners he could not have landed,' says the fog dispersal report, which goes on to say that, at 16,000 gallons for a three-hour burn, the petrol consumption was excessive due to a broken feed-pipe. No doubt the ground near the burners was well and truly saturated, and smoking might have been a hazardous pastime for some while afterwards. It is surprising to read that after the burn 665,000 gallons of petrol remained in the storage tanks; more than would have been left in many of the English airfield installations.

The only other occasion when FIDO was known to have been used at Epinoy was on the night of 10/11 March 1945. The target area of 138 Wing stretched from Leeuwarden into north-west Germany, and as far east as Osnabruck. Twenty-four aircraft were detailed. Eighteen of them completed their attacks by 22.30 in conditions of 'cloud practically down to the deck', by which time the other six had been recalled. The low cloud everywhere made it advisable to light the marker burners to ensure lining up with the runway as the Mosquitos returned, ten of them landing safely. One was flown by US Major D.D. Button, with Larry Melling as navigator:

> On that night, 107 was the only squadron operating because of widespread ground fog. It was so prevalent that the Germans assumed that there would be no night activity, and when we arrived over our patrol area it was alive with road and rail transport. The squadron had a very successful night raid indeed.
>
> When we returned to base, we landed using FIDO. The only way I can describe it is that it was like descending into the mouth of hell. The heat was so intense that we actually felt the bump as we passed over the end of the runway and my pilot had to take very great care to stay exactly in the centre of the runway and not to overshoot. The whole squadron got down safely and we were very proud of the lineshoot, 'only squadron operating', but our feelings about FIDO were a bit mixed. The system undoubtedly worked; it lifted the ground fog about 300 ft, which was just enough, but we wondered how it would be in a damaged aircraft, perhaps on one engine, trying to maintain the essential dead straight approach. We were told that if by any mischance we hit the piping while taking off or landing, that section would automatically shut off. We were not too sure that we believed it, and in a wooden aircraft the whole idea seemed dicey. Luckily we never had to use the system again, but it did work.

The fog dispersal report for this operation records that only 3,699 gallons of petrol were used during a two-hour burn, compared with 16,000 for a three-hour burn on the previous occasion. Meantime Haifox's designer Denys Fox and his colleagues had been very busy. On 13 March it was reported that eight portable burners were to hand at Staines, and that fifty sets were to be ready for collection from the contractors for delivery by transport of the 2nd American Air Division the following day.

We do not know if the fifty burners ever formed part of an installation at Epinoy, but FIDO hit the headlines, in military circles at any rate, some months later. Apparently, after the cessation of hostilities, instructions were given for the system to be dismantled. Whoever was responsible for carrying out the order did so in a big way for AVM Edgar James recalls: 'It seems that a couple of enterprising Air Traffic Controllers flogged the steel pipes to some local entrepreneur for a very large sum and made off into the blue!' Another correspondent tells us that it became a court martial case, but the accused 'got away with it', because no specific instructions had been given as to how FIDO should be disposed of once it was dismantled!

TWENTY

The Aleutians

... even when the winds are blowing at 15 to 25 knots, the fog just sits there
Christopher A. Long, US Navy Civil Engineer Corps

Although the attention of Second World War historians has generally concentrated on the central and south Pacific theatres of war, an equally fierce conflict took place in 1942 and 1943, when Japanese forces advanced eastwards and northwards to the Aleutian Islands. The Japanese Aleutian operation was one element of a larger, complex plan, intended to capture Midway Island in the central Pacific and to draw into battle and destroy the US Pacific Fleet.

In the event, the Midway offensive failed, but it was decided to continue with the Aleutian thrust. The Japanese attacks were anticipated, but insufficient forces were available to prevent carrier-borne air raids on Dutch Harbour, at the eastern end of the Aleutians on 3 and 4 June 1942 and the occupation of the undefended western islands of Attu and Kiska three days later.

The Japanese were never able to extend their foothold in the Aleutians, but it was many months before United States and Canadian land, sea and air forces capable of expelling them and restoring national pride could be assembled. Initially, retaliation against the occupation forces on Attu and Kiska, totalling some 8,500 men, comprised, weather permitting, attempts at bombing and naval bombardment, together with surface and submarine patrols. The main battle, however, was against the weather – extreme cold, rain or snow, gales and almost perpetual fog.

Veterans who served there have a very sanguine view of this wilderness:

> Of all the places that the military could have picked to fight a war, the Aleutian Islands was one of the worst in the world. . . . There are few places where men and vehicles can move easily on the mountainous islands. The low areas generally consist of muskeg, under which are layers of waterlogged, slimy, volcanic ash, mud, sand and finally, volcanic rock. . . . It is the incessant wind, however, that is the most noticeable scourge to human sanity. Coming down from the north with an average speed of 12 knots, they frequently blow at 24 knots for 24 hours and more. The Aleutian Islands are the only place where high winds and fog occur at the same time. . . . There are few islands which are large enough or flat enough and lend themselves to the construction of airfields. Amchitka and Shemya are the exceptions.

Despite such atrocious conditions and logistical shortcomings, airstrips were gradually established closer and closer to the enemy-held islands. Eventually the decision was taken to utilize unpopulated Amchitka, only 60 miles from Kiska. In gale force winds which wrecked three of the four transports involved, engineers struggled ashore on 11 and 12 January 1943. Their immediate task was to build a 4,000 ft long fighter airstrip, from which P–40 fighter-bombers flown by US and Canadian pilots could operate against Kiska.

Working in a sea of mud, frequently unable to see across the runway, 813 Engineers Battalion buckled down to their formidable task. For weeks on end they moved up to 20,000 cu. ft of infill daily, to establish a firm foundation for aircraft taking off and landing. The first fighters were able to operate from runway 'Fox' within five weeks. A 10,000 ft runway, capable of accepting heavy bombers, was commenced immediately after this, adjacent to the airstrip. By 5 May, 36 Bomb Squadron was able to mount a mission with its B–24s from the 5,000 ft of runway 'Baker' which was complete.

Later that month, after five days' delay because of fog and gales, an American invasion force landed on Attu to trap the defenders, who fought bitterly to the end. The official army history recorded: 'The price of victory was high. In terms of numbers engaged, Attu ranks as one of the costliest assaults in the Pacific.' While the battle was still going on, plans were laid for other airstrips to be built at the western end of the Aleutians; on Attu itself and on Shemya, only a few minutes flying time away. Reconnaissance parties who landed there on 28 May 1943 found the island 'devoid of any human habitation'. Japanese troops had landed on Shemya in November 1942 with a view to establishing an airstrip, but nothing had come of the project and they had withdrawn shortly afterwards.

American engineers planned a site for a 3,000 ft fighter strip, which would later be extended to 10,000 ft for heavy bombers. The fighter strip was operational by 21 June and sufficient of the enlarged runway was completed for B–24s to land on Shemya by 13 August.

Meantime, a massive armada was being built up for the invasion of Kiska, in anticipation of a battle as fierce as that for Attu. When the time came for the assault, however, it was discovered that the entire Japanese garrison had been evacuated under cover of foul weather.

The liberation of the Aleutian Islands necessitated a reappraisal of the role of the enormous ground and air forces which now controlled the archipelago. It was envisaged that many would be released for service elsewhere, and that the 11th Air Force might now be redeployed to carry the war across the sea to the Japanese homeland and the Kuril Islands. With an 800 mile trans-ocean flight, sans landmarks, a substantial offensive in that direction was a project which required different planning from the campaign thus far. Lessons had been learned from several missions which had been flown to the Kurils before the capture of Kiska. From these it emerged that the prime enemy was the weather. There were 184 operational losses, mainly due to fog. Only forty-one were directly attributable to enemy action.

With such a serious factor to consider, it was fortunate that successful landings in fog with the aid of FIDO had recently been made back in England. Through Bomber Command's liaison officer Wg Cdr John Wooldridge, the United States air authorities had been kept informed of progress in the realm of fog dispersal, and in the autumn of 1943, Wg Cdr Wooldridge and his American counterparts, Cdr J.P. Lunger and Lt Sinclair, explored its potential for the United States Navy and Air Forces.

Several transatlantic consultations took place, and on 4 October it was requested that the United States Bureau of Yards and Docks install an experimental fog dispersal system based on the Haigill Mk III burners, at the Naval Air Station, Whidbey Island, Washington, whence several naval air units had been sent in the Aleutians wind-down. A further meeting took place on 30 November, during which the site was designated Station XVIII.

Early in 1944 there were second thoughts on the most urgent need for FIDO, and Cdr Lunger visited the Aleutian Islands to ascertain the requirements of the northern Pacific Fleet and the US 11th Air Force there. In a report of 4 February Wg Cdr Wooldridge submitted that:

The chief difficulty is the remarkably barren and hilly nature of the country. In the immediate neighbourhood of all of the airfields under consideration here, rocky hills may be found, rising steeply to a height of 1,500–1,800 ft within a few yards of the runways. As conditions are usually extremely windy, these hills cause considerable amounts of turbulence and no definite wind directions can be forecast. The general feeling is, however, that under the existing conditions, any aid to landing, such as FIDO, would be of great advantage, especially in view of the light thrown up by and visual penetration of the burner lines through fog. Cdr Lunger has not yet returned from the

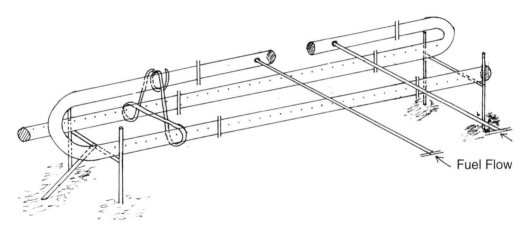

Fuel Flow

Fig. 26 Fog dispersal burner, Amchitka, 1993 (Christopher Long)

islands, and a full report on his visit will be forwarded to London as soon as he gets back. The Works and Docks Department of the US Navy places very high priority on this project and it is hoped that the work of construction will start very soon after Cdr Lunger's return.

John Wooldridge's hopes were swiftly realized for, on the commander's return, it was directed that the installation should not go ahead at Whidbey Island, but at Amchitka. Records show that the months of June, July and August were the worst periods for fog in the Aleutians. An average of 455 hours of fog was experienced during those three months, 30 per cent of the time with visibility down to 50 yd. Knowing this, it was hoped to complete a fog dispersal system at Amchitka before the onset of the 1944 fogs. Since the conditions in the Aleutians were substantially worse than on mainland America, and since experience gained in England was to hand, the American engineers elected to install burners based on the later Mk IV burners.

A company of the 79th and the 509th Construction Brigades (the Sea-Bees), was selected to build the installation on runway Baker, and set about the task with a vigour which would have made John Wayne's chest swell with pride. Sited precariously among a mixture of jagged peaks and treacherous tundra, construction of the 10,000 ft runway had daunted but not defeated earlier engineers and they took the addition of a FIDO system in their stride. The detachment from the 79th reached Amchitka on 30 March. Initially a double row of 30-therm burners 6,000 ft long was to be built flanking the 300 ft wide Baker runway. The Sea-Bees were learning as they went along – but they learned quickly. Fabrication workshops were built on the runway itself and three 40 yd burners were made from material locally available.

After consultation between the air base commander and the resident engineer at Amchitka, changes were made as construction progressed. The overall length of the burner lines was reduced from 6,000 ft to 4,000 ft with the approach from the east. The inner and outer lines of burners were relocated, to be further from the runway centre-line. Because of the very elongated shape of the airfield site, the FIDO storage tank farm was repositioned closer to the head of the runway. Portable burners to facilitate sealing of hardstandings and taxiways adjacent to the runway were eliminated. We do not know whether the burner lengths remained at 40 yd each, but jet holes were altered to $\frac{3}{32}$ in diam. at 4 in centres.

Materials for construction arrived on 17 April and the first production burner was completed two days later. All welding and pipe bending was done on site. The jet holes were drilled after the burners were fabricated to ensure the correct angle to the top, pre-heater pipe. The two-shift assembly line produced 100 burners by 29 April. Construction of the tank farm began on 22 April and six 350gpm pumps were installed by the eastern end of the runway.

Because paving of the runway was not yet completed and flight tests could not be carried out, Lt Cdr R.L. Champion, the Bureau of Yards and Docks representative, went to England to be appraised of progress made there, with particular reference to the difficulties being experienced at St Eval. As a result of his report, further changes were made to the system. The output of the outer lines of burners was raised from 30 therms to 50 therms. Marker burners were added at the east end of the runway. Additional burners were added to fill gaps and the inner and outer lines were connected to each other, 3,500 ft from touchdown.

An innovation which would have caused palpitations on a British airfield was that, 'since tests have indicated that wind velocities of 20 knots or over caused improper heating of burners, 5ft earth windbreaks were placed on the upwind side of all burner lines'. While such obstructions would have been unthinkable in Britain, where a billiard-table surface was sought, John Wooldridge noted that Canadian airmen had no fears of such barriers, 'as snow was frequently piled 3 ft high only a few feet from the edge' of airfields in Nova Scotia. No FIDO airfield plan exists, but Fig. 27 conveys the general layout.

Tests of the whole system were carried out from the middle of June 1944. Clear visibility along a mile of runway was obtained, but there was substantial intrusion of fog at the eastern end. As a result of this test, the marker burners there were replaced by a double row of cross-burners.

Another test took place on the 16th. This time an 8 knot cross-wind was blowing from the south. Ceiling was 150 ft and surface visibility only 150 yd. Two thousand yards of runway was cleared of fog to a height of 300 ft. After ten minutes, the system was extinguished, and visibility dropped to only 100 yd.

A month later, when surfacing of the runway was complete, the first flight trials were undertaken by Lt Cdr F.R. More, CO of Patrol Squadron VP–62, Pacific Fleet Air Force, in a Catalina amphibian and Capt W.M. Campbell in a United States 11th Air Force Dakota. There was zero ceiling and 150 yd visibility on the morning of 24 July 1944, with a 12 knot cross-wind from the south-west; 4,000 ft of outer and inner burners on the upwind side of the runway were lit at 05.50 and evaporated 300–500 ft of fog in only 5 minutes. Downwind of the burners, clearance extended across the muskeg for at least a mile – up into the foothills in fact. Lt Cdr More's PBY–5A was airborne before reaching the last burner, and disappeared into the fog, from which point he flew on instruments.

Returning to the airfield about 10 minutes later, still on instruments, he broke into clear air at 150 ft over the cross-burners. 'On landing, the aircraft hit the runway hard, in what closely

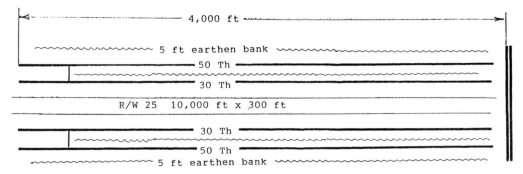

Fig. 27 US 11th AFB Amchitka, FIDO layout

approached a three-point landing,' concluded the pilot's report. Following his experience, he recommended that at least 40 minutes notice be given prior to the use of the system and that operation of the burners be restricted to two hours at a time. Lt Cdr More also recommended 'power landing' right down to the deck, to overcome 'errors in depth perception'.

At 05.45 on the 25th Capt W.H. Campbell and Lt W.P. Patrick flying Dakota 42–24274 took off in conditions of zero ceiling, zero visibility and a 14 mph head wind. Four thousand feet of the inboard and outboard lines of burners on the southern side of the runway were lit, as well as the eastern end cross-line burners. The C–47 became airborne after 3,500 ft and disappeared into zero everything long before it cleared the airfield boundary. Capt Campbell flew clear of the fog at 400 ft and reported that the runway and burners were clearly visible below, as was a substantial area downwind of the airstrip. Circling above the fog and the hills for some time, Dakota 42–24274 plunged back into fog at 500 ft east of the runway, approaching at 120 mph. The aircraft was talked down, but the pilot did not espy the airstrip until over the eastern cross-burners at a mere 50 ft. A successful landing was achieved, although a great deal of turbulence was experienced.

Messrs Campbell and Patrick's report concluded: 'Under the existing conditions, a landing could not have been made without the benefit of the fog dispersal unit. The pilots agree that this is a plausible solution to the hazard of fog in zero-zero conditions.' FIDO was in use for 65 minutes, consuming 80,704 (US) gallons of petrol. At the end of the tests, the system was handed over to the 11th Air Force as fit for operational use.

One week later FIDO was put to the test in earnest on Amchitka Island. A naval escort covering a visit by President Roosevelt to northern Pacific waters requested anti-submarine air cover while within range of Aleutian air bases. On 2 August, six Catalinas of Patrol Squadron 62 were alerted to fly 'a six-lane special mission' from the base. Ceiling on Amchitka was only 100 ft and visibility 400 yd, with drizzle borne on a 10 knot westerly wind as the time for their staggered take-off approached. FIDO was lit, inside lines only, and burned clearly in time for the first take-off at 13.22, through to the last at 14.03. Throughout the burn, ceiling was maintained at 300 ft and for the full 4,000 ft length of the burners, beyond which the PBYs disappeared into the gloom. There is no record that fog dispersal was needed for their eventual return.

Following FIDO's proving, Lt Cdr Champion urged: '. . . that a slot burner installation, a wind curtain installation and a sonic system be made at this station in time for development to be utilized in the Aleutians by June 1945, the advent of the next fog season'. By that date, however, the conclusion had been reached that rapid improvement to the Amchitka system was not possible, due to lack of materials and experienced personnel, who had by now been posted elsewhere. No completion within a year was foreseen, and with the reduced importance of the Aleutians, the anticipated cost of $276,000 was not justified. The fog dispersal system subsequently fell into disrepair, and what little the weather had not rendered inoperable was dismantled early in 1946.

In the cold-war period, Aleutial military stations became vital links in the air defence of the North American continent. During the 1950s Amchitka was part of the US early warning network. Later, it was the site of underground nuclear testing and subsequently it became a National Wildlife Refuge. In 1986 Amchitka was again used for radar experiments, but advancing technology rendered the base surplus to requirements and it was decommissioned in September 1993. Christopher A. Long of the USN Civilian Engineer Corps supervised the evacuation and penned the following obituary on the eve of departure:

Portions of the original fog dispersal system can still be found around the 25 approach end of what was originally 'Baker' runway. In the year that I have been stationed on the island, I have had no idea what those remnants of elevated pipes sticking out of the ground were, exactly.

The only guess I could venture was some sort of sprinkler system, but with the weather conditions up here, they certainly did not need one of those! The runway was reconstructed prior to the AEC use in 1988, as part of our construction efforts. The majority of the fog dispersal system was, however, far enough away from the main runway not to interfere with the reconstruction.

Now that I know what it was, I can certainly tell you that I wish it still worked. The fog on Amchitka during the months of July and August is absolutely atrocious. Even when the winds are blowing at 15–25 knots, the fog just sits there. I cannot count the number of days on which we had no ceiling, and zero visibility. I can tell you that, even with advanced landing systems, we were only able to land seven out of twenty planes during those two months. That is bad news when you have only got one plane a week to ferry people, groceries and mail!

Before he left, Christopher Long photographed the remains of FIDO on Amchitka (Pl. 74–7), now left in the sole care of Mother Nature.

As has been mentioned earlier, the airstrip on Shemya became operational for bombers on 13 August 1943. It was a long while before the runway offered anything beyond the crudest landing facilities. In fact, not until August 1944 was the surface at the paving stage. The engineer's report for that month recorded that: 'In order to ensure maximum use of the runway, and safety of planes and their crews, a fog dispersal unit is being laid concurrent with the paving operations. As now planned, units will be installed on each side of the east end of the runway, for a distance of at least 5,000 ft. When in operation, the fog dispersal unit will burn 50,000 gallons of white gasoline per hour.'

The runway in question ran approximately east–west across the southern part of the island, close to the shore. Another runway ran in a NW–SE direction further north. Construction of the NW–SE runway was fraught with every kind of difficulty, not least being the existence of twenty ponds on the site. 'Ponds' was a euphemism for stretches of water of indeterminate depth, some of which would not have shamed the title of lagoon. One thing veterans agreed they all had in common was that in whichever direction one chose to go, a pond would be in the way! Six of these ponds lay directly along the course of the runway. It is understood that military planners originally intended to base giant B–29 bombers on the island, but the persistently poor weather caused the joint chiefs of staff to abandon the idea in September 1944, 'due to pending plans for relocating the Air Base which are yet to materialize.'

There is no evidence that the fog dispersal systems planned for Shemya ever got beyond the surveying stage. In April 1945 Admiral Ramsey, Chief of the US Bureau of Aeronautics, recommended that the installation of a unit at Shemya 'should not be considered because the installation could not be completed in time for the 1945 fog season due to the lack of harbour facilities and other difficulties'. The Aleutians Air Department withdrew their request on 16 August and the Operations Division of the General Staff in Washington officially closed this chapter of FIDO's history on 6 June 1946.

And finally – the story is told of the occasion when the Inspector General visited a FIDO-equipped airfield. After a day in which everything was suspiciously in order, he retired to his quarters and sent for the duty bugler. When the lad reported to him he was asked what his duties were when FIDO was to be lit.

'Well, sir,' replied the airman, 'I sleep in the guardroom near the Tannoy control panel, and if Flying Control ring through, I press the switches for the FIDO crew, crash crew, ambulance and mobile cranes and then play the FIRE! call.'

'Right,' said the Inspector General. 'I'll see you in the guardroom at three o'clock tomorrow morning', and added as the bugler turned to leave, 'Don't say anything about this to anyone.' Needless to say, within ten minutes the station commander sent for the lad and bullied all that had transpired out of him.

Promptly at 3 a.m. the Inspector General strode through the guardroom door where everyone was unusually alert.

Plate 74 Modified Mk IV burner as used on Amchitka, 1993 (Chris Long)

Plate 75 Remains of outer line of burners at runway head. Top, vaporizer, pipe missing. Reinforcing rods driven through to rock beneath. Earthen bank to right. Inner row of burners dismantled during runway reconstruction (Chris Long)

Plate 76 Main petrol supply pressure regulator and control (Chris Long)

Plate 77 Control valves, main petrol supply to individual burner units (Chris Long)

'Now,' barked his lordship, 'Switch on and play the last post!'

'But, sir,' stammered the bugler.

'The last post!' growled the Inspector General . . .

As the plaintive notes of the funeral call drifted across the aerodrome, the crash tender thundered around the perimeter track, the ambulance clanged its way from the sick bay, two mobile cranes, like stiff-necked dinosaurs, plunged across the grass, their crews hanging on like monkeys, and the flames from the FIDO burners roared up into the night sky . . .

They say that for a long time afterwards, if you telephoned the blanket store of a certain RAF outpost somewhere east of Suez, the telephone was answered by a Group Captain!

Notes

Throughout the book, personal reminiscences are acknowledged as they occur.

1

Unless otherwise indicated, operational details and losses are from *The Bomber Command War Diaries*, by Martin Middlebrook and Chris Everitt.

2–3

Unless otherwise indicated, the technical and meteorological details in these chapters have been drawn from the following reports:

1. E.G. Walker and D.A. Fox, *The Dispersal of Fog from Airfield Runways*, and Mr Fox's own recollections.
2. W.T. Moore, *History and Development of Hades and Rapex Burners*, and Mr Moore's own recollections.
3. H. Edge and L. MacPherson, *Meteorological Aspects of Fog Dispersal by Heat*, and Mr MacPherson's own recollections.

Additional material has been provided by *Dispersal of Fog on Airfields*, Progress Reviews 1 and 2 in the Imperial War Museum (IWM) and copy of A.C. Hartley's diary in the same place. Progress reports on the construction of FIDO at individual airfields and monthly operational landing and petrol consumption figures are also at the IWM. Material submitted to the postwar Court of Claims for Awards to Inventors has been made available by Denys Fox. I am also grateful to Mrs Margaretta Wooldridge for permission to examine the papers of her late husband Wg Cdr John de Lisle Wooldridge.

4 Hartfordbridge/Blackbushe

Operational details have mainly been drawn from the station Operations Record Book (PRO, Air 28/342) and from Christopher Shores' *2nd Tactical Air Force*, neither of which contains any reference to FIDO. Trevor Harvey's *A History of Blackbushe* is much more helpful. Blackbushe's fog dispersal reports are in the papers of Geoffrey Lloyd (85/46/16/B10, IWM). They are less informative than for most other FIDO aerodromes. Fortunately, Bill Beaumont has been good enough to furnish me with a copy of his records compiled for the Court of Claims for Awards to Inventors, which fill many gaps. See also the introduction to Ch. 2 notes.

5 Bradwell Bay

Operational details are mainly drawn from the station ORB (PRO, Air 28/105) which contains few references to FIDO. The ORB is supplemented by information from *The*

Bomber Command War Diaries and Roger A. Freeman's *The Mighty Eighth War Diary*. Bradwell Bay's fog dispersal reports are in the papers of Geoffrey Lloyd (85/46/16/Bll, IWM). They do not contain as much information on FIDO as one would wish. See also the introduction to Ch. 2 notes.

6 Carnaby

General descriptions of Carnaby and its activities are contained in Brian Rapier's *White Rose Base* and Bruce Halpenny's *Action Stations 4*. Emergency landing incidents are mainly drawn from the station ORB (PRO, Air 28/125), supplemented by reference to *The Bomber Command War Diaries* and *The Mighty Eighth War Diary*. Carnaby's fog dispersal reports are in the papers of Geoffrey Lloyd (85/46/16/C16–2 files, IWM). See also the introduction to Ch. 2 notes.

7 Downham Market

A general account of Downham Market appears in Michael Bowyer's *Action Stations 1*. Operational details have been drawn from the station ORB (PRO, Air 28/213), and the all-over pattern into which they fitted, from *The Bomber Command War Diaries*. One day's operations have been particularly highlighted in an extensive quote from Alex Thorne's *Lancaster at War 4: Pathfinder Squadron*. Downham Market's fog dispersal reports are in the papers of Geoffrey Lloyd (85/46/16/D13, IWM). See also the introduction to Ch. 2 notes.

8 Fiskerton

A general account of Fiskerton and its squadron's operations is in Bruce Halpenny's *Action Stations 2*, and in *The Military Airfields of Lincolnshire* by Messrs R. Blake, M. Hodgson and W. Taylor. Operational details are in the station ORB (PRO, Air 28/283), though there are few references to FIDO, supplemented by *The Bomber Command War Diaries*. Fiskerton's fog dispersal reports are in the papers of Geoffrey Lloyd (85/46/16/F26, IWM). I am indebted to Clive Roantree for permission to quote extensively from his book, *To Fly Lancasters*. See also the introduction to Ch. 2 notes.

9 Foulsham

A general account of Foulsham and its operations is contained in Michael Bowyer's *Action Stations 1*. Operational details are in the station ORB (PRO Air 28/287), which contains few references to FIDO, supplemented by *The Bomber Command War Diaries*. Foulsham's fog dispersal reports are in the papers of Geoffrey Lloyd (85/46/16/F27, IWM). I am indebted to Len Bartram for a very helpful tape-recorded description of RAF Foulsham 1942-7, and a copy of his book of the same title. See also the introduction to Ch. 2 notes.

10 Graveley

A general account of Graveley and its operations is contained in Michael Bowyer's *Action Stations 1*. Operational details are in the station ORB (PRO Air 28/322) and the background within which they were set in *The Bomber Command War Diaries*. Graveley's fog dispersal reports are in the papers of Geoffrey Lloyd (85/46/16/G9, IWM). I am grateful to Mr D.H. Foreman for a copy of his touch of nostalgia, 'Return to Graveley', and to Anne Bishop for one of her *History of Graveley*. See also the introduction to Ch. 2 notes.

11 Ludford Magna

A general account of Ludford Magna is contained in Bruce Halpenny's *Action Stations 2* and *The Military Airfields of Lincolnshire* by Messrs R. Blake, M. Hodgson and W. Taylor. 101

Squadron's time at the base is well covered in *Bomber Squadron at War*, by Andrew Brookes, and a wartime close-up of station and squadron is presented by Carl Olsson in 'Twenty Lancasters', *Illustrated* magazine, 25 March 1944. Useful references to Ludford Magna occur in *Weather*, January and February 1988, in articles by R.J. Ogden. Ludford's station ORB (PRO, Air 28/501) contains more references to FIDO than that of any other airfield. The fog dispersal reports for Ludford are in the papers of Geoffrey Lloyd (85/46/16/L9, IWM). *The Bomber Command War Diaries* provide the setting for 101 Squadron's operations. See also the introduction to Ch. 2 notes.

12 Manston

Manston's earliest history is recorded in *Wings over Westgate*, by the present writer. Later accounts occur in *A History of RAF Manston*, ed. R. Stockman, and in Chris Ashworth's *Action Stations 9*. Its role as an emergency airfield was determined by the activities of RAF Bomber and Fighter Commands and the US Eighth Air Force, whose operations are covered in *The Bomber Command War Diaries* and *The Mighty Eighth War Diary*. Manston's ORB is (PRO, Air 28/515), and the few fog dispersal reports are in the papers of Geoffrey Lloyd (85/46/16/M22, IWM). See also the introduction to Ch. 2 notes.

13 Melbourne

A good general history of RAF Melbourne is Brian Rapier's *Melbourne 10*, supplemented by Bruce Halpenny's *Action Stations 4*. The station ORB is (PRO, Air 28/530) and the scheme of things into which 10 Squadron's ops fitted is detailed in *The Bomber Command War Diaries*. Melbourne's fog dispersal reports are in the papers of Geoffrey Lloyd (85/46/16/M23, IWM). See also the introduction to Ch. 2 notes.

14 Metheringham

General accounts of Metheringham appear in *Military Airfields of Lincolnshire* by Messrs R. Blake, M. Hodgson and W. Taylor, and in Bruce Halpenny's *Action Stations 2*; 5 Group operations in which 106 Squadron was involved are in *The Bomber Command War Diaries*. The station ORB is (PRO, Air 28/536), and its fog dispersal reports are in the papers of Geoffrey Lloyd (85/46/16/M24, IWM). See also the introduction to Ch. 2 notes.

15 St Eval

A general account of St Eval is contained in Chris Ashworth's *Action Stations 5* and a series of articles by R.A. Bell in the station magazine *Westwings*. The station ORB is (PRO, Air 28/730), and its fog dispersal reports are in the papers of Geoffrey Lloyd (85/46/16/S18, IWM). Extensive use has been made of episodes in Arthur C. Clarke's *Glide Path*. See also the introduction to Ch. 2 notes.

16 Sturgate

A general account of Sturgate appears in Bruce Halpenny's *Action Stations 2*. The station ORB is (PRO, Air 28/802), and Sturgate's fog dispersal reports are in the papers of Geoffrey Lloyd (85/46/16/S19, IWM). See also the introduction to Ch. 2 notes.

17 Tuddenham

A general account of RAF Tuddenham appears in Michael Bowyer's *Action Stations 1*. Further information is included in 90 Squadron's history *Sing High*, though nothing referring to FIDO. Several quotes have been made from *Chocks Away* by Eric Wannop. 90 Squadron's operations are covered in 3 Group references in *The Bomber Command War Diaries*. The station ORB is (PRO, Air 28/859), and Tuddenham's fog dispersal reports are in the papers of Geoffrey Lloyd (85/46/16/T13, IWM). See also the introduction to Ch. 2 notes.

18 Woodbridge

A general account of Woodbridge is included in Michael Bowyer's *Action Stations 1*. Gordon Kinsey also covers some of its activities in his book *Bawdsey*. Both *The Bomber Command War Diaries* and *The Mighty Eighth War Diary* are invaluable in recording the operations which FIDO at Woodbridge backed up so well. The station ORB (PRO, Air 28/954) is more informative than most. The fog dispersal reports are in the papers of Geoffrey Lloyd (85/46/16/W11, IWM). See also the introduction Ch. 2 notes.

19 Epinoy

Brief accounts of the history of Epinoy and its squadrons appear in *Les Aigles de Cambrai* by Michel Bacquet (Médiathèque Municipale Cambrai, 8207421) and *La 12 Escadre de Chasse* (Bibliothèque Municipale Cambrai Flash 103, no. 44), though they make no reference to FIDO. Epinoy's few fog dispersal reports are in the papers of Geoffrey Lloyd (85/46/16/E5, IWM). See also the introduction to Ch. 2 notes.

20 The Aleutians

For background material for this chapter I am indebted to John H. Cloe, Chief of History, 11th Air Force, Elmendorf AFB, Alaska, for a copy of his book *The Aleutian Warriors*; and articles on 'The Aleutians' by D. Colt Denfield and Erwin N. Thompson in *After the Battle* magazine, No. 62, 1988, though neither source makes reference to FIDO. IWM material relating to FIDO in the Aleutians is to be found in the papers of Geoffrey Lloyd (85/46/15&17, IWM).